MUIRHEAD LIBRARY OF PHILOSOPHY

AN admirable statement of the aims of the Library of Philosophy was provided by the first editor, the late Professor J. H. Muirhead, in his description of the original programme printed in Erdmann's *History of Philosophy* under the date 1890. This was slightly modified in subsequent volumes to take the form of the following statement:

'The Muirhead Library of Philosophy was designed as a contribution to the History of Modern Philosophy under the heads: first of Different Schools of Thought—Sensationalist, Realist, Idealist, Intuitivist; secondly of different Subjects—Psychology, Ethics, Political Philosophy, Theology. While much had been done in England in tracing the course of evolution in nature, history, economics, morals and religion, little had been done in tracing the development of thought on these subjects. Yet "the evolution of opinion is part of the whole evolution".

'By the co-operation of different writers in carrying out this plan it was hoped that a thoroughness and completeness of treatment, otherwise unattainable, might be secured. It was believed also that from writers mainly British and American fuller consideration of English Philosophy than it had hitherto received might be looked for. In the earlier series of books containing, among others, Bosanquet's *History of Aesthetic*, Pfleiderer's *Rational Theology since Kant*, Albee's *History of English Utilitarianism*, Bonar's *Philosophy and Political Economy*, Brett's *History of Psychology*, Ritchie's *Natural Rights*, these objects were to a large extent effected.

'In the meantime original work of a high order was being produced both in England and America by such writers as Bradley, Stout, Bertrand Russell, Baldwin, Urban, Montague, and others, and a new interest in foreign works, German, French and Italian, which had either become classical or were attracting public attention, had developed. The scope of the Library thus became extended into something more international, and it is entering on the fifth decade of its existence in the hope that it may contribute to that mutual understanding between countries which is so pressing a need of the present time.'

The need which Professor Muirhead stressed is no less pressing today, and few will deny that philosophy has much to do with enabling us to meet it, although no one, least of all Muirhead himself, would regard that as the sole, or even the main, object of philosophy. As Professor Muirhead continues to lend the distinction of his name to the Library of Philosophy it seemed not inappropriate to allow him to

A

recall us to these aims in his own words. The emphasis on the history of thought also seemed to me very timely; and the number of important works promised for the Library in the very near future augur well for the continued fulfilment, in this and other ways, of the expectations of the original editor.

H. D. LEWIS

MUIRHEAD LIBRARY OF PHILOSOPHY

General Editor: H. D. Lewis

Professor of History and Philosophy of Religion in the University of London

The Analysis of Mind BERTRAND RUSSELL 8th impression

Clarity is Not Enough by H. D. LEWIS

Coleridge as Philosopher by J. H. MUIRHEAD 3rd impression

The Commonplace Book of G. E. Moore edited by C. LEWY

Contemporary American Philosophy edited by G. P. ADAMS and W. P. MONTAGUE 2nd impression

Contemporary British Philosophy First and second series edited by J. H. MUIRHEAD 2nd impression

Contemporary British Philosophy third series edited by H. D. LEWIS 2nd impression

Contemporary Indian Philosophy edited by RADHAKRISHNAN and J. H. MUIRHEAD 2nd edition

Doctrine and Argument in Indian Philosophy by NINIAN SMART

Ethics by NICOLAI HARTMANN translated by STANTON COIT 3 vols

Freedom and History by H. D. LEWIS

The Good Will: A Study in the Coherence Theory of Goodness by H. J. PATON

Hegel: A Re-Examination by J. N. FINDLAY

Hegel's Science of Logic translated by W. H. JOHNSTON and L. G. STRUTHERS 2 vols 3rd impression

History of Æsthetic by B. BOSANQUET 2nd edition 5th impression

History of English Utilitarianism by E. ALBEE 2nd impression

History of Psychology by G. S. BRETT edited by R. S. PETERS abridged one-volume edition 2nd edition

Human Knowledge by BERTRAND RUSSELL 4th impression

A Hundred Years of British Philosophy by RODOLF METZ translated by J. H. HARVEY, T. E. JESSOP, HENRY STURT 2nd impression

Ideas: A General Introduction to Pure Phenomenology by EDMUND HUSSERL translated by W. R. BOYCE GIBSON 3rd impression

Imagination by E. J. FURLONG

Indian Philosophy by RADHAKRISHNAN 2 vols revised 2nd edition

Introduction to Mathematical Philosophy by BERTRAND RUSSELL 2nd edition 10th impression

Kant's First Critique by H. W. CASSIRER

Kant's Metaphysic of Experience by H. J. PATON 3rd impression

Know Thyself by BERNADINO VARISCO translated by GUGLIELMO SAL-VADORI

Language and Reality by WILBUR MARSHALL URBAN 3rd impression

Matter and Memory by HENRI BERGSON translated by N. M. PAUL and W. S. PALMER 7th impression

The Modern Predicament by H. J. PATON 3rd impression

Natural Rights by D. G. RITCHIE 3rd edition 5th impression

Nature, Mind and Modern Science by E. HARRIS

The Nature of Thought by BRAND BLANSHARD 3rd impression

On Selfhood and Godhood by C. A. CAMPBELL

Our Experience of God by H. D. LEWIS

The Phenomenology of Mind by G. W. F. HEGEL translated by SIR JAMES BAILLIE revised 2nd edition 5th impression

Philosophical Papers by G. E. MOORE 2nd impression

Philosophy and Religion by AXEL HÄGERSTRÖM

Philosophy in America edited by MAX BLACK

Philosophy of Whitehead by W. MAYS

The Principal Upanishads by RADHAKRISHNAN

The Problems of Perception by R. J. HIRST

Reason and Goodness by BRAND BLANSHARD

The Relevance of Whitehead by IVOR LECLERC

Some Main Problems of Philosophy by G. E. MOORE 3rd impression

The Theological Frontier of Ethics by W. G. MACLAGAN

Time and Free Will by HENRI BERGSON translated by F. G. POGSON 7th impression

The Ways of Knowing: or The Methods of Philosophy by W. P. MONTAGUE 6th impression

Values and Intentions by J. N. FINDLAY

Muirhead Library of Philosophy

EDITED BY H. D. LEWIS

THE FOUNDATIONS OF METAPHYSICS IN SCIENCE

BY ERROL E. HARRIS

Nature, Mind and Modern Science
Revelation Through Reason

THE FOUNDATIONS
OF METAPHYSICS IN
SCIENCE

BY
ERROL E. HARRIS

Roy Roberts Professor of Philosophy
in the University of Kansas

London
GEORGE ALLEN AND UNWIN LTD
RUSKIN HOUSE MUSEUM STREET

PRINTED IN GREAT BRITAIN
in 11 on 12 Imprint Type
BY UNWIN BROTHERS LIMITED
WOKING AND LONDON

CONTENTS

A*

PREFACE

To fulfil its purpose adequately, this book is too short. I am well aware that, apart from the omission from Parts I–III of much scientific material which is germane, Part IV is far too condensed and abbreviated. I can only hope that the interest of the reader may induce him further to explore the scientific field, and that by close attention to the final arguments he will grasp the links which brevity may have obscured. The book would have been even worse without the help, criticism and advice of scientific friends and colleagues; none of whom, however, are responsible for the philosophical opinions expressed in it. Those to whom I am indebted are: Professor Henry Margenau, of Yale University, Professor Bernice Wheeler, of Connecticut College, Professor Leone, of the University of Kansas, Professor James Drever, of the University of Edinburgh, Dr. Peter Caws, sometime Rose Morgan, Professor in the University of Kansas, and Dr. R. K. Jennings. Each of them has read some part of this work in draft and has done much to save me from misunderstanding technicalities and from making errors in consequence. Of my gratitude to them this preface is testimony.

My thanks are also due to the Bollingen Foundation of New York for financial assistance which enabled me take time off from my teaching duties in order to work on the book. Without this advantage it would have taken much longer to write.

E. E. H.

High Wray,
October, 1964.

INTRODUCTION

CHAPTER I

SCIENTIFIC PHILOSOPHY

I

In 1914 Bertrand Russell reproached Bradley and the Idealists for their adherence to the classical tradition in philosophy and their consequent failure to adapt their thought to the scientific temper of the age. He obviously believed that he was himself developing a philosophy in harmony with this scientific temper, and, in the great stream of empiricist thought that has issued from the beginnings which he made, frequent claims have been asserted that philosophy had now become scientific. But these claims have never seriously been put to the test, and when investigated many of them prove to be groundless. Russell's own voluminous contribution and those of many others who have followed his methods and developed his ideas have run contrary to some of the most characteristic and significant trends in modern science, and have not infrequently been in conflict with their own professed empirical ideals. The purpose of this book is not polemical and the detailed critique of current doctrine implied in what follows will, for the most part, have to be inferred by the reader; but some brief statement here may serve to support the allegations made above.

Few, if any, philosophers who make the claim to be scientific in their philosophical methods seem carefully to have considered what being scientific means and requires. What scientific criteria must we use to discover when and whether a philosophy meets the requirements of science? Those which some philosophers have offered are so ill-founded that critical examination at once discovers their unacceptability. Hans Reichenbach, who made the claim quite unreservedly, offered two criteria of the scientific: (i) logical analysis and (ii) adherence to the 'vertifiability theory of meaning'. The second is now generally discredited, and the first suffers from ambiguity and vagueness. 'Logical analysis' means different things to different philosophers. Russell, Moore, Wittgenstein, Carnap, Wisdom, Ryle and Austin have all professed to practice it and each has done something different in its name. Russell, by the phrase, covered both the analysis of facts into 'hard data' and the analysis of descriptions as incomplete symbols (the two are not wholly unconnected); Moore analysed propositions by means of verbal paraphrase; Wittgenstein (at first) sought to analyse compound statements into elementary propositions which would 'show forth' the form of the facts; Carnap analysed statements in the material mode into others in the formal mode, and yet other philosophers, influenced by Wittgenstein's later views, which rejected and replaced some of those he had expressed earlier, confined themselves to the analysis of linguistic usage, in the course of which they unveiled confusions and 'superstitions' in the beliefs of all previous analysts. Hardly any two of these philosophers have pursued what might be described as an authentic method recognizably common to both, and where analysis pretended to reduce either facts or language to simple and primitive terms, it is nowadays generally repudiated as 'reductive' and impracticable as well as unrewarding. It is, accordingly, not clear in the least in what precise respect 'logical analysis' is scientific.

If, however, a more natural interpretation of the phrase be adopted, as a rigorous, self-consistent and systematic critique, then the first criterion offered by Reichenbach plays havoc with the second, for the whole positivistic doctrine, on which the verifiability theory of meaning rests and which he advocates, proves under examination to be self-refuting, logically inconsistent and question-begging.[1] There is little need to repeat here arguments which I have developed elsewhere at some length, nor need I summarize the quite voluminous critique made by others of the verification principle.[2] Suffice it to say that, if it is intended to assert only that a proposition is meaningless, which is in principle non-verifiable (i.e. one the truth or falsity of which could

[1] *Vide* Hans Reichenbach, *The Rise of Scientific Philosophy* (University of California and Cambridge, 1951).

[2] *Vide* B. Blanshard, *Reason and Analysis* (London and LaSalle, 1962), Ch. V; 'The Philosophy of Analysis', reprinted in *Clarity is not Enough* (London, 1963), pp. 76–109; C. D. Broad, 'Two Lectures on the Nature of Philosophy', *ibid.*, pp. 48–49; Errol E. Harris, *Nature, Mind and Modern Science* (London, 1954), Ch. XVI; 'Scientific Philosophy', *Philosophical Quarterly*, II (1952), pp. 153–65; G. R. G. Mure, *Retreat from Truth* (Oxford, 1958), pp. 135, 138–39; W. V. O. Quine, *From a Logical Point of View* (Harvard, 1953, Ch. II; J. O. Urmson, *The Philosophy of Analysis* (Oxford, 1958), Chs. 9 and 10; G. J. Warnock, *English Philosophy since* 1900 (Oxford University Press, 1958), Ch. IV; J. Weinberg, *An Examination of Logical Positivism* (London, 1936), pp. 48–56, and *passim*.

in no conceivable way be established) the principle is true but vacuous; for by definition a proposition is an assertion which is either true or false. If on the other hand it is intended to maintain, as it normally is by its proponents, that no factual proposition is meaningful unless some immediate report of pure sense-experiences is relevant to its verification, it makes an impossible demand and puts an end to all significant discourse. This is because, as is now generally agreed, immediate reports of pure sense-experiences cannot be meaningfully expressed, and because, if they could, they could never be made relevant to the verification of any factual proposition. To demonstrate at length what must now be familiar to all informed students of philosophy would be merely tedious. The crux of the matter is that all facts involve relations, more or less complex, and no ostensive proposition (could any ever meaningfully be framed) includes the report of relations. Spatial and temporal settings are, therefore, of necessity excluded from them as well as all the other multifarious relational elements necessarily involved in even the simplest statement of fact. What has to be verified is precisely that to which ostensive propositions could never be relevant and verification by references to them is never possible. To offer the verification principle as a criterion of scientific procedure is thus to pervert science and make it an impossible pursuit. The theory which offers this criterion can, in consequence, hardly sustain the claim to be itself scientific. We may not talk of scientific philosophy before we can give a satisfactory account of what it is to be scientific, and this means forming a clear conception of what science is and does.

The desire of philosophers that their discipline should rank as science is not a new, or exclusively a twentieth century, aspiration. Descartes, less self-consciously perhaps than the moderns, and Kant, with more humility, were influenced by the same ambition. But it is rather more typical of our own day than of any earlier period that thinkers should emulate the natural scientists, not only because the natural sciences have been the most successful and have made the most spectacular progress, but also because they have exercised so profound an influence upon our life and thought that they have acquired unquestioned and almost unchallengeable authority over our outlook and practice. There can be no doubt whatever that the temper of the age is scientific, and no question but that every serious philosopher must, in these days, take account of science, its methods and achievements and what it discovers of the world we live in.

It is, however, neither justified nor profitable to attempt to find out the nature of scientific thinking by making metaphysical assumptions about the nature of the world and our knowledge of it, and then interpreting science and its methods in light of these. Such an approach puts the cart before the horse, for if we assume a theory of knowledge from the start, we affect to know what science is and does. On the other hand, the search for answers to these questions is itself a quest for a theory of knowledge, and its outcome ought not to be prejudged. Yet this question-begging approach is very prevalent. Hans Reichenbach could see in Einstein's theories only an application (and vindication) of the verifiability theory of meaning,[1] failing to notice that if the criterion of significance laid down by the verifiability theory is strictly applied the theory of relativity should be meaningless. The positivistic doctrine asserts that a factual statement which cannot be empirically verified is without scientific significance. Yet, that all Galilean (inertial) systems are equivalent, is such a statement; for no Galilean system can be experimentally identified or constructed, and none has or ever could be observed, so that to compare such systems and find them equivalent by empirical observation is impossible. Yet this statement of the equivalence of Galilean systems is the very foundation of the special theory of relativity. On the other hand, Reichenbach dismissed as a 'creed', 'a primitive form of guessing', heuristically useful but quite unscientific and unphilosophical, Einstein's stated conviction of the harmony of the Universe, presumably because it did not accord with his own metaphysical views. Yet, as we shall see, there are good grounds in science for Einstein's statement.

Similarly, Professor R. B. Braithwaite, in the introduction to *Scientific Explanation*, declares that 'a scientific hypothesis . . . is an empirical proposition in the sense that it is testable by experience', and he goes on to explain that what he means by experience 'covers all the facts which in ordinary language would be said to be observed facts'.[2] But there are numerous scientific propositions, some of which even rank as laws, which cannot possibly

---

[1] *Vide* H. Reichenbach, 'The Philosophical Significance of the Theory of Relativity', in *Einstein: Philosopher-Scientist*, Ed. P. A. Schilpp (New York, 1949).

[2] R. B. Braithwaite, *Scientific Explanation* (Cambridge, 1953), p. 2.

be tested by what would ordinarily be called observed facts, but at most by what have been termed *Gedankenexperimente*, and there are some observed facts which have been deliberately set aside by scientists in favour of well attested theories.[1] Professor Braithwaite's statements are simply the result of assuming an empiricist epistemology in advance of investigation. He explicitly accepts Hume's view that scientific laws express nothing other than the constant conjunction of events and claims to be able to show the adequacy of this view 'in the development of a theory of science which includes it'.[2] If this is not prejudging the issue, what could be? Braithwaite makes no secret of his espousal of the orthodox empiricist viewpoint. He takes it for granted that 'observation' is something simple—a direct acceptance of given sensuous data—and he analyses it no further than to distinguish observation of material objects from that of sense qualities, dismissing as irrelevant to a theory of science all questions of their interrelation. That it is the primary source of scientific knowledge and the sole test of scientific hypotheses he does not question. But Empiricism is an epistemology elaborated by philosophers quite independently of any systematic examination of the actual procedures of natural science. Its original authors, in the seventeenth century, were necessarily ignorant of present-day scientific positions, and it would therefore be very surprising if its tenets should today prove adequate as an element in a theory of contemporary science.

These brief strictures must be taken only as exemplifications and are not put forward as final criticisms of the views concerned. That would have to be undertaken in a study the main purpose of which was epistemological and must be deferred to another place and time.

The critique of the large body of analytic philosophy, in the development of which the claim to be scientific has been made or assumed, is already voluminous and at this stage needs no augmentation.[3] It has come both from without and from within, and despite the fact that external criticism has been largely ignored by analytic philosophers, there is remarkable agreement between

[1] Cf. Results of experiments by W. M. Hicks and D. C. Miller modifying the result of the Michelson-Morley experiment. *Vide*, Michael Polanyi, *Personal Knowledge* (London, 1958), pp. 12–15.

[2] Op cit., p. 11.

[3] Cf. references given above, p. 18 n2.

the objections raised to their successive positions by external critics and the analysts' own recognition of former errors and the reasons they give for rejecting views earlier approved within the movement.[1] This I have pointed out in a recent article in *Dialectica* (Vol. 17, No. 1, 1963) where I have shown how the logical atomism which was the starting-point of contemporary analytic philosophy remained the presumed foundation of successive changes of viewpoint until its incoherence and self-refutation came to be recognized. The internal critique, I have argued further, has finally demolished the philosophical grounds on which the entire movement rested, and it may legitimately be treated as a phase that has passed.

My object in this book and what is planned as its sequel is to make a fresh start. Conceding that the spectacular advances in natural science have made a profound difference to man's outlook and have resulted in a typical new twentieth-century conception of the world, I wish to take cognizance in some detail of what science tells us and from that to derive conclusions as to the appropriate form of philosophy for the second half of the century. This method of approach I believe to be more truly empirical than Empiricists themselves have made; for the sciences concerned are universally regarded as empirical sciences and are the most systematic and developed forms of empirical investigation in their several fields. To begin from their discoveries, therefore, and to proceed from them to philosophical theory must surely be unimpeachable from an empirical point of view.

An approach of this kind, however, by no means entails the profession of philosophical Empiricism, which is really a metaphysical theory (whether or not acknowledged) and is not by any means always reached by empirical argument. The empirical method so much prized in science is not the same thing as the philosophical doctrine of Empiricism. The admission, freely to be made, that observation and experiment are valuable and indispensable means of scientific investigation does not necessarily commit one to the belief in the primacy of sense. On the contrary, to test the truth of Empiricism, attention must be paid to the actual practice of scientists and the character of scientific progress. An examination of these may be empirical in spirit and may nevertheless (as Professor N. R. Hanson's recent book bears

[1] *Vide* Urmson, op. cit. and Warnock, op. cit.

witness)[1] throw serious doubt upon the fundamental assumptions of Empiricism.

What then is the precise character and significance of the scientific spirit of the age? It can only properly be understood after a thorough examination of scientific knowledge: the deliverances of the sciences, the sort of world that they reveal to us, their methods, how they acquire their data and arrive at their conclusions, their validity, how they establish their standards and commend themselves to our credence, their place in the system of man's activity, their relation to other fields of human experience.

2

Empiricism, with its derivatives, is nowadays the brand of philosophy most prone to claim to 'tread the sure path of a science'. Its starting-point, tacitly or openly, is always the fortuitously occurring data of sense. These are assumed to be simple and irreducible particulars without mutual connection, though they are, of course, variously conjoined. It is the conjunction of these primary data that constitutes matters of fact and it is solely through our experience of them that we can and do acquire knowledge of the world. Matters of fact are, therefore, on this view, mutually independent. Though conjoined, there is no discoverable necessary connection between any two of them. The world is thus presumed to consist entirely of unconnected, mutually independent facts, described as atomic, any one of which could be other than it is without changing any of the others, or could remain the same despite alterations elsewhere. Similarly, propositions in which such facts are stated are atomic and are logically independent of one another. No factual proposition is deducible from any other by virtue of its factual content, though such deduction is sometimes possible in consequence of formal characters of the propositions.

Professor A. J. Ayer has called it a 'logical truism that if two states of affairs are distinct, a statement which refers to only one of them does not entail anything about the other'.[2] If, by this statement, Ayer intends no more than a definition of distinctness between states of affairs, so that if statements are mutually

---

[1] *Patterns of Discovery* (Cambridge, 1958).

[2] *The Problem of Knowledge* (Penguin Books, Harmondsworth, 1956), p. 29.

entailed the facts to which they refer are not distinct, then the arguments which he alleges depend upon the 'truism' do not follow from it. These are the proof that no cognitive state of mind could be infallible, and Hume's proof that no effect can ever be logically deduced from its cause.[1] Some other reason than such a definition of distinctness would have to be available in both these cases, (i) to show that statements about a cognitive state of mind *could* not entail the truth of what it apprehended, (ii) that statements about effects *could* not be entailed by statements about causes. For unless we can show that the states of affairs are distinct—i.e. that the statements referring to them are not mutually entailed—the question will have been begged. It is clear therefore that Ayer intends something different. He assumes that distinctness between facts is always apparent—as Hume says, 'the effect is totally different from the cause'—and the alleged 'truism' then is that whenever the facts are different, statements referring to either do not entail the other.

This, however, cannot be a 'logical truism' because it is sometimes false. That the velocity of light is invariant for all observers is one state of affairs, and that two events, simultaneous for one observer, are successive for another moving with high velocity relative to the first, is another state of affairs (or perhaps two other states of affairs); and they are quite distinct, in the sense of being clearly distinguishable (like Hume's causes and effects). Yet the statement referring to one of them does entail the truth of the other (or others), according to the special theory of relativity. When Professor Ayer says that a statement is a 'logical truism', he means that its truth is linguistically guaranteed, which in this case it certainly is not. If, however, it is assumed (as it was by Hume) that facts always are and can only be collections of simple data, there can be no mutual connection between them which is rooted in their content; and this is a metaphysical doctrine that lacks scientific substantiation.

As, in this doctrine, all facts are particulars or conjunctions of particulars, general propositions about similar facts must always be taken in extension, and are always the result of inductive generalization asserting nothing more nor less than the occurrence of constant conjunctions. Causal laws have no other basis, for there can be no evidence of essential connections between facts. They are merely general statements about the constant conjunc-

[1] Cf. loc. cit.

tion of specified events with the presumption that such conjunctions will continue in the future.

Relations between facts are thus purely external, as must
inevitably be the case if primary data are entirely simple, and,
in this philosophy, if the phrase 'internal relations' is ever permitted, it refers only to those between the internal parts of a
combination of simples. But these relations, like all others, are
external to their terms. The notion that they could in any way
be constitutive of their terms is rejected as paradoxical (for what
then could they relate?), though it is at times admitted that some
relations are definitive of their terms and so essential to and
inseparable from them.

In a world of unconnected, simple particulars, logic is always
extensional and is either purely formal or, if informal, is concerned
solely with the use of linguistic forms. Particulars may be collected
into classes by virtue of their similarities, and no other notion
of a class is available than a collection of similar particulars. Taking
classes in extension, a formal calculus of class inclusion and
exclusion is then possible. The connections between the propositions concerned are purely formal, for it is not their material
content that determines these connections. Whether or not a
particular belongs to any class is a purely empirical matter, as
is the question which classes are included or excluded by which.
But once these have been empirically decided, the formal characteristics of the propositions expressing the facts make deductions
possible of their mutual relations. This depends ultimately upon the
definition of terms, of logical constants and upon the rules for their
use and for transformation of symbolic expressions—all of which
may be more or less arbitrary. Logical connection is then (in so
far as it is necessary) tautological according to the rules; and
logic, being purely formal, gives no information about the world.
Hence, necessary logical connection between propositions has no
factual bearing and no new fact can be discovered by its means;
while, on the other hand, no factual connections (for strictly
there are none) are ever the basis of logical inference. As the
informal rules for the use of linguistic symbols operate similarly
to, but less rigorously than, the formal rules of a logical calculus,
the informal analysis of language may also be included under
logic.

The positions outlined here have all been held at some time
by some Empiricists; some have been held at all times by all

Empiricists, but not all Empiricists have held all these views all the time. Within that very wide and varied school there have been differences and disputes on many of the points here laid down. There is no need to pursue the divergencies and aberrations of different branches or periods in the development of the doctrine. Throughout all variations of Empiricist theory the fundamental tenet is that knowledge of matters of fact always derives ultimately from sense-observation in some form, which is what it is, independent of conceptual, theoretical or logical connections; and any statement or proposition expressing the brute facts so observed is logically independent of every other such statement. Philosophers who profess to have given up this tenet must have given up Empiricism, and some who make the profession continue to argue and propound theories which still presuppose the principles they profess to have repudiated.

In dealing with matters of fact this philosophy is in a perpetual difficulty, to overcome which it has gone through innumerable contortions. Though one fact cannot be inferred logically from any other, yet the frequent recurrence of conjunctions can be recorded and general statements can be made about them in the form of scientific laws.[1] These laws can then be made premises for the prediction of future events. Here, however, two main problems arise: (i) by what logical procedure do we form general statements on the evidence of purely particular cases—this is the 'problem of induction'; and (ii) how, if matters of fact may not be inferred one from another, do we deduce future particulars from empirical hypotheses, and how are these predictions confirmed—this is the problem of verification.

Both of these problems will receive attention in the proper place. Here I am anxious to stress only this, that they arise out of a philosophical position which follows directly from the assumptions most characteristic of Empiricism, that the primary facts of the world are atomic, that the elementary data of knowledge are simple particulars, and that they are logically and factually independent of one another without discoverable connection between them. These assumptions are metaphysical, are usually made dogmatically, and if they are false we need not be unduly disturbed by the problems to which they give rise. Whether similar problems would arise out of different assumptions is a matter for further investigation, but a more important and urgent

---

[1] Cf. Braithwaite's doctrine referred to above.

question is whether and how metaphysical assumptions of this (or any other) kind could be tested. Is it possible to discover whether or not they are true?

Ironically, the sort of philosophy we have been outlining frequently abjures metaphysics, on the ground that metaphysical statements cannot be empirically verified. If this were true it would stand condemned by its own touchstone of validity. But empiricists of this ilk do assert that sensible statements about the world belong exclusively to the sphere of the empirical sciences. It should then be possible to discover by consulting the natural sciences whether or not the world divides into atomic and logically unconnected facts, whether relations between facts, between objects and events, are all external or if they may in some (or even in all) cases be constitutive of their terms. This is one of my objects in the investigation which follows, and I shall not be deterred by those who say that the facts are already known and that no new evidence will throw light upon these questions. Facts that are already known to scientists are sometimes overlooked and disregarded by philosophers, and though the evidence we need may be already in our hands, it may not have been recognized. Nor shall I be deterred by those who contend that the questions to be considered are really linguistic. It depends, they may argue, only on the accepted uses of words like 'relation', 'fact' and 'atomic' whether relations may be called 'internal' or 'external' and whether facts are 'atomic', and the way we use such words as 'infer' and 'connect' will determine whether matters of fact can be inferred one from another and how intimately they are connected. We might meet these strictures by representing our investigation as research into the way in which scientists use such terms. Are relations as understood (e.g.) in physics between, let us say, length and duration, mass and energy, constitutive of or external to their terms? As the word 'fact' is used in science, is the fact that two events are simultaneous essentially dependent upon the motion of the observer, or is it independent of all other facts? An examination of scientific theory should enlighten us. I shall not go out of my way to present the investigation as a linguistic study, but if anybody wishes to regard it as such, the results will probably not be seriously affected.

I think it is possible to show that the scientific evidence at our disposal is directly contrary to empiricist presuppositions and that it favours an entirely different conception of the world supporting a radically different philosophy and demanding a conception of logic wholly other than that which, fostered by Empiricism and elaborated by symbolic techniques, has gained such widespread prestige at the present day. Philosophical reflection upon contemporary science leads us back to a type of philosophy which has more in common with what Russell originally castigated as unscientific; but this fact has been missed because few, if any, philosophers have felt competent to examine the pronouncements and methods of the sciences in detail, and those who have the competence have not, until recently, had the inclination. Meanwhile, the resurgence of empiricism has largely distracted attention from the sort of enquiry that might have revealed the fact. The recent empiricist developments have in fact been an interruption in the natural development of philosophy which, in the work of Samuel Alexander, of Bergson and of A. N. Whitehead was pursuing a line much more in keeping with 'the temper of the age' than anything that has issued from the pens of Wittgenstein, the members of the Vienna Circle, G. E. Moore or the Oxford linguists. The Oxford philosopher who saw this most clearly, at the time when what he called 'the cardhouses' of analysis were beginning to look most imposing, was R. G. Collingwood, and he laid the foundation for a new phase of progress, which had it been heeded and built upon, would have been the beginning of a much firmer edifice. For a brief assessment of the relevance of Bergson, Alexander and Whitehead to contemporary scientific progress reference should be made to *Nature, Mind and Modern Science*. There is of course much more to be said, especially about Whitehead, than I have written there, but commentary on philosophical systems is not my present purpose. There will be occasions for pointing out the appropriateness of certain theories as we proceed, and at a later stage I shall make use of the lead given by Collingwood, but my intention is to try to develop *ab initio* the metaphysical theory which the discoveries of science demand and for which they provide the empirical grounds.

3

We have long had it dinned into our ears that metaphysicians have no right to pose as superior savants with means of discovering the nature of the real exceeding those of the natural scientist in scope and perspicacity. Nor indeed have metaphysicians any such means. The nature of the world cannot be deduced *ex nihilo*, but can be discovered only by patient and careful investigation and research, involving, in its proper context, experiment and observation. Even if such knowledge could be divinely revealed, scientific investigation would still be necessary to test the authenticity of the revelation. It can therefore only be through the natural sciences that a comprehensive knowledge of the world can be approached. But none of the special sciences aspires to a conspectus of the total field, for each special scientist is inevitably immersed in the interconnected details of his own branch, for the study of which he must acquire specific techniques. Interdependence between the sciences, intimate though it is, has not led to a super-science combining all of them, in all their ramifications, into a single discipline, and it is doubtful if any such super-science is even possible. The need accordingly remains for the metaphysician's effort to see things together, as Plato recommended—not to correct, outdo, or modify the pronouncements of science, but to reflect upon them, to develop their implications and mutual connections, examine their presuppositions, and to form as complete and systematic a conception of the world as the available evidence permits.

Further, no natural scientist, as such, concerns himself with the credentials of his own methods and their results, except so far as the immediate progress of his science requires it. Where progress is impeded by obscurities and confusions (as it was at the turn of the century in physics) concerning the legitimacy of certain key concepts, the special scientist may be constrained, temporarily and to a limited extent, to turn epistemologist. But the general question of the validity of scientific knowledge, in particular the question with which this chapter opened—by what criterion is any study properly held to be scientific?—does not fall within his scope. The reason for this is clearly connected with the inability of the specialist, *qua* specialist, to range over the whole domain of science; for in order to decide what it is to be a science, all sciences must be taken into account and a wide variety of their methods and practices must be considered. Further, comparison must be made between the special sciences and other claimants to and forms of knowledge, a task that does not belong to any of the special sciences, as such. Not even a 'sociology of knowledge' would answer the central questions relevantly, however much valuable material and light upon them it might provide, because those questions are not about science as a social manifestation, but concern its competence and truth.

It must not, however, be imagined that, because the philosopher inquires into the criteria of scientific competence, he is presuming either to sit in judgement upon the methods of the scientist or to dictate standards for his observance. On the contrary, science sets its own standards and its competence can only be presumed by the philosopher at the start. He cannot dictate, if only because he is (initially at least) ignorant of the criteria and credentials which validate science, and for this reason he must, in order to discover what they are, examine the practice of scientists.

The task of the philosopher is thus two-fold. He must use the evidence provided by the sciences to construct a comprehensive and coherent conception of the universe, and he must examine the methods of scientific investigation and discovery and the process by which the sciences advance, in order to discern the insignia of reliability that entitle any discipline to be called by the name of knowledge—that is, science. I propose to attempt the first of these tasks as a preliminary to the second, as well as for its own sake. For until the first has been completed, we shall not be in a favourable position to undertake the search for the validating criteria of science. A descriptive account of scientific practice is not enough by itself to reveal these criteria, for description does not validate. To test the credentials of a body of knowledge it is necessary, not only to review its contents and methods, but also to understand the aim and purpose of knowledge as such, its significance and function as a form of human activity; and that involves, further, an understanding of human activity and its place in the scheme of things. Consequently, the critical examination of scientific method is inevitably made in the light of a conception of the world and of man, which must either be assumed in general or worked out in detail. But, if metaphysical presuppositions are not to be made at the outset, it cannot be gratuitously assumed; and if it is to be discovered, the only source of enlightenment that can provisionally be accepted as reliable is science itself. The aim of science is a theory of the real, or of that department or aspect of the real which is being specially studied, and the collection of these theories of departments and aspects, taken together, provide the most carefully sifted evidence we have of what reality is like.[1] But when this evidence is viewed together and systematized to form a single whole, our conception of each section treated separately by the sciences may well be modified in the light of its synthesis with the rest, and some features which in the special sciences are less strongly emphasized may gain new and illuminating significance.

My plan, then, is first to consider the findings of the natural sciences and to try to determine from them the sort of world-picture with which they present us, in the hope that subsequently it will permit of a decision as to the place of the human mind and its scientific endeavour—of science itself—within the total scheme of things. For clearly science and man are part of the world which they study and cannot rightly be omitted from the scientific account of it. In this way, perhaps, a metaphysical theory may be outlined and a theory of knowledge may be approached which have some semblance of scientific stability. Epistemology is not the propaedeutic, but the final achievement of science and philosophy, and is the fruit of reflection upon all stages of knowledge, pre-scientific, scientific and (what I believe to be only an extension of the foregoing) philosophical. And knowledge itself is not the precursor but the outcome of a long and arduous development in nature, examination of the course of which should throw light upon its products.[2]

4

The task proposed would seem to call for superhuman capabilities. To perform it adequately one would have to be both a scientist, trained and competent in every branch of natural science and a practised philosopher as well. But in these days that is beyond the capacity of the most brilliant. Ideally it is an

[1] Cf. Bertrand Russell: 'Science is at no moment quite right, but it is seldom quite wrong, and has, as a rule, a better chance of being right than the theories of the unscientific.' *My Philosophical Development* (London, 1959), p. 17.

[2] Here, once more, I find myself in happy agreement with Bertrand Russell, who believes it to be a mistake 'to begin with how we know and proceed afterwards to what we know ... because knowing how we know is one small department of knowing what we know'; and 'for another reason: it tends to give to knowing a cosmic importance which it by no means deserves'. *My Philosophical Development*, p. 16. Russell's subsequent elaboration of his second reason is somewhat obscured by his failure to define the term 'mental', but those whom he criticizes often fail equally to clarify its meaning.

enterprise that should be carried out conjointly by scientists and philosophers in collaboration. But, unfortunately, it is difficult to find a team of specialists with the time and inclination to undertake it, who are all sufficiently intelligible to one another and all sufficiently persuaded of the value and necessity of the project. Philosophers particularly in recent years have preferred to seek short cuts to what they term 'professional status' by adopting limited techniques without critical examination of the presuppositions that support them or sufficient validation of their scientific status, neglecting the sort of question which might contribute to a philosophy of nature, and thus leaving the scientists who might be willing to cooperate without philosophical guidance. Moreover, the esotericism of the philosophers often alienates the sympathy of the scientist seeking elucidation of the philosophical implications of his discoveries. And, in consequence, the effort towards synopticism is neglected.

My own ability to fulfil the requirements single-handed of so large a project is obviously and lamentably inadequate. But, while acutely conscious of my shortcomings, I hope that I may be able to provide an outline sufficient to stimulate the interest of more able thinkers and to indicate the value of the undertaking by properly qualified experts. To expound scientific theories I do not pretend, nor yet to cover any special field in detail. I attempt only to report, with as much indication as seems necessary of the process by which they were reached, general conclusions in the main branches of science, in order to discern the overall tendency, and to see how far they fit together into a coherent world-concept. I shall do this, not on my own authority, but on that of the recognized leaders of thought in the sciences concerned. Where they disagree (for it is only a vulgar myth that science is so assured a route to truth that disagreement between doctors is excluded), I shall endeavour to be impartial, and if I show any preference for one of two or more rival theories, it will only be when it seems more easily compatible with what is best established in related fields.

The first part of this essay will be devoted to reviewing, in turn, the findings of the physical, the biological and the psychological sciences, and to considering if and how they contribute to a general doctrine of the nature of things. The second stage of the enquiry (to be reserved for a separate volume) will move to an examination of what James Conant has called 'case-histories' of scientific discovery and reasoning, with a view to determining the general character of scientific procedure and explanation, and of the process of scientific advance. From this, in conjunction with the conclusions emerging from the first part, I shall try to develop a theory of knowledge, estimating as I do so, the extent to which the scientific evidence supports current and traditional epistemologies. In short, I hope that from these lines of enquiry, metaphysical and epistemological theories will emerge in harmony with one another and with the scientific temper of the age. Whether or not they may be regarded as examples of 'scientific philosophy' will depend upon what we decide as we proceed about the criteria of science and the scientific, and when these are established the final judgement may safely be left to the reader.

PART I
THE PHYSICAL WORLD

CHAPTER II

THE PHYSICAL WORLD

I

The twentieth-century revolution in physics presents us with a conception of physical nature so radically different from that entertained by classical physics that the philosophical outlook conditioned by the latter is no longer viable either as a metaphysical theory or as a tacit presupposition of other sciences. That as yet philosophers, with a few notable exceptions, have not recognized this fact is one of the intellectual incongruencies of the age. For what is overtly styled the philosophical revolution of the present day—the 'analytical' movement led by Russell, Moore, Wittgenstein and Carnap—has gone diametrically in the opposite direction. Some biologists and psychologists also seem still to lag behind in their awareness of the extent to which modern physics has cut away from under their sciences the old materialist-mechanist conceptions of reality. The word here to be emphasized is 'old'. Modern physics has not abolished matter, or replaced it by 'spirit', it has given a fundamentally new account of it; and mechanism has not given way to 'vitalism' or anything of that sort, but has more or less been rendered meaningless by the new developments. In deposing the old ideas, contemporary physics has not enthroned their equally outdated philosophical rivals, it has evolved out of them something significantly different from either.

This has been done in two main phases, which have been historically concurrent. First, the theory of relativity completely transformed the conception of the world in space and time. From a vast collection of individualized particles externally related to one another and to the infinitely extended containers, space and time, which were independent not only of them but also of each other, it transformed the idea of the world into one of a single, continuous, unbroken space-time whole, constituted by a web of interrelated events themselves determined by the geometrical properties of the field in which they occur and from which they and the physical properties of the entities participating in them are inseparable. For classical physics empty space and time were prior to matter both logically and (conceivably, at least) temporally. Space and time could not, as Kant declared, be thought away, though their entire filling could.[1] A time before the creation of the universe could be (though need not be) imagined in which nothing existed except the space which might potentially contain entities and there might again be time after the end of the world unfilled by events; but events themselves cannot be thought as timeless.[2] For relativity physics, in contrast, events and space-time are concurrently real, mutually constitutive and altogether inseparable either in fact or in thought. Space-time is the metrical and physical field in which events and things are nodal regions, 'folds' or 'pleats' (as Eddington was fond of calling them). The salient effect of relativity physics is unification—the coalescence of space, time, matter and energy into a single systematically articulated continuum, from which none of these factors can be extricated. Further, where classical physics envisaged a space extending infinitely in all directions and a time without beginning or end, the general theory of relativity offers a self-contained, self-complete, yet boundless universe of finite extent—a whole which excludes nothing though it is not endlessly extended. So, instead of an interminably incomplete world of separate and externally related particles, we have a single, intricately interwoven structure of mutually constituting elements.

The second phase of the revolution in physics, carrying with it fundamental changes of philosophical outlook, was the development of the quantum theory. The effect of this is to create in the physical microcosm the same sort of transformation as relativity has produced in the physical macrocosm. What classical physics conceived as an indivisible, hard, irreducible atom, quantum physics sees as a physical system in which the elementary particle is, as it were, in solution. Within this system, and in its systematic inter-relation with other elements, the particle is sometimes distinguishable but is inextricable as a separate entity. For the isolable mass-point of classical physics, the quantum theory substitutes what may be styled a physical pattern, or *Gestalt*, identifiable as a whole and containing within it distinguishable features. These may sometimes be represented as if they were particles, sometimes as if they were waves, but they are not

[1] *Vide Kritik der Reinen Vernunft*, A 24, B 38–9 and A 31, B 46.
[2] Cf. Milic Capek's lucid exposition in *The Philosophical Impact of Contemporary Physics* (New York, 1961), Chs. II and III.

themselves identifiable as separable and individualized entities. Here again all relations prove to be internal, and the system takes precedence over the particular components in the mutually constitutive inter-play of primal activity.[1]

The physical world is thus seen as a macroscopic totality encapsulating within it microscopic totalities all constituted on similar principles of unified order. It is a complex system to which the constituent elements are integral and mutually formative. In the light of this conception, any talk of atomic facts is wholly incongruous and the sort of logic based on mutually independent propositions is obviously inappropriate. Necessary connections, which Hume has banished, are now seen to be indispensable, and the idea of factual truths that are both synthetic and logically cogent, so far from being evidently impossible as empiricists maintain, is inescapable. If the implications of modern physics are taken seriously, whole edifices of current philosophy must be assigned to the house breakers and a new metaphysic and a new logic must be sought.

2

In the chapters which follow I shall try to give some account of the way in which this revolutionary change comes about, dealing first with the transmutation of the classical idea of the world by the special and general theories of relativity. Next, consideration will be given to the new conception of space-time and its character as an inherently articulated system, variously manifesting and exemplifying a unitary principle of order. Thirdly, the cosmological conception will be outlined and examined, to bring out the essentially inter-connected character of fundamental physical facts, and the mutual dependence of what, at first sight, might seem to be remote and unrelated factors within the physical universe. Fourthly, the complex ramifications, both in physics and in philosophy, of the new theory of matter will be reviewed: the complementarity of the notions of wave and particle, the conflict and its possible resolution between the discontinuity of matter and energy and the essentially continuous character of relativistic space-time, the far-reaching influence of Pauli's Principle of Exclusion as a source of organization and system. Lastly, I shall sum up the position resulting from the theories of

[1] See below, pp. 131–139.

contemporary physics and try to outline the general conception of the physical world which it forces upon us. This will conclude the first section of our review of the scientific account of nature, to be followed by a similar treatment of the biological sciences seeking to discover the significance of life as a further stage in the organization of the world.

CHAPTER III

RELATIVITY

I

The starting-point of the classical mechanics was the conception *in abstracto* of a mass-point free of all external influences; not that any such thing had been or ever could have been observed, but the phenomena of movement which are observed could be most intelligibly explained in terms of a set of postulates of which the Law of Inertia was one of the most important. That the motion of such a free material point is uniform in a straight line is not subject to experimental confirmation. The nearest we could come to a practical demonstration of it would be by causing smooth balls to roll along a surface as even as we could make it, eliminating as far as was practicable the sources of friction, and observing the degree of approximation to uniform rectilinear motion which would result from the proportionate reduction of external forces. Even so, gravity and a host of other physical influences would in practice defy attempts to eliminate them altogether, and the balls themselves would not be mass-points, even though they might be assumed to be aggregates of particles. Nor could we construct on the Earth's surface a runway which is smooth and rectilinear, and if we could the result of the experiment would still not confirm our hypothesis. None of the heavenly bodies is observed to move uniformly in a straight line, and in fact if anything ever were observed to do so, it would still be questionable how far its absolute freedom from external forces could be empirically discovered. The implausibility of much current epistomology in the light of the non-empirical character of this and other important scientific principles is something we shall have to consider hereafter. At this point we need only observe that this conception of isolated, free-moving particle is the key to the entire idea of the physical world which became current during the two centuries immediately following Newton's *Principia*—a world of separate and independent particles brought into mutual relation by external and fortuitous causes.

The exertion of a force upon a freely moving particle, it was next presumed, would change its velocity in proportion to the

B*

force applied and in the direction of its application. Accordingly, the knowledge of the position and velocity of such a particle, as well as of the forces acting upon it at any instant of time, provides data sufficient to calculate its future movement and to determine its position and velocity at any subsequent instant. These forces, however, in classical mechanics, are consequent upon the action of other particles and are dependent upon their masses, positions and movement. Thus, in any system of moving bodies, if the mass, position and velocity of each is known at any particular instant, the position and velocity of all is calculable for any other instant of time. In the words of Louis de Broglie:

'Thus for a system formed of N material points we obtain an array of 3N differential equations of second order with respect to time between the 3N coordinates of the N material points. Mathematical analysis then shows that the solution of this array of equations is entirely determinate if we know at a certain initial instant the position and velocity of all the points of the system.'[1]

The particles were pictured as moving in space as in a vast receptacle. Space was the theatre of operation and they were in it, not of it. Their movement took time, which was conceived as a sort of separate and absolute movement independent both of space and of the bodies whose motion was correlated with it. Yet, though space and time were, on the one hand, mere containers for bodies to exist and move in, they also, on the other hand, provided those bodies with some of their most fundamental properties: extension and duration. An odd inconsistency here infects the classical mechanical conception of the world, about which scientists, before the beginning of the twentieth century, remained unconcerned, though some philosophers were worried by it. Space and time were something external to bodies—a mere field of their mutual relations—and yet at the same time essential to and constitutive of them. The spatio-temporal properties of bodies which for Locke and his contemporaries were 'primary' were seen to be 'such as are utterly inseparable from the body, in what estate soever it be ... and the mind finds inseparable from every particle of matter'. Extension, figure and mobility were listed among them. Yet the existence and changes of these spatio-temporal objects left unaffected the absolute, immutable, brooding presence of the space and time in which they occurred.

[1] *The Revolution in Physics* (London, 1954), pp. 30-1.

The location, duration and motion which for Newton constituted the spatio-temporal quantities inherent in the real world
were not the apparent or relative measures commonly attributed
to physical entities as perceived, but only their 'true, mathematical
or absolute' measures. The true places of bodies and times of
events were taken to be immutable parts of space and time. 'It
is from their essence or nature that they are places', writes Newton,
'and that the primary places of things should be movable is
absurd'. The same is held of time; and 'translations out of those
(primary) places are the only absolute motions'.[1] Thus bodies
have length, duration and motion as intrinsic properties, which,
however they may be disguised in their appearance to us due to
relativity to one another and to our positions and motions relative
to them, are their own absolute attributes. For example, each end
of a rod has its absolute place so that the distance between them
is a fixed and absolute length, and if the rod is moved from its
primary place, defined by these positions and their mutual
distance, its consequent absolute motion is its intrinsic and
peculiar activity. This movement is essentially the uniform,
rectilinear, inertial movement, modifications of which only occur
as a result of the impingement of external forces, and any such
forces will themselves be the result of the position and movement
intrinsic to other bodies.

The world of classical mechanics was thus a particulate world,
the substances of which were material points each with its own
intrinsic primary properties including mass, position, figure and
motion. The influence of each upon the others was exercised
from a distance and was extrinsic to the passive participant,
affecting it, no doubt, yet doing so only as permitted by its own
intrinsic characters. These were primary and fundamental and
were the source of any secondary qualities with which the substance might be credited. The secondary characters were to be
listed among the relative and apparent properties resulting from
its relation to our perceiving and more truly attributable to the
perceiver than to the perceived, being effects produced by the
object upon his consciousness.

To such a world the categories of substance and attribute
were plainly appropriate and the subject-predicate form of
proposition specially applicable. Bodies were in the last resort
atomic with their particular properties inherent in them. The

[1] *Principia*, Definitions, Scholium.

statement of any such inherence of a property in a substance was the statement of an atomic fact, as was that of the external relations determining the influences from without to which they were subject. It was at least *prima facie* a world of metaphysical and logical atomism of which it would be plausible to say:

'The world divides into facts.

'Any one can either be the case or not be the case, and everything else remain the same.'[1]

But even of the world of classical physics this would have been a superficial description, if only because one of the forces acting between bodies was that of universal gravitation, dependent upon their masses and spatial positions; and even if these were regarded as intrinsic properties, the mutual attraction which resulted determined the motion of particles in such a way that all must be dependent upon each. It was precisely for this reason that, from the knowledge of the positions and velocities of all the particles in any system at one instant, the state of the system at any other instant was held to be calculable.[2] Thus the falsity of the statement that any of the constituent facts might be or not be the case while everything else remained the same ought to have been patent.

Yet the ease with which any such system could be analysed into its constituent parts, and the success with which the results of combining such parts could be calculated from the data that the analysis provided, rendered the atomistic approach particularly appealing, and this may be one of the reasons (though not the only one) for its persistence into the twentieth century. Moreover, classical physics, as it developed, pursued several relatively separate paths simultaneously in optics, mechanics, thermodynamics and electrodynamics. The assumption of the particulate character of the material world for long served as a tenable basis for theories in all these branches, but their underlying unity remained to be demonstrated. Towards the end of the nineteenth

[1] Wittgenstein, *Tractatus Logico-philosophicus*, 1.2, 1.21.

[2] 'In particular, if you have committed yourself to a system of mechanics in which accelerations are produced by external forces, and if you are committed to the view that these forces are interactions between particles, it would seem that before you can make any progress in the subject you would need to know, not only the configuration of the universe, but also very detailed information about the nature of the forces involved.' Professor G. Temple, 'From the Relative to the Absolute', in *Turning Points in Physics*, ed. A. C. Crombie (Amsterdam, 1959–60), p. 71.

century, however, the mechanistic interpretation of the physical world, of which the main outline has just been sketched, proved progressively less satisfactory until it finally broke down and, with the theories of relativity and quanta, the particulate picture of reality was superseded, leaving the atomistic philosophy of latter-day Empiricism as a curious anachronism.

2

The special theory of relativity effected the break which occasioned this conceptual transformation. The allegedly intrinsic primary properties of bodies were their measurable features and by measurement alone could they be precisely determined. Yet absolute place, time and motion defy measurement because no absolute standard can be discovered against which to measure them. The progress of physics revealed the impossibility of identifying an absolute inertial system in which bodies could be truly at rest. Every reference body available is in motion relatively to some other reference bodies or systems. The earth having lost her central fixity at the very inception of modern scientific development, the sun was taken as a more reliable origin for axes of reference. But the sun moves round the galaxy and the frame it provides is not absolute. The fixed stars next seemed to afford the appropriate absolute reference system; but they are not fixed. Whether galactic or extra-galactic, they are all in motion, relative to one another and to our galaxy, as our galaxy is to the sun. Physicists then turned to interstellar space itself, having filled it with a substance, the luminiferous aether, which might serve as the required absolute standard of measurement. With the complexities and paradoxes involved in theories of the aether we need not here trouble ourselves; that motion relative to it is systematically undetectable was finally established by Michelson, and nothing was left to which appeal could be made as an absolute criterion of position and motion. This discovery led to Poincaré's enunciation of the Principle of Relativity, 'that a uniform translatory motion, which is possessed by a system as a whole, cannot be detected by observation of phenomena taking place wholly within that system'. In short, there is no way of determining absolute motion. Accordingly, any frame of reference moving uniformly is an inertial (or 'Galilean') frame equivalent to any other Galilean frame, and its velocity being relative to every other is no fixed quantity but depends upon the reference body with which we choose to compare it.

The very fact that disqualified the aether as an absolute standard and established this universal relativity of co-ordinate systems, the defiant invariance of the velocity of light, made length and time incurably relative quantities, variable systematically with the velocity of the co-ordinate system used as a standard of reference. There can be no simple location in space or time, no length or motion intrinsic to mutually independent bodies. These properties are no more than relations between the object and the observer[1] and depend on the local conditions of observation. Many of the most obvious 'primary' qualities (motion, and rest, length and duration) have thus become 'secondary' in a manner hardly contemplated by Berkeley (who demolished the distinction on the strength of more subjective considerations), through the conception of measurement itself and the physical means of its application.

The velocity of light as measured by all observers, irrespective of their own motion, is found to be invariant, and this cannot be because a luminiferous aether is carried along with the observer nor because the light participates in the motion of the source of propagation. The Doppler and Fizeau effects prove that the former is not the case, and the latter is disproved by the absence in the appearance of rotating double stars of any discrepancy due to variation, with the velocity of its source, of the velocity of their light. Consequently the measurement of simultaneity of distant events, for which purpose light (or radio) signals are the only means at our disposal, will differ for observers moving with different velocities relative to one another. This is neatly illustrated by Sir Edmund Whittaker as follows:[2] Let us suppose two rigid rods of equal length AB and DE, are moving relatively to each other with a velocity sufficient to be significant in comparison with that of light. Let there be observers at C, the midpoint of AB, and at F, the midpoint of DE. Suppose that simultaneous light signals are

$$A \qquad\qquad C \qquad\qquad B$$
$$D \qquad\qquad F \qquad\qquad E$$
$$D_1 \qquad\qquad F_1 \qquad\qquad E_1$$

---

[1] Cf. Eddington, *Space, Time and Gravitation* (Cambridge, 1953), Ch. II.

[2] *Vide From Euclid to Eddington* (Cambridge, 1949), pp. 57-8.

are flashed from C to A and B and from F to D and E. Each observer will then record as simultaneous the arrival of his signals at the end points of his own rod. If the emission of the signals is presumed to occur when the rods are coincident, the arrival of the signals at the end points of the rods will occur when DE has travelled some distance from AB and A will no longer coincide with D nor B with E. Let us represent the new position of DE as $D_1 E_1$. The distances of these new points from C are not equal. As the velocity of light is invariant for all observers, the signals could not, for the observer at C, have reached D_1 and E_1 simultaneously, yet they must have done so for the observer at F (F_1). For the latter the signals could not have reached A and B simultaneously, though they must have done so for the observer at C. Therefore, simultaneity has a different meaning for observers in different frames of reference.

The simultaneity of the events at A and B, or at D and E, depends, however, upon our knowledge of the equality of the distances AC and CB, DF and FE. For the observer at C, AC= CB; for the observer at F, DF=FE. But for the former, $CD_1 \neq CE_1$. If events are found to be simultaneous in experience their actual temporal relation can be calculated only from a knowledge of the distance between them. But the distance of moving points (and there is nothing absolutely at rest) can be measured, in the last resort, only with the help of light rays. The velocity of light is thus bound to affect our measurements both of time and of space, and as it is invariant, these measures, both spatial and temporal, as made by observers moving with different velocities relative to each other, are bound to diverge. Thus the interdependence of measurements of space and of time becomes inescapable.

The divergence of measures resulting from relative motion can be computed by the use of the Lorentz transformations and results obtained in one Galilean frame of reference can be transferred to any other by their application. The Lorentz transformations are a set of formulae which enable us to determine measurements in any and all inertial systems moving uniformly with different velocities from the knowledge of their values in any one such system. Each frame of reference provides a unified system for measurements applicable throughout the entire universe, yet each gives different values to the quantities determined by reference to it. Nevertheless they are all systematically interconnected by

the Lorentz transformation formulae, which are specially constructed to take account of the invariant velocity of light in every
system, so that fundamental laws of physics will remain constant
in all. This is not an invention of the mathematician or a piece
of chicanery on the part of the physicist to force reality into a
mould that suits his purposes. The physical laws are themselves
what represent the real world and their invariance is the hallmark
of their objectivity and independence of special subjective and
observational conditions. If it could not be maintained and if
every frame of reference gave measures irreconcilable with every
other, no coherent account at all could be given of the physical
phenomena. It was indeed the failure of the classical mechanical
approach to give such an account consistent with the Michelson-
Morley experiment and with other physical facts, some of which
have been mentioned above, that forced its supersession by the
theory of relativity. Newtonian mechanics are not, however,
false; they give virtually accurate results where velocities in
relation to light are so small as to make negligible difference to
measurements of length and time. But the range of their justifiable
applicability is limited to such cases.

It is already apparent that the effect of the special theory of
relativity is that of unification of the world by way of essential
interrelationships between the erstwhile independent primary
qualities of bodies. These now become interlocked, not only in
any one separate body, but with those of other bodies relative
to which it is moving; not only with reference to the co-ordinate
system in which they are measured, but also by virtue of the
essential interrelation of all Galilean systems. It is, moreover,
to be remembered that these primary properties are no mere
adjuncts of the entities they characterize but are intimately
constitutive of them, and they are now seen to be mutually
inseparable and determinable only in relation to one another.

There is, however, a still more far-reaching interdependence
established by the theory: that of spatial distance and temporal
lapse. In summing up the conception of space and time to which
the special theory of relativity leads us, M. Émile Borel writes:
'The essential point is the absolute impossibility of separating
the measurement of space from the measurement of time'.[1] To
assess the interval between events both must be taken into account
together in a four-dimensional space-time frame with the product

---

[1] *Space and Time* (London, 1931), p. 161.

of the time and the velocity of light as the fourth co-ordinate. The divergent results of measurement of the same phenomena in different co-ordinate systems then reflect varying modes of separating space from time by observers moving relatively to one another with different velocities, or alternatively, the rotation of axes in a Minkowski four-dimensional world.[1] But in every frame the space-time interval between events is invariant.

What we have here is a generalization of Euclidean geometry to four dimensions, amalgamating space and time. So, likewise, the relativistic mechanics prove to be simply a generalization of the classical mechanics, and for small velocities the two are virtually indistinguishable.

Our separation of space from time thus proves to be 'subjective', in the sense that it is contingent upon the conditions of observation. But the 'objective' fact remains as the invariant interval between events. Those constituting the history of any entity can be regarded as a continuous line in the four-dimensional continuum, known as its world-line, which is the same for all observers in inertial co-ordinate systems, and the intervals between these events are invariant. All observers, in every such system, will discover the same world-lines for physical objects.

The 'primary' qualities of length and duration, figure and motion have turned out to be purely relative; what so far remains 'primary' and 'objective' is embedded in a space-time matrix. The interval is neither a length nor a duration but both at once; it is strictly not the quality of a body quasi-independent of the spatio-temporal field in which it exists, but a series of events co-ordinately analysable[2] in various ways according to the frame of reference adopted. And these events are not separable occurrences, but rather distinguishable phases in a continuous spatio-temporal process. This is equally true whether they constitute the world-line of a physical thing or some process of translatory motion (be it of light signals or any other agency) involved in the performance of measurement. Space-time is of their essence, yet apart from them (as we shall see) there is neither space nor time.

In the classical mechanics, mass was at least as important a quality of bodies as length and duration. But in contemporary

[1] *Vide* Einstein, *Relativity, The Special and General Theory* (London, 1954), p. 122.
[2] Cf. Whitehead, *Process and Reality* (Cambridge, 1929), p. 408.

physics this too has become a relative quantity varying with the frame of reference. As the velocity of light is a limit which cannot be exceeded, the acceleration of a moving body is resisted as it converges to that limit, not only in proportion to the inertial mass of the body (as in classical mechanics), but also in proportion to the velocity already attained. Increase in velocity is accompanied by increase in kinetic energy, which is now indistinguishable from (for it has precisely the same effect as) increase in inertial mass. The relativistic formula for this increase contains the expression mc^2, which Einstein recognized as the quantity representing the energy of the body before augmentation—in other words the energy of its rest-mass. He could thus establish a general equivalence between mass and energy in the equation $e=mc^2$, the far-reaching implications of which will become more apparent later. What is to be noticed here is that the mass of a moving body is not a fixed quantity because it depends on velocity, which is relative; and there is no identifiable state of absolute rest. Mass has become a 'secondary' quality in the same way as length and duration, for it depends on the conditions of observation and measurement peculiar to the particular frame of reference chosen.

The picture of a world of mass-points, of bodies consisting of aggregates of such particulate masses, moving in an absolute field of space and time, has thus been transformed into one of a unified space-time continuum, in which events can be distinguished, but out of which they cannot be dissected—events constituted by their mutual relations in a world of correlative elements, inseparable and interdependent, constituting a single complex whole.

The mutual dependence of these constitutive relations is, moreover, not simply factual but logical. It is entailed by the very concepts of the properties concerned. Position, length, figure, duration, mass, are all terms necessarily implying measurement, comparison and the mutual interrelation of parts. Position is a meaningless term apart from co-ordinates of some kind (be they only molar objects crudely used as references for orientation). A co-ordinate system is a minimal requirement for definition of any determinate extensive quantity. Any statement, therefore, referring to the determinate position of an object entails reference to a co-ordinate system and so necessarily and immediately entails other statements about other actual and possible positions.

Length depends upon the relation between at least two such determinate positions and carries similar entailments. The precise definition of a length implies a standard of measurement with which it must be compared, and an instrument for making the comparison embodying the standard. Thus any statement referring to length logically entails a statement of comparison with a presumed standard—one may say, is logically equivalent to such a statement. But the theory of relativity teaches us that no such statement has a simple or absolute meaning, but expresses a value that systematically alters with the velocity of the co-ordinate system in relation to the object measured. Velocity, however, is a concept logically involving those of length and time and its quantitative determination in any particular case involves a comparison between lengths, durations and positions, and all these quantities are mutually determinant. No statement about any one of them is free from entailment of statements referring to some or all of the others. Every measurement of length entails one or more measurements of time and both imply and are implied by measurements of velocity.

It might be argued that the actual length of a given rod may or may not be a certain quantity, and that it can be discovered only through the performance of an actual process of measurement, the result of which is contingent. But, even if this were conceded (and we shall later see that there are good reasons for denying it), no act of measurement can be performed and no result can be obtained that does not logically (and mathematically) involve, tacitly or explicitly, reference to a co-ordinate system and to its velocity relative to the object measured. That is to say, every statement of the result of a particular measurement necessarily entails statements (specific and precise) of the results of other measurements.

If then Professor Ayer is right, and it is a logical truism that a statement referring to one of two distinct states of affairs does not entail anything about the other, there can be no distinct states of affairs in the physical world; but if the length of a rod (to take but one instance) and its velocity relative to any observer, are distinct states of affairs, then Professor Ayer must be wrong, because any statement referring to one of them will entail some statements referring to the other. What follows in the rest of this chapter will reinforce this point even further.

3

An intermediate stage between the conception of a particulate universe and the four-dimensional space-time world, was marked by the notion of 'field' that came into the foreground of physical theorizing with the development of electro-dynamics. A charged particle or a magnet is surrounded by a configuration of lines of force along which a free body subject to electrical or magnetic forces will be accelerated in the direction in which the force acts. This configuration is known as the field of force of the particle or the magnet. The direction of movement of a test body is described as being from a higher to a lower potential of the force, and the field might be defined as the structure or distribution of potentials associated with the source of energy. When the interrelation of electric and magnetic forces had been recognized, the electromagnetic field was defined and the equations determining its structure were evolved by Clerk Maxwell. In the first instance, it was the attempt to understand electromagnetism in terms of the classical notions of forces acting between particles that gave rise to the idea of the field. But phenomena for the interpretation of which the new concept was most successfully used did not conform to the older ideas.[1] In fact, as field physics developed, particles became relatively unimportant and attention was concentrated upon the field filling the space between them. 'In the new field language', we learn from Einstein and Infeld, 'it is the description of the field between the two charges, and not the charges themselves, which is essential for an understanding of their action. The recognition of the new concepts grew steadily [these writers continue], until substance was overshadowed by the field.'[2]

As the field fills the whole of space and time, no part of the physical universe is completely unaffected by it (even though, for most practicable purposes, its effects may cease to be considerable beyond a limited region). The introduction of the concept, therefore, indicative of the crumbling of the classical mechanics, gives rise to a more unified picture of the material world, in which

[1] *Vide* Einstein and Infeld, *The Evolution of Physics* (New York, 1954), Ch. III, and Einstein, *Relativity*, pp. 146 ff.

[2] Op. cit., pp. 157–8. The distinction was later to break down altogether. *Vide* Ch. VI, below, pp. 112, 126–131, 140 f.

every particle becomes, in a sense, all-pervasive[1] and each becomes involved with every other in a complex of overlapping fields. For every particle is the centre at least of a gravitational field and may also have electrical and magnetic fields associated with it, the limits of none of which can be sharply drawn and which modify the physical environment of every other particle.

At first, however, the field was represented as a region of wave propagation, the velocity of which was precisely determined as Maxwell's constant c—the velocity of light in a vacuum—and the waves were imagined as occurring in a material medium, aether. Difficulties concerning its texture and mechanical properties soon proved insurmountable, but still greater were the difficulties concerning the velocity of the wave propagation relative to that of its source and of the observer measuring it. As Professor Temple has recently reminded us,[2] the frame of reference in which this propagation is supposed to occur is not specified. If the aether provided an absolute frame, velocity relative to it should be detectable, but that was found to be impossible. Yet it cannot be a Galilean frame, for all such frames are equivalent and transformation of measures from one to another would involve a modification of the velocity of light, whereas the evidence is incontrovertable that the velocity of light is independent of that of its source. Consequently the medium had to be abandoned, while the field remained somehow to be accommodated within the four-dimensional continuum envisaged by the special theory of relativity. This was successfully accomplished in the general theory.

4

The first step was the recognition by Einstein of the identity between inertial and gravitiational forces and his enunciation of the principle of equivalence. As bodies behave relative to an accelerated frame of reference in exactly the same way as if they were in a gravitational field relative to an unaccelerated frame, it is immaterial which of the two frames is taken to be 'at rest'.[3]

[1] Cf. Pierre Teilhard de Chardin, *The Phenomenon of Man* (London, 1959), pp. 41 and 45.

[2] *Vide* 'From the Relative to the Absolute', *Turning Points in Physics*, p. 74.

[3] Cf. Einstein, *Relativity, the Special and General Theory*, Ch. XX, and *The Meaning of Relativity* (London, 1956), p. 56.

Relative to the presumed inertial frame an accelerated body will respond to inertial forces precisely equivalent to those of a gravitational field which would be presumed by an observer using a frame attached to the accelerating body. The principle of equivalence, therefore, states (in Eddington's formulation): 'A gravitational field of force is precisely equivalent to an artificial field of force [i.e. one produced by accelerated motion], so that in any small region it is impossible by any conceivable experiment to distinguish between them'.[1]

As Eddington puts it, a field of force appears as soon as the observer and his measuring appliances are deflected from their 'natural track' in space-time, that is, the one which traverses the longest interval between events in which the observer and his instruments are concerned.[2] He therefore substitutes a new law of motion for Newton's first law, which he finds tautological because the only way in which we can tell whether or not a body is affected by impressed forces is to discover whether or not its motion is uniform in a straight line. The new law states: 'Every particle moves so as to take the track of greatest interval-length between two events, except in so far as disturbed by impacts of other particles or electrical forces'.[3] These 'natural tracks' are geodesics in space-time.

As the interval-length is invariant for all frames of reference, this natural track or geodesic is absolute and the same for all observers, but, according to the frame selected, it may appear to be straight or curved in any of a number of different ways. Its apparent curvature will correspond to acceleration—or alternatively to the 'forces' acting upon the moving body—and the degree of curvature to the magnitude of the acceleration (or force). But, as every body in the known world is in non-uniform motion relative to some other bodies, no frame can be selected in which all curvature is eliminated. There is, in short, no completely Galilean frame, though approximations to Galilean conditions can be found in limited regions. Thus whatever frame we care to choose, gravitational fields will be observable, though they will be different for different frames. Nevertheless,

---

[1] *Space, Time and Gravitation*, p. 76. The limitation to small regions is necessary, for it is not always possible to choose a frame of reference that will cancel a gravitational field throughout its extent.

[2] Op. cit., p. 69.

[3] Op. cit., p. 82. Electrical forces are given separate consideration later.

the law of gravitation, as a fundamental law of physics, must be the same in all. This condition is realized when the fact is recognized that measuring instruments (rigid rods and clocks) behave differently in gravitational fields of varying intensities (i.e., frames accelerated in varying degrees) and that, accordingly, the geometry of space-time in different regions is not uniform.[1] Alternatively, we may say that the applicable geometry is non-Euclidean; the co-ordinates used cannot be Cartesian but must be Gaussian, and the four-dimensional geometry resulting is Riemannian. This is equivalent to representing space-time as variously curved, its curvature governing the relations between the measurements in different co-ordinate systems which map out the structure of fields of force in any region. The type and degree of curvature involved is discovered by examination of the mathematical equation necessary to determine the invariant interval between events.

When Gaussian co-ordinates are used, this equation is a generalized form of that required by Cartesian co-ordinates. The new equation involves a series of coefficients which are functions of the co-ordinates, and the mathematical properties of which define the type of curvature of the continuum to which they refer. These coefficients are found to correspond to the potentials (inertial or gravitational according to the view-point taken) of the field of force indicated by the curvature of the geodesic in the co-ordinate system chosen. The gravitational field is thus seen as a geometrical peculiarity of the spatio-temporal manifold.

In space-time the motion of every particle is traced as a world-line, and, as only physical interactions are observable, all discoverable events are intersections of these world-lines. These are points determined by different co-ordinates in different systems, but their relations to one another correspond for all observers and their mutual order is the same in every system. This order constitutes the physical structure of the world in an absolute sense. Eddington pictures the network of world-lines as embedded in a jelly, which may be deformed in any way without altering the order of intersections. We can introduce any kind of co-ordinate system we find convenient to determine their positions,

---

[1] Cf. Einstein, *Relativity*, Ch. XXIII, and *The Meaning of Relativity*, pp. 55–9. The constancy of the law of gravitation operates here analogously to that of the velocity of light in the special theory.

and the intervals and the order of encounters between world-lines will be the same in all. As Eddington points out, there is no difference between distorting the jelly after having introduced (say) a rectangular co-ordinate system, and introducing the system after the distortion of the jelly, nor is there any criterion for deciding which representation is better; both are equally valid.

The geometry of space-time, its real curvature, is not determined by the co-ordinate system applied to it for the purposes of measurement, but by the physical laws which determine the structure of the field. These, now seen as laws of geometry, restrict the possible kinds of space, or of metrical field, that can exist in nature. The 'field of force' is a relative or secondary character in the world, but the kind of space which determines how it will occur is not, and this depends upon the laws of physics. Alternatively, we may say that the co-ordinate system used is arbitrary, within the limits set by the curvature of space (for not every type of co-ordinate system is applicable to every kind of space, as a strictly Cartesian system is inapplicable on a spherical surface), but there is a real property of the physical world which the curvature of space represents. In fact, to speak of 'curvature' is to speak analogically, imagining the geometrical properties of a certain type of space (e.g. Riemannian) as displayed upon a curved surface in Euclidean space. It is not, however, the curved surface that is real, but the geometrical properties of the metrical field. If we represent these by means of a curved surface in Euclidean space we do so only to aid our imagination and our talk of curvature is then metaphorical.

In this way the gravitational field is, in Meyerson's phrase, 'resorbed' into space-time, becoming simply a characterizing feature of its geometrical properties, and the idea of field in general is accommodated within the four-dimensional continuum under the concept of curvature. There is no need to presume the exertion of any peculiar physical force, for gravitational and inertial forces are no more than the effects we experience as we traverse the contours of space. Their existence or non-existence, their character and magnitude, depend on the frame of reference in which we make our measurements. They are secondary properties like length, duration and mass. The primary reality is immersed in the spatio-temporal continuum, is governed by its geometrical structure, and manifests itself in invariant quantities, such as interval and action (the product of energy and time), and the covariant laws of physics. This continuum is a single, seamless totality, containing undeniably a plurality of distinguishable elements, but elements which are distinguished in ways that are dependent upon the variable conditions of observation and are therefore not permanent or absolute divisions within the real.

5

Electrical and magnetic forces, the phenomena that originally gave rise to the field conception, have so far been left on one side, but an extension of Einstein's theory has been made to account for them in a similar manner. This was no mere adjunct to the theory but an essential expansion of it. Schrödinger writes:

'In Einstein's theory of gravitation matter and its dynamical interaction are based on the notion of an intrinsic geometric structure of the space-time continuum. The ideal aspiration, the ultimate aim, of the theory is not more and not less than this: A four-dimensional continuum endowed with a certain intrinsic geometric structure, a structure that is subject to certain inherent purely geometrical laws, is to be an adequate model or picture of the "real world around us in space and time" with all that it contains and including its total behaviour, the display of all events going on in it.'[1]

He goes on to say that the theory embraced from the outset every form of dynamical interaction and that gravitation was only the simplest case. Any agent whatsoever, he points out, producing ostensible accelerations does so in the form of 'an energy-momentum tensor', and produces it through the medium of the gravitational field connected with it. Whereas pure gravitation is simple in kind, because the energy-momentum tensor is regarded as located in minute specks of matter (mass-points) and as having a particularly simply form, the tensor connected with a charged particle is spread out throughout the space around it and is of a complicated form even when the particle is at rest. The laws of the electro-magnetic field, Schrödinger continues, are also to be regarded as purely geometrical restrictions on the structure of space-time.

[1] *Space-Time Structure* (Cambridge, 1950), p. 1.

Matter gives rise to a gravitational field, in consequence of its characteristics of mass, momentum and the like. But according to the special theory mass and energy are equivalent, and the general theory has shown that energy is susceptible of gravitational attraction. The presence of an electromagnetic field should, therefore, give rise to or modify a gravitational field. In other words, it should take the form of space-time curvature more complex than that corresponding to the simple gravitational field.

Einstein was able to show that various degrees of space-time curvature existed, progressively increasing from empty space, through space in the vicinity of matter and that in which electro-magnetic fields exist, to space filled with matter. But matter and electricity remained foreign to space-time in the sense that they did not appear to be a natural consequence of its geometrical properties and were imported from alien sources. The introduction by Weyl of a still more generalized form of geometry made it possible to assimilate at least the electromagnetic field, and a further generalization of Weyl's geometry developed by Eddington enabled him to deduce important consequences tending to link the results of relativity and those of quantum mechanics and to relate some of the essential properties of elementary particles to the geometry of space-time.

It is an assumption of Riemannian (as of Lobachewskian and Euclidean) geometry that the units of measurement (the gauge system) remain the same in all reference frames, so that two unit rods which coincide at one point will continue to coincide at any other point in space-time irrespective of the routes by which they might severally have been transported. Weyl treated this assumption as unwarranted. If it is, and if standards of length are susceptible of alteration on transference, the interval between events ceases to be invariant. Eddington shows that the assumption is precarious by pointing out that transference of standard rods and clocks from one reference frame to another would involve an abrupt change in their velocities which could quite conceivably alter their magnitudes and workings.[1] To overcome this difficulty Weyl developed a geometry requiring an additional space-time curvature. As in Riemannian geometry direction is non-transfer-able in consequence of the curvature of space, so in Weylian geometry distance is non-transferable because of a further

[1] *Space, Time and Gravitation*, pp. 167 f.

curvature (known as distance-curvature) involving the gauge-system in each region of space-time. This new curvature introduced into the description of the metrical field four functions additional to the ten which in Einstein's theory correspond to the potentials of the gravitational field and are expressive of direction-curvature. The new functions proved to be identical with the potentials of the electromagnetic field, and the new tensor equations were found to coincide with Maxwell's equations.

Where direction-curvature is absent, far from matter, Galilean conditions obtain and the gravitational potentials in our formulae vanish or remain constant. Where distance-curvature vanishes, space-time is non-Weylian and the potentials of the Weylian tensor disappear. In other words, far from matter there is no gravitational field and direction is transferable, but where direction is non-transferable a gravitational field exists; and similarly, where distance is found to be non-transferable an electro-magnetic field is present and where this is not the case distance-curvature vanishes. Yet not all curvature can completely disappear at any point in space-time, because the standards of measurement—constituting the gauge-system—are determined by it. Weyl maintains that the radius of curvature at any point provides a 'natural unit', and if space were completely flat this radius would be infinite and there would be no 'natural gauge' to serve as a standard.

In Einstein's theory the interval and the tensor equations characteristic of space-time curvature are independent of the co-ordinate system but not of the gauge system. The quantities in Weyl's theory which are independent of both co-ordinate and gauge systems have been styled (by Eddington) 'in-tensors' and 'in-invariants'. It is these now that must be regarded as the intrinsic quantities of reality in a world represented as a single, continuous, space-time whole, the geometrical properties of which account for all the physical manifestations we experience as length, duration, mass, gravitation and electromagnetic force.

6

The precise effect of this revolution in physical thinking has been well described by Sir Edmund Whittaker:

'From time immemorial the physicist and the pure mathematician had worked on a certain agreement as to the shares which they were respectively to take in the study of nature. The mathematician was to come first and analyse the properties of space and time, building up the primary sciences of geometry and kinematics; then, when the stage had thus been prepared, the physicist was to come along with the dramatis personae—material bodies, magnets, electric charges, light, and so forth—and the play was to begin. But in Einstein's revolutionary conception the characters created the stage as they walked about on it; geometry was no longer antecedent to physics, but indissolubly fused with it into a single discipline.'[1]

Further, the coalescence (so to call it) of the world is revealed in the deposition from predominance of Euclidean geometry because, in assuming the possibility of establishing immediately relations between points which are a finite distance apart, it tacitly presupposes action at a distance. In the Riemannian and Weylian geometry of the relativity theory no such assumption is permitted. 'In the new world', says Whittaker, 'no direct relations exist at all except between elements that are contiguous to each other.'[2] Relations between separate events are thus mediated by contiguities, and contiguity is essential to a world that is indisseverably one. No split or crack can be contemplated in this continuum, for it would disrupt all possible relations. Moreover, as the contiguous elements are events, not mere Euclidean points, they are always four-dimensional and their continuity is that of a process—a growing into and out of one another without break or cleavage. There can be no hiatus anywhere, for not only are world-lines unbroken threads in the continuum, but also the relation between events in different world-lines is mediated by the space-time curvature guiding the co-ordinate and gauge systems with which it is measured. It is, so to speak, generated out of the metrical properties of contiguous, infinitesimally small regions of the space-time matrix by the equations of differential geometry.

The only physical reality remaining in any way extrinsic to space-time is matter, so far as it appears in particulate forms. No way has hitherto been found of resolving electrons and protons into the electromagnetic field. Nevertheless we have seen that the field has taken precedence over the particle for the purposes of physical description and prediction, and has (so to say) spread

---

[1] *From Euclid to Eddington*, p. 117.   [2] *Ibid.*

the particle throughout space and time. Moreover, the gravitational field around a particle has been described by Eddington as a hummock in space-time such that it cannot be rounded off but culminates in a kind of infinite chimney. Eddington suggests that this chimney may be replaced by a higher degree of curvature than that of the gravitational field, a curvature representing the presence of matter. 'The region', he writes, 'cannot be empty, because the law applying to empty space does not hold. We describe it, therefore, as containing matter.'[1]

Furthermore, we have seen that energy and matter are not different substantial forms, but only different manifestations of the same reality, and we are shortly to find that the quantum theory permits no absolute distinction between particle and field, matter and radiation; and though the quantum of action has not yet been finally geometrized, the theory of relativity makes action (which Eddington identified with the curvature of the world) an absolute quantity. Though Planck's constant h, which plays so important a role in atomic physics, is perhaps not the natural unit of action, it may well have some significant relation to it.[2] Further, by a generalization of Weyl's geometry, Eddington developed a theory that enabled him to link the law of gravitation with the known facts and quantitive relationships of atomic phenomena, by way of a physical theory of the universe as a whole. To these ideas we shall return in Chapters V and VI. What we wish to emphasize here is that, through a continuous series of generalizations of Euclidean geometry and Newtonian mechanics, all physical phenomena have been resolved into the structure of space-time in a unified world. First, the special theory of relativity showed length and duration, mass and energy to be inseparably united; then the general theory geometrized the gravitational field; Weyl's extension of the theory assimilated to it the phenomena of electrodynamics, and, finally, Eddington attempted to include the structure of matter within the geometry of the four-dimensional whole. In the words of A. d'Abro:

'The ultimate goal is one of unification. We wish to succeed in representing the entire physical universe in terms of the relationships of structure of the fundamental space-time continuum. Einstein's space-time enabled us to account for gravitation in

---

[1] *Space, Time and Gravitation*, p. 98.
[2] Cf. Eddington, op. cit., p. 177.

this way, but the electromagnetic field appeared as a foreign invasion. None of the known elements of structure seemed capable of accounting for it. It seemed as though the world of space-time, gravitating masses and energy might just as well have existed in the absence of this electrical intrusion. Now, we have every reason to believe that such cannot be the case, for since matter is built up of protons and neutrons, the annihilation of electricity would entail that of matter, gravitation and energy, and possibly also of space and time. In order to overcome this difficulty, it appeared necessary to generalize our conception of space-time, obtaining thereby a continuum presenting additional elements of structure which might be identified with electric and magnetic forces. And so we were led to Weyl's generalization, which permits the electromagnetic field to enter into the general synthesis, no longer as a foreign adjunct, but as a constituent element of space-time structure. But besides the field there is the electron, and the field alone does not seem to afford us the possibility of building up the electron; we cannot account for atomicity or for the quanta of action. Therein resides the problem of matter. . . . So long as these mysteries remain unsolved, it is only natural that we should seek new elements of structure by proceeding with further generalizations. Eddington's theory was conceived with this object in view.'[1]

The effort of the scientist is thus to bring all physical phenomena under laws, each of which is a specific expression or special exemplification of the pervasive metrical properties of the space-time continuum. The world is conceived as an unbroken, unified whole, or four-dimensional process, not indeed blankly uniform, but richly differentiated into distinguishable parts and elements variously determining the metrical properties of the locality. These differentiations, however, are not fixed and simply located in space-time, but depend on the particular system of interrelated elements with reference to which they are considered, and of such systems there is an indefinite possible variety. Nevertheless, the relativistic principle (or set of principles) governing the variations from one system to another is universal and regulates the structure of the whole.

Within this totality, the distinguishable contents are mutually determined and their most intimate and constitutive qualities are

[1] *The Evolution of Scientific Thought from Newton to Einstein*, pp. 337–8.

generated by their relations one to another. This is a close and intricate interdependence in the process of determination (or definition) of constituent factors, not a rigid determinism of the Laplacian form. On the contrary, something very different is implied, as will emerge in later discussion. Motion and its velocity, whatever it is that moves, is relative to the motion and velocity of whatever else is compared with it. Upon this comparison, again, depend the spatial dimensions, the temporal duration and the mass of all moving bodies; so likewise do electrical charge and magnetic moment. Electrical charge and magnetic moment have, moreover, proved to be the ultimate constituents of matter, so that in the last resort, every entity of the physical world is and comes to be what it is by virtue of its complex interrelations with others. Terms and relations are mutually dependent and are determined in detail by the principle of organization which knits them all into a single system.

Unity and diversity in this conception are of equal importance and neither may be stressed at the expense of the other. With its internal cohesion and continuity the four-dimensional space-time world is no 'block universe', such as Bergson deprecates and (latterly) Milic Capek has repudiated as a misrepresentation of the world-picture offered by relativistic physics.[1] Capek is right to insist that relativity does not spatialize time. On the contrary, the classical notion of static space has been altogether abolished and the unity of space-time becomes a dynamic unity. But it is a unity nevertheless. The element of process in the contemporary world-picture is ineradicable, but it is none the less correlative to, and inescapably implicative of, a coherent oneness that is equally indispensable. In the next chapter this matter will be discussed more at length and we shall find that Capek's salutary insights are nevertheless somewhat one-sided. In his protests against every form and shade of Eleaticism, he acknowledges its persistent recurrence in the history of philosophy, but fails to see in this fact evidence of an equally persistent demand imposed upon thought by the very nature of succession and process, for a unity and connection that transcends and comprehends all flux and passage. He seems to overlook this aspect, which is quite definitely present, in the philosophy of Whitehead, whom he so generally supports; and, in his aversion to Parmenides, he comes at times perilously near to embracing Heraclitus.

[1] *Vide The Philosophical Impact of Contemporary Physics*, Ch. XI.

CHAPTER IV

THE PRIMORDIAL MATRIX

I

The metaphysical conception engendered by the theory of relativity is one in which the space-time continuum functions as the primordial stuff or substance of the material world. Implicit in the structure of its intrinsic diversification are the existence, physical properties and behaviour of material bodies. Space-time is consequently no featureless void but an ordered plenum, in which both the aspect of fullness and that of internal organization have far-reaching philosophical significance. It is important to note that the fullness and the order are interdependent characters of the continuum; form or structure is, as we shall later have even stronger reason to insist, fundamental to the physical existence of spatio-temporal entities, and there is no rift or possible separation between the structured reality and the field or expanse in which it is ordered. This is a direct consequence of the character of space-time as a self-differentiating and unified continuum, a specially important type of unity, the nature of which has been partially recognized by philosophers in the past, in different and often complementary ways. The whole momentous topic of form and matter and their interrelation is here involved. To discuss it in detail and with reference to all the important thinkers whose theories bear upon it would involve a digression from my main theme unwarranted at this point, but there are some features of the idea of space-time so far outlined that we shall find prolific of later results, and these I shall try to bring into relief by comparison with some earlier doctrines.

In Newtonian science, space, time and matter were each separate existences and the world was envisaged as one of particles poised in a void. It was essentially the Democritean picture, which had been handed down at the time of the Renaissance, through the revival of interest in Epicurus and his version of atomism as an alternative to Aristotle. Space by itself was empty and had an absolute existence of its own—and so had time. Matter and its changes simply inhabited these two forms of extension but made no difference to them. The legacy from Democritus and the

Ancients was a reality comprising nothing except atoms and the void. But the void was strictly non-being, and so for classical physics, although space was absolute and independent of matter, it was *per se* utterly empty, a mere receptacle for reality which properly consisted only of matter. The same might be said of time, but less simply, for time was somewhat confusedly conceived, not only as the scale or series of moments in which events occurred, but also as itself some sort of independent movement or passage. Though no material events should occur, yet time was regarded as passing on or moving forward into the future. What moved in the process of pure, empty time it was impossible to say, or what could be the 'passage' of time in which nothing happened. Material motion must occur in space, but the movement of time itself left space eternally unaltered. In fact, the relation between space and time posed a perennial problem, for the passage of time seemed to be imaginable only in spatial terms and yet all spatial movement presupposed the passage of time. In short, pure time devoid of events was lapse without change, duration without occurrence, movement without alteration of place, yet the receptacle of all change, all occurrence and all spatial movement.

The difficulties and contradictions involved in these conceptions of empty and absolute space and time have exercised philosophers for centuries. But the theory of relativity has so radically altered the aspect of space-time-matter interrelations that such philosophical questions as are still relevant today are very different from those of the past. Yet the relativistic ideas are not discontinuous with earlier philosophical thought. Not only are they foreshadowed by both Berkeley and Kant,[1] but the theory of

[1] *Vide* Berkeley, *Principles of Human Knowledge*, Part I, §§ 110–17, where, having (in Sections 97 and 98) repudiated the conception of absolute time, Berkeley explicitly criticizes Newton and rejects also the ideas of absolute space and absolute motion: 'I must confess it does not appear to me that there can be any motion other than *relative*: so that to conceive motion there must be conceived at least two bodies; whereof the distance or position in regard to each other is varied. Hence, if there was one only body in being it could not possibly be moved' (§ 112). Again, '. . . the philosophic consideration of motion doth not imply the being of an *absolute Space*. . . And perhaps, if we inquire narrowly, we shall find we cannot even frame an idea of pure Space exclusive of all body' (§ 116). Cf. also *De Motu*, §§ 52–3, 58, 63–4.

Cf. Kant, *Metaphysische Anfangsgründe der Naturwissenschaft*, Erstes Hauptstück, Grundsatz: 'Eine jede Bewegung als gegenstand einer

C

relativity in some measure justifies and reconciles the views of Descartes and Leibniz concerning space.

Descartes, because he denied that non-being could have magnitude or extension, refused to countenance empty space, and maintained that all extension was substantial and all space a *plenum*. For him, space is simply extended substance and the distinction between bodies within it no more than the demarcation of different figures and magnitudes, the changes of which constitute motion.[1] Leibniz also rejected the notion of empty space as an entity with its own absolute existence. He held both space and time to be no more than forms of order of the relations between substances: space an order of co-existence and time an order of succession.[2] For Descartes extension is substance; for Leibniz substances, through their interrelations, generate extension. Each in his own way anticipates something of Einstein's theory; Leibniz in that he recognizes space and time to be constituted solely by the mutual relations of substances, as Einstein, in the special theory, sees space-time as the structure of relations between physical objects and the observer (between reference-frames); and Descartes in that he insists upon the plenitude of space and time, as Einstein, in the general theory, identifies the metrical with the gravitational field and (in effect) rejects empty space. 'The true kernel of Descartes' idea,' he says, 'is that there exists no space "empty of field".'[3] And, as matter is inseparable from the field, the modern doctrine also postulates a *plenum*, if

möglichen Erfahrung kann nach Belieben als Bewegung des Körpers in einem ruhigen Raume, oder als Ruhe des Körpers und dagegen Bewegung des Raumes in entgegengesetzter Richtung mit gleicher Geschwindigkeit angesehen werden.' And Viertes Hauptstück, Lehrsatz 1: 'Die Geradlinichte Bewegung einer Materie in Ansehung eines empirischen Raumes ist zum Unterschiede van entgegengesetzten Bewegung des Raume ein blos mögliches Prädikat. Eben dasselbe in gar keiner Relation auf eine Materie auzer ihr, d.i. als absolute Bewegung gedacht, ist unmöglich.' But Kant was too good a Newtonian to do away altogether with absolute space and retains it as an *a priori* form of intuition independent of all experience.

[1] *Vide Principles of Philosophy* II, xiii–xxv. Here again there is the germ of a theory of relativity.

[2] *Vide IIIme. Lettre à Clarke*, 4, *The Leibniz Clarke Correspondence*, Ed. H. G. Alexander (Manchester University Press, 1956), pp. 25–6: 'I hold space to be something *merely relative*, as time is: I hold it to be an *order of co-existences*, as time is *an order of successions*.'

[3] *Relativity*, p. 156.

not of 'body', yet of metrical structure dependent upon and continuous with matter.

The theory of relativity combines and reconciles the Cartesian and the Leibnizian views. According to the general theory, the curvature of space is intimately connected with the mean density of matter, and this curvature determines the size of the universe (a feature of the theory to which we shall recur in the following chapter). The extent of space is thus dependent upon the presence of matter, or as Eddington puts it:

'A region outside the field of action of matter could have no geodesics, and consequently no intervals. All the potentials would then necessarily be zero.... Now if all intervals vanished space-time would shrink to a point. Then there would be no space, no time, no inertia, no anything. Thus a cause which creates intervals and geodesics must, so to speak, extend the world.'[1]

But intervals and geodesics are relations between events (spatio-temporal entities) and they are generated by the 'action of matter'. In short, it is true both that space-time is the order of relations between things and events, and that matter ('*res extensa*') extends space; and we shall see that matter is most probably not, in the last resort, foreign to space-time. Physical space, the space of the real world, is not the amorphous space of pure mathematics, but is the metrical field of physical science, revealed in the behaviour of physical things, like measuring instruments. It is the system of metrical interrelationships of physical phenomena —what d'Abro calls 'a relational synthesis of physical results'.[2] This is the Leibnizian doctrine, but it is also and equally Cartesian, for the metrical field is not pure mathematical space, but is a sort of physical medium continuous with matter, filling, as it constitutes, the whole of space-time.[3]

If space and time are thus welded together into a single manifold, which is, moreover, a plenum—a continuous all-pervasive field impregnated throughout with energy and the primordial stuff from which solid matter is, as it were, precipitated out (though this metaphor is not wholly appropriate and will later have to be changed)—if this is how space-time is conceived, no question

---

[1] *Space, Time and Gravitation*, pp. 157 f.
[2] Op. cit., p. 54.
[3] Cf. d'Abro, op. cit., pp. 56–9.

can arise about the relation between the space in which a body is situated and that which is the body's own extensity, no question can arise about the kind of movement attributable to pure empty time, or about the relation of this movement to the time-occupying translations of bodies through space. And no such questions arise because the distinctions that they presuppose between space and time and their occupants cannot be made. The total reality is one continuous process of physical activity, the structural character of which *is* space-time, and an element in the dynamic character of which is spatio-temporal motion.[1]

The relativistic conception of space leads to a position in some ways reminiscent (despite obvious differences) of Plato's account of the 'receptacle' in the *Timaeus* (49–52). Though identified with place, this 'receptacle' is something very different from the receptacle-like space of Newton, for it is no mere container for bodies but the matrix ($\mu\hat{\eta}\tau\epsilon\rho$) of the generated world. But whereas the Platonic 'receptacle' (or 'recipient') has no form of its own and simply receives the forms imposed upon it, Einstein's space-time has an intrinsic structure which regulates the order of events (and so of all spatial relations and movements) within it. The 'receptacle' of the *Timaeus* is the forerunner of Aristotle's primary matter, which, when informed by the opposite qualities, hot, cold, moist and dry, becomes proximate matter to the elementary forms of earth, water, air and fire, and these again proximate matter to higher forms. But Aristotle did not identify primary matter with space, though he refused to admit the void. 'Place' for him is the potentiality of the presence of body, but is not its primary matter. Yet Aristotle recognized two aspects of matter (and criticized Plato for failing to do so[2]): as a positive substratum, and also as a bare potentiality (or privation of form). Place is the second of these without the first, and so is not to be identified with ὕλη. Nevertheless, Aristotle avoided the error of conceiving pure space—the void—as a positive entity, prior in effect to matter, as it had come to be for the Atomists and was later conceived by Newton and the classical physicists.

It is this independent, infinitely extended void, imagined as existing all at once in every instant of time, that the theory of relativity abolishes; and the conception is internally incoherent. Space, so conceived, is an extensive unity without diversity which

[1] Cf. my 'Time and Change' in *Mind*, Vol. LXVI N.S., 1957.
[2] *Physics*, I, 9.

is strictly unthinkable. Diversity can be introduced into it only by the idea of distance (which is the peculiar relation between its constituent parts). Instantaneous distance, however, is distance traversed with infinite velocity, so that different points are literally occupied at the same time. Nothing, however, can occupy diverse positions simultaneously. Two positions concurrently occupied by the same thing must be identical. Consequently, instantaneous positions are all one and indistinguishable and distance disappears, so that instantaneous space cannot be differentiated into distinguishable parts.

2

In more recent times Samuel Alexander attempted to correct this defective conception of space in a doctrine which amalgamates space with time as the matrix of all things (analogous to Aristotle's ὕλη), within which certain special configurations of point-instants (corresponding to 'form' in Aristotle) give rise to emergent qualities: first energy; then from special energy patterns, matter; from material configurations, life; and so on, producing an Aristotelian-type *scala naturae*. This scalariform arrangement of grades will engage our attention more fully hereafter; what is of immediate interest is the account given of the first-stage and its identification with space-time as the original matrix. Alexander recognizes the importance of the intrinsic patterning and organizing function of space-time, the dynamic character and creative potentialities of its order. Despite some obscurities and inconsistencies, therefore, it may repay us to give some brief consideration to the exposition of his doctrine and try to elicit its more suggestive features.

Any attempt to appreciate Alexander's theory is liable to be hampered partly by a certain vagueness in his exposition and partly by confusions arising out of the gratuitous and irrelevant deference he pays to Empiricism. First, it is not clear how far his doctrine is consciously based on the work of the physicists. He refers to the work of Lorentz, Einstein, Minkowski and others associated with the beginnings of the theory of relativity, and it is apparent that he was influenced by their ideas, but he mentions these thinkers specifically only to underline differences between his own views and theirs, while at the same time arguing that his doctrine is not incompatible with the scientific theories. And, indeed, the account which he himself gives of space-time is highly original, though often obscure because he never explicitly acknowledges the main idea (presently to be noticed) which might make it more easily intelligible.

Secondly, he protests that his approach is purely empirical and that it is the empirical character of space and time that he is describing, without any attempt, as he puts it, 'to preside over their creation' by means of *a priori* deductions from first principles. Yet he does not mean by this to exclude the use of concepts from his description nor to give any specially privileged position to the senses.[1] By 'empirical character', however, we naturally understand those features which are apparent to us in our common experience rather than highly abstract, analytical relationships imputed by the theorist. Yet Alexander insists that he is here concerned only with pure space and time, not with their sensible (i.e. empirically accessible) filling of qualified objects and events, though he sometimes makes use of these as aids to the imagination in drawing attention to the properties of pure space and time. Alexander himself begins with the remark that space and time 'look and feel like extensions', which gives the impression that he intends to describe what they look and feel like in more detail; but many of the properties that he subsequently discovers are neither obvious to sight and touch nor commonly accepted on the evidence of what is directly perceived. They seem rather to be deduced, and not always cogently, so that it is often difficult to grasp precisely to what they refer.

In summary the theory is as follows. Space is said to be full of time and time of space, and this is explained as the differentiation by time of the blank unity of space, which it is maintained, taken as a mere whole of co-existence, would have no distinction of parts. Distinction is introduced by variously dating the different points, each being united with its appropriate instant. Similarly, time by itself is a bare succession of nows without mutual connection, for the earlier is over and gone before the later begins. The continuity of time, therefore (it is alleged), can be effected only by its union with space in which each instant 'occupies' a point, and each point 'occurs' at an instant. Presumably the succession of discontinuous nows is united by the continuity of co-existence among points, and the blank unity of space is diversified by the successiveness of the instants at which the points

[1] Cf. *Space, Time and Deity*, Vol. I, pp. 4–5 and 40–1.

occur; but the discontinuity of spatial points on account of their mutual distance—for no two can coincide—seems to have been overlooked, as well as the continuity implicit in non-spatial succession. Alexander, however, does also assert that space diversifies time and that time unifies space,[1] for without space the bare now of time would be without distinction from other nows, such distinction being possible only within the unity provided by the continuity of space. Again, time unifies space by distinguishing the points to be united, a co-existent blank being without content and so no real whole at all.[2] Consequently there is no space without time, nor time without space, no mere points or bare instants but only space-time constituted of *pure events* or point-instants.

The cogency of this argument is not at first sight overwhelming for almost every step seems equivocal. It does however establish the mutual implication of unity and diversity in both space and time, though not that this unites them in a single manifold. Alexander goes on to deny that each instant occupies every point in space and that every point endures throughout time. He maintains that the occupancy of points by an instant is selective and that successive instants occupy different selections of points. Further, any point may be repeated at different instants (not necessarily successive). In other words, successive events may occur in different places and different events may occur in the same place. In this way instants are said to be distributed among points and, with the passage of time, are constantly being redistributed.

It is not easy to see immediately what all this means. We do not commonly observe spatial points popping in and out of existence at different instants, or temporal instants darting about in space; and even if it be allowed that we do observe *events* occurring in different places at the same time and at different times in the same place, it is still true that what we observe are not pure, unqualitied events, not point-instants. We may, however, derive a little illumination by applying the analysis made on p. 69 above. It is never explicitly made by Alexander, yet is constantly suggested by his argument. He maintains that space-time and motion are the same thing and that space-time is 'a system of motions',[3] and this offers us a possible clue to his meaning. Difficult though it is to conceive of motion without any moving body, it is possible to think of it simply as translation or transition through space—

[1] *Space, Time and Deity*, I, p. 60.   [2] *Ibid.*, p. 47.   [3] *Ibid.*, p. 61.

the bare tracing of distance between points. Now spatial distance cannot be conceived without any appeal to time, in the sense of some sort of lapse. That nothing can be simultaneously at two separate points, *a* and *b*, is precisely what is meant by their being apart. In other words, some time must be taken to effect transition from *a* to *b*. Thus only can the unity of co-existent places in space be diversified, for distinction between points in pure space can only be made in terms of the distance between them, and if this is what takes time to traverse, it is time that diversifies space through motion.

But unqualified motion is not sufficient to determine the distance between points, for the time which elapses varies with velocity. The velocity may not be infinite, for if it were, distance would be traversed in no time and points incapable of distinction would coincide. On the other hand, if the velocity of the diversifying motion is variable or relative, distance will be indeterminate. The implication, therefore, is an absolute and invariant velocity somehow inherent in space-time that can serve to define distance. One is immediately reminded of the part played in the theory of relativity by the velocity of light; but Alexander makes no reference to it at all, nor, in this connection, to the velocity of motion; and to fit the idea explicitly and consistently into his theory would require considerable reformulation. Nevertheless, if his descriptions are interpreted as referring to motions and not simply to static points and instants, they become more intelligible, though not altogether free from inconsistency; for, although a movement involves the occupancy of successive points at successive instants, passage through these points does not annihilate those not simultaneously occupied. They must in *some* sense coexist throughout the movement, otherwise the distance as a whole cannot be defined in terms of temporal lapse, and motion would degenerate into a succession of disconnected occupancies (or here-nows) as exceptionable as any discontinuous series of instants. Unless this coexistence of spatial points all at the same time is assumed, the continuity of motion and of the time involved disintegrates. But if it is assumed, then every point must occur (in *some* sense) at every instant, and also adjacent points be occupied successively, though space and time need not therefore fall apart in the manner deprecated by Alexander. They seem to do so only when the account given of them is too abstract and 'occupancy' is left vague and undefined. Not instants but that which moves occupies different points successively, and the absolute velocity that defines distance, taken as the fourth co-ordinate ($\tau = ict$), amalgamates space and time into a single continuous manifold.

It is unfortunately just this that Alexander refuses to admit (except as 'a means of mathematical manipulation') and he distinguishes sharply between the four-dimensional continuum of Minkowski and the space-time of his own theory. 'The relation between space and time which we have found empirically', he says, 'appears to be of a much more intimate kind, with time embracing in its one-dimensional order all three dimensions of space.'[1] His attempted proofs that this is so are obscure and fail to convince, though they further illustrate his struggle to identify the principle of diversification in space as time; for, unless they are quite fallacious and sophistical, they depend throughout on the treatment of time as a movement along a spatial track (or a number of concurrent spatial movements).[2]

3

The same sort of oversight seems to infect the argument put forward by Capek[3] for the complete abolition of co-existence and of juxtaposition in space. For these he substitutes 'extensive becoming'. Relativity, he says, has wholly eliminated instantaneous co-existence and has infused time into all space, so that the conception of pure spatial extensity is no longer legitimate. We may now speak only of contemporaneous durations. On the other hand, time has not been spatialized in the sense that the time axis has become a fourth static space dimension, but no more is it left as a mere uni-dimensional series of unextended and durationless instants. Time has an expanded and expanding content, it has breadth and volume. But the spatial implications of these terms have not their former timeless significance, for distance has meaning only in terms of causal sequences and so is never devoid of temporal succession. In Capek's view, therefore, while pure space has been altogether discarded, temporal progression still has an important place in the contemporary world-picture.

In the main all this is sound enough so long as we remember

[1] *Space, Time and Deity*, I, p. 59.
[2] *Vide Space, Time and Deity*, I. Ch. II.
[3] *Vide Philosophical Impact of Contemporary Physics*, Ch. XI.

C*

that *pure* time and space are *pure* abstractions and that neither are components of the real world. The actuality is the process of events out of which neither space nor time can be independently extracted. But it is equally true that even relativistic physics can completely dispense with neither space nor time. The extensive becoming of the world is no less spatial than temporal. Its extensiveness still requires co-existence, and juxtaposition cannot be altogether abolished, though it ceases to be a purely spatial idea and is, perhaps, better conceived as contiguity. For any expanse must have co-existent parts, otherwise it is not an expanse but a mere multiplicity if *un*related points—precisely what Capek would promptly reject.

For, as he admits, in relativistic thinking simultaneity of distant events is not annihilated; it is only made relative. Distant events, as he concedes, are contemporaneous, but their simultaneity cannot be simply or absolutely determined. In the diagram representing the relativistic four-dimensional world, the 'here-now' is the apex of a double cone, the meeting point of absolute past and absolute future:

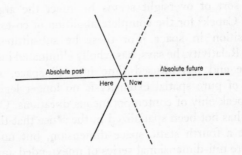

but the interval between the two cones is not a void. Schrödinger felicitously called it a '*Toleranzbreite*'. It is the contemporary world filled with events whose precise location in space-time is not simple but varies with the frame of reference. In this respect, however, they are no different from any other events, for in different frames different time series will be applicable, and simple dating is no more possible than simple location.

The temporality of causation and the consecutiveness of causal processes undoubtedly remain essential for relativity. But the consequence of this is that causal chains linking distant events always have the form of motion (e.g. the propagation of radiation), and motion can occur only between contiguous positions in space, which must therefore be *juxta*-posed. This juxtaposition is, as it were, pushed further afield in the causal process, and its propagation (so to call it) is both spatial and temporal. The truth of the matter is that juxtaposition has not been abolished but it has become temporal as well as spatial, and can never be one without the other. Similarly, if time is to have structure and expanse as well as bare succession, there must be co-existence of places, if not we are restricted to bundles of unrelated causal lines, each without any spatial breadth, and without mutual communication. Capek seems to lean towards such an idea; but this, as we have seen, is not what the relativity theory demands. There is a connection between contemporary events but they are differently correlated in different frames. There is co-existence, but it is not instantaneous, and simultaneity is not a timeless cut across the four-dimensional manifold but a *Toleranzbreite*.

Capek is anxious to put out of court those who assert the unreality of time, but he seems to forget that, of those who do, the majority deny the reality of space for the same or similar reasons. He himself, in company with Bergson, is not unwilling to degrade space to the level of appearance, but is reluctant to forego the reality of time. But, on his own showing, the two are 'inseparable'. To speak of appearance and reality is not very fruitful without defining terms. Capek is well aware that any appearance must be founded in, and explained in terms of, reality (who more than Kant and Bradley have insisted on this), and that if temporal succession is confined to the mind, it still remains a feature of experience and is not eliminated from the real. But it must not be forgotten that our awareness of time is curiously ambiguous because, while it is incurably successive, it is so only so far as our consciousness spans an epoch of some duration and apprehends it as a whole within which the succession takes place. Bare 'nows' cannot constitute a succession and cannot maintain continuity. They must coalesce in a 'specious present', which, as J. D. Mabbott has convincingly argued,[1] is emphatically *specious*, and may comprehend almost any span depending upon the universe of reference of our thought. It is not, and cannot be, wholly perceptual and can constitute a time-series (as Kant saw)[2] only

[1] *Mind*, LX (1951).
[2] *Kritik der Reinen Vernunft*, Second Analogy, A 189, B 233 ff.

if conceptually ordered as an objective sequence. This objective sequence must be conceived as a whole or else the succession within it, if at all it could then properly be recognized as such, becomes incoherent and devoid of order.

Time is no more than the metric of becoming, which is the presentational form of the concrete reality that becomes. Capek explains lucidly how a single space-time interval between two events may be differently measured by two observers in different frames of reference because they use different metrics.[1] The result is different local times; but they are secondary characters which do not affect the actual process of 'creative advance'. In a valid sense they are different appearances of it. In this sense, then, time *is* mere appearance, though the process of events is not. And this process, we should have learnt from Whitehead, is one of '*concrescence*', of continuous realization of 'definiteness', wholeness, or form. Mere succession is meaningless and unintelligible. It must be a sequence or series of continuous and coherent structures. What has no form can be no part of a succession, so successive instants are strictly inconceivable, and the idea serves a purpose only as an abstraction from that of successive changes. What changes must have some form, and this form must alter to produce the change and the succession. Succession necessarily implies difference and 'successive identities' is a contradiction in terms. *A fortiori*, empty, identical instants cannot succeed one another. If succession thus implies form and structure it equally requires continuity of successive forms in the process of change. That is to say, it equally involves pattern of change in order to be intelligibly continuous and successive. This is the foundation on which the idea of causality rests and Kant's recognition of it constitutes his great advance upon Hume. Without recognizably continuous pattern of change, successive '*Vorstellungen*' are purely subjective, disordered and incapable of precise temporal relation. The same, of course, is true of spatial order, but there the aspect of togetherness is easier to recognize than in the case of time, while the equally essential aspect of differentiation gets somehow frozen, and the wholeness of space appears static and binding, while the wholeness of time tends to escape notice altogether.

This wholeness or totality is what frightens Capek, who very rightly is anxious to avoid 'the night in which all cows are black',

[1] Op. cit., p. 218.

the block-universe, *tout donné*; and he feels that the continuous flow of time can save us from these. Indeed it can, but not because it breaks the bounds of wholeness and structure; not because it is for ever incomplete—for it as much implies completion as does spatial order. It saves us from the blank unity of the Parmenidean One, because it is the primary form of diversity and differentiation. As soon as diversification of a uniform being is contemplated it takes the form of change and must be presented serially. This is why relativity forces upon us the infusion of space with time—to diversify its otherwise blank and unintelligible oneness. Difference of position is distance; and distance takes time to traverse.

4

The glimmer of this truth is what Alexander sensed, and its consequence is that the differentiated whole of interfused space and time must be construed in terms of motion.

Throughout the confusions and obscurities of his exposition the effort is discernible to find some principle of order and discrimination systematically diversifying the blank unity of the spatio-temporal continuum. Alexander assigns this function in the main to time. At a later stage he asserts that the relation of time to space is analogous to that of mind to body—'time is the mind of space'. It is not that time is really a form of mind, but that mind is rather a form of time. 'In the matrix of all existence, space-time, there is an element, time, which performs the same function in respect of the other element, Space, as mind performs in respect of its bodily equivalent.'[1]

Precisely what this is intended to mean is never made very clear; nor are the grounds for the formula very illuminatingly explained. Alexander does little more than set out the differences between the spatio-temporal and the corporo-mental relationship. But he does maintain that each instant of reference is the 'mind' of its point, continuous with the 'minds' of all points along its line of advance. And earlier he speaks of a centre of reference as a percipient 'full of memory and expectation' observing the distribution (and its changes) of instants among points.[2] All this suggests rather strongly that the mental function is that of

[1] *Space, Time and Deity*, II, p. 44.
[2] *Ibid.*, I, p. 71.

systematic diversification within a continuous whole. Yet it is by no means the case that Alexander himself thought of mind as the organizing principle of the body. Mind for him is something quite different. It is the 'quality' of consciousness supervening upon a constellation of neural activity. His theory of its nature and relation to matter is not without value, nor yet without obscurity and paradox, but we cannot embark here on any detailed examination of it.[1] Our present purpose is simply to draw attention to the insight that there is something analogous to mind in the primordial matrix of things.

This suggestion is by no means unique, and Alexander was not the first to make it. It can be traced back in the history of philosophy at least to Anaxagoras. Alexander's great contemporary, Whitehead, insisted that every actual entity created in the process that is the substratum of reality has a mental as well as a physical pole. More recently Pierre Teilhard has expressed conviction that all things have a mental and conscious 'within', atoms and molecules no less than organisms and men,[2] and he quotes J. B. S. Haldane in support of this idea.[3] Can it be so interpreted as to refer to facts for which there is any scientific evidence? Until something more has been said about the nature of consciousness and mind, the question hardly admits of any precise answer. The unqualified assertion that space-time and all things else possess consciousness is merely fantastic. Though the ancients believed something of the kind, they did so, for the most part, on mythological rather than on scientific grounds. And much will depend upon what consciousness, on investigation, turns out to be, an enquiry that cannot be pursued at this point. Of interest and importance, however, is the clue provided by Alexander (inadvertently or otherwise) that the function of mind is systematization—the differentiation of a uniform continuum, and the unification through order of a disparate multiplicity. Though he says that space and time perform this service for each other, it is the element of order, which seems to him to belong more properly to time, that proves most important; hence it is time that is named as the analogue to mind.

[1] See, however, my *Nature, Mind and Modern Science*, Ch. XVIII, pp. 405 ff.
[2] Cf. *The Phenomenon of Man*, Ch. II and *passim*.
[3] *The Inequality of Man* (London, 1932), p. 113.

5

The theories of relativity leave us in no doubt that the space-time matrix of the world involves just such an aspect of order and systematization. The continuum is a seamless unity, but it is by no means devoid of structure. That belongs to the metrical field with its inherent geometry, which permits measurement with reference to co-ordinate systems of determinate kinds and is the source of laws governing the behaviour of all spatio-temporal objects. Motion is regulated by the form of its geodesics, and its curvature provides the foundations of the mathematical formulae which effect the transformation of measures from one co-ordinate system to another—all essentially interrelated by their common yet various applicability to the one fundamental continuum. If, in this sense, we could speak of a mind of space-time at all, we must identify it with its metrical character. But it would be better, for the present at least, to refrain from any such self-committal language and to confine ourselves to what may safely be maintained: that, for modern science, physical space-time does possess intrinsically a character of systematic diversity consequent upon the ordered variegation of its continuity. There is essential to it a systematic interdependence of distinguishable parts and elements, which is reflected in and expressed by the mathematical calculi of its geometry, and which governs the behaviour of physical things.

'The innumerable foci which share a given volume of matter', Pierre Teilhard remarks, 'are not . . . independent of each other. Something holds them together. Far from behaving as a mere inert receptacle the space filled by their multitude operates upon it like an active centre of direction and transmission in which their plurality is organized.'[1] In short, space-time involves and imposes on its contents a principle of organization. One may say that space-time *is* such a principle, or is a system of such principles. Spatio-temporal relations are *organizing* relations, and without them there is no physical space-time at all. This point is constantly stressed by Eddington, and for the theory of relativity it is inescapable. We shall find as we go on that principles of organization are intrinsic to and largely constitutive of all things, and later that the relation of such principles to whatever it is they organize has a special bearing upon the nature of

[1] *The Phenomenon of Man*, pp. 41–2.

mind. Alexander's intuition, therefore, that there is some analogy between the elements of order and system in space-time and the human mind is not altogether misguided.

6

The objection might be raised that this systematic articulation of the continuum is not really intrinsic to space and time, but is simply the mathematical apparatus by means of which the scientist co-ordinates his observational data. It is imposed upon the world, it may be said, by the mathematical physicist, and is not its inherent structure. But this cannot be the case, for, as has already been noted, the space-time of physics is not the amorphous continuum of pure mathematics. It is the actual field of physical events and its geometry is revealed in the behaviour of the physicist's measuring devices. The laws of physics are bound up with it, and to allege that the theorist imposes its geometrical structure upon the world is tantamount to crediting him with the fabrication of physical laws. Some eminent physicists have, it is true, favoured a Kantian view, that the laws of nature are the inevitable consequences of human intellectual and observational equipment and procedures. But this is an epistemological theory, the cogency of which we are as yet in no position to assess. Our first task must be to examine the comprehensive view of the world offered us in the actual findings of scientific investigation, and only after that can we consider the place and function of human knowing within it. At this stage, we must simply record that the theories of relativity (special and general), as theories of the physical world, show its kinematic and dynamical properties to be implicit in the geometrical character of the metrical field.

Moreover, there are a number of other possible geometries, besides those applied in the theory of relativity. Any of these might be imposed on space-time if it were just a matter of arbitrary choice. But not all of them have been found compatible with the observed physical phenomena. It could rightly be maintained that even the pure mathematician does not capriciously invent these alternative geometries, but discovers them as alternative logical possibilities.[1] It is even more certainly the case that the

[1] Cf. W. C. Kneale, 'The Idea of Invention', *Proceedings of the British Academy*, 1955.

physicist does not choose arbitrarily among them whichever he fancies. He has to discover which of them will render intelligible and coherent the experienced behaviour of physical objects—he has to discover what the geometry of space-time in the real world actually is.

What he has discovered is a four-dimensional world, which is one and continuous throughout, but which is complexly and systematically articulated in such a way that its various parts and their geometrical properties are mutually implicated, so that from the knowledge of some of them, by the appropriate mathematical procedures, others can be calculated. Its wholeness and continuity is constituted by these interdependences of distinct parts, and they, in turn, are consequent upon it. More properly, wholeness and continuity, on the one hand, and interdependence of distinguishable parts, on the other, are alternative aspects of the same fact about the nature of space-time, of which each is a complementary expression. Let us consider some examples.

(i) Any co-ordinate system provides a frame of reference for measurements throughout the whole of space-time, relating vectors to one another in such a way that from the knowledge of some of them others can be deduced by the application of the appropriate calculus. One of the simplest cases of this is the inferability of the interval traversed by the movement of a particle from the sum of the squares of the differences of the respective co-ordinates involved:

$$s^2 = \Delta x^2 + \Delta y^2 + \Delta z^2$$

variously extended and generalized forms of which are used in relativity theory.

(ii) Measurements of the same phenomena will differ when referred to Cartesian co-ordinate systems moving relative to one another with uniform velocity. But the values in any one such system can be derived from those in any other by applying the Lorentz transformation formulae. So we have a multiplicity of different systems, each covering the whole of space-time, and each uniting in its own way all the phenomena throughout the physical world by interlocking relationships; and all these systems are related to one another by similarly interlocking relations.

(iii) Co-ordinate systems in non-uniform motion relative to one another are Gaussian. They each extend, as before, throughout all space and time and unite all phenomena in relations of mensuration. Each determines these relations differently, but, again, they are all so related to one another that the values obtained in any one can be calculated from those obtained in any other by means of the tensor calculus. 'The knowledge is expressed in terms of tensors which have a fixed system of interlocking assigned to them; so that when one tensor is altered all the other tensors are altered, each in a determinate way. By assigning each physical quantity to an appropriate class of tensor, we can arrange that, when one quantity is changed . . . all the other quantities change automatically and correctly. We have only to let one item of knowledge run through its changes—to turn one handle—to get in succession the complete observational knowledge of all . . . observers.'[1]

For the mathematical physicist space-time is a system of systems, each of which differentiates and interrelates distinguishable elements, in accordance with a definite principle of order, within the single unity of the whole.

This kind of whole or system is what we may call (if the invention of a word be permitted) a polyphasic unity. A unity, not empty and analytic nor blankly uniform and featureless, but one in which a variety of different elements is distinguishable, each expressing—each a particular manifestation or realization of—the principle that unifies them all and relates them to one another systematically. It is thus a unity or whole with many different facets, displaying its articulate nature in numerous different ways, presenting to an observer a multiplicity of appearances each representing in its own way the principle of order that constitutes the whole and which relates the elements of the multiplicity to one another in such a manner that they are mutually deducible if the principle of order is known.

Perhaps the purest and most abstract exemplification of a principle of unity governing a polyphasic whole is to be found in mathematics as the function of a variable. Every such function determines the relations between quantities in a systematic way and unites them into complexes whose mutual relations are similarly systematic. Yet it is itself a single principle and each of its many different expressions, when different substitutions are made for the variable, is a co-ordinated whole of distinguishable elements. All these expressions taken together—the range of the function—form a system of which the function is again the uniting

---

[1] Eddington, *The Philosophy of Physical Science* (Cambridge, 1939), pp. 86-7.

principle. It is a unity of differences constituted by their mutual relations, because those relations are the expressions or particularizations of a single principle of organization. Thus x^2 is a formula representing all square numbers, each of which is a complex formed by a specific operation upon two equal quantities (their product), and all of which form a class determined by the possession of the resulting character of 'squareness'. Each is the sum of the first x consecutive odd numbers, and so the range of the function is a whole of systematically interrelated members. Moreover, the organizing relation displays itself in different forms both in the number series and in geometrical shapes, and these different forms are similarly systematically interrelated. Stated as a mathematical formula, a function at once signifies the uniqueness and cohesion of the totality and regulates the distinguishing relations of the elements of which it is composed and in and through which the organizing principle is expressed.

A somewhat more complex example is the equation

$$f(x, y, z) = 0$$

in which x, y and z are the three rectangular co-ordinates of a Cartesian system, and which is sufficient with a suitable choice of function (f) to define any surface whatsoever in Euclidean space, however complicated or irregular it may be.[1] Such a function, though not impossible to determine, would in some cases be quite unmanageable as a means of deducing the details of the surface; but it is the possibility, in principle, of constructing it and not its usefulness that is of interest, for its shows, not simply that any surface, however irregular, is a polyphasic unity, but that Euclidean space is such a unity with properties determining its contents in systematically related ways, so that it is possible to represent any surface within it as a single function of three variables.

Mathematical order and relation are in this way typical of what we have sought to denote by polyphasic unity, and the mathematical character of such theories as those of relativity is an indication of the fact that the reality to which they refer is polyphasic. The evidence for this fact accumulates as we proceed further. Contemporary theories of the universe, to which we are about to turn, give impressive corroboration and theories of matter

[1] The example is cited by E. Borel, *Space and Time*, pp. 173–5.

still more. In fact, we shall find this type of wholeness making itself evident in increasing degrees of complexity throughout the world as revealed by the different sciences of nature, and it is therefore important to recognize its presence from the start in the space-time whole which, according to the theory of relativity, forms the basis of the physical world. It is to the credit of Alexander's philosophical insight that he realized (if not always clearly or to the full) that this essential character of space-time is fundamental to all reality, and to this extent he may well have been justified in regarding it as the matrix from which all things emerge. We have already see some, and shall presently see more, grounds for crediting this belief. Further, though we should not wish to endorse his distinction of time from space, as the 'mental' factor in contrast to the 'bodily', the principle of order, which seemed to him specially to belong to time, but which we have found inherent in space-time as a single manifold, may prove to be the same as that which, on another plane and in a different way, characterizes human mentality.

CHAPTER V

THE EXPANDING UNIVERSE

I

The question whether the space of the universe extends to infinity or comes eventually to an end—Kant's first Antinomy—vanishes in the light of modern relativistic cosmology. Matter, if nothing else, introduces curvature into space, and perfectly flat space is a physical impossibility (though local approximations are not excluded). Consequently the three dimensions of the world bend round and turn in upon themselves, so that, though it is boundless, its volume is finite. The physical universe must be conceived as a self-contained and self-sufficient totality without ragged edges. It does not shade off into an inconceivable infinity of emptiness, but is complete in itself. Not only does relativity unite and integrate all things as a system of internally related entities in a four-dimensional continuum, which knits together their properties, movements and everything that makes up their substantial being, but it moulds the entire universe into a self-contained unity, the parts of which cannot rightly be understood in isolation, or by any process of more than provisional dissection. This is to some extent true of all contemporary cosmological theories, but in those which seem to be most coherent and are best supported by evidence it is incontestable.

The Newtonian theory of gravitation presents the cosmologist with a dilemma. If matter were not uniformly distributed throughout space, the mutual attraction of bodies would result in their concentration in 'a single mass.'[1] On the other hand if it were uniformly distributed over infinite space, the gravitational field at any point would either have to be regarded as infinite or could be arbitrarily assessed in incompatibly different ways. Any point in space, so conceived, could be regarded as the centre of an Euclidean sphere in which the mass of uniformly distributed matter would be proportional to the volume of the sphere (i.e. to R^3), and the gravitational field anywhere on the surface would be proportional to $\dfrac{\text{Mass.}}{R^2}$ The gravitational field thus varies with R and approaches

[1] *Vide* Isaac Newton, *Four Letters to Bentley*, I.

infinity as R increases. But in such a universe, any point may legitimately be regarded as centre and the gravitational field in consequence may be anything up to infinity in any region.[1]

An alternative way of stating the matter is given by d'Abro as follows:

'Newton's law, when applied to the interior of a continuous distribution of matter [viewed as a cloud of dust particles] is expressed by Poisson's equation

$$(1) \quad \Delta \phi = 4 \pi k \mu$$

where ϕ is the Newtonian potential, k the gravitational constant and μ the density of matter. For our dust cloud to retain uniform distribution to infinity, no forces, on an average, must be acting on the dust particles; and this requires that the Newtonian potential ϕ should retain a constant value throughout infinite space. If, however, we set ϕ=constant in Poisson's equation (1) we obtain $0 = 4\pi k \mu$, and so μ=0. We conclude therefore that the only possible uniform distribution of matter is one in which there is no matter; and this is but another way of saying that a uniform distribution is impossible.'[2]

Astronomical observation shows that the nebulae are approximately evenly scattered throughout as much of the universe as is known, and if this is taken as normal for the whole, it must be assumed that matter is on the average uniformly distributed. Einstein, accordingly, adopted a modified equation for the law of gravitation, $G_{ik} = \lambda g_{ik}$, which, by introducing the cosmical term λ, eliminated infinity.[3] His argument is briefly the following. According to the general theory of relativity, the presence of matter introduced curvature into space, so that the radius of curvature is proportional to the average density of matter. If matter is uniformly distributed, therefore, space will curve round into and close upon itself. It forms a Riemannian three-dimensional curved surface in four-dimensional space-time. The universe is then conceived as a hypersphere, finite in volume but unbounded (like the finite but unbounded area of the surface of a

[1] The argument is Seeliger's. Cf. J. G. Whitrow, *The Structure of the Universe* (New York, 1959), pp. 99–100, and Einstein, *Relativity, the Special and General Theory*, p. 126n.

[2] *The Evolution of Scientific Thought from Newton to Einstein*, pp. 299 f.

[3] Cf. Eddington, *The Expanding Universe* (Cambridge, 1933), p. 21, and Jones, Rotblat and Whitrow, *Atoms and the Universe* (London, 1956), pp. 211–12.

Euclidean sphere).[1] The uniform distribution of matter, though it is ubiquitous, is not infinite, and the Newtonian dilemma no longer arises.

Einstein's formula gave a static universe in which the relative velocities of its material contents were taken to be zero. That, at the time (1917), was in accordance with what was known of the velocities of the fixed stars. World-lines in the time direction, therefore, were straight and parallel and the universe as a whole curved only in space. Einstein's universe is known, in consequence, as the cylindrical universe. De Sitter, however, developed a formula giving a space curvature independent of the density of matter, which in any case, as observed atsronomically, is very small. He simply disregarded matter and treated the cosmical constant as an intrinsic feature of space-time. The omission from the gravitational equations of the material tensor gave rise to a solution representing a universe curved in all four dimensions, in which time slows down at increasing distances from any point of reference until it comes finally to a standstill in the region of extreme remoteness (the four-dimensional antipodes). This is not actually a return of time upon itself, which sphericity of a four-dimensional world would suggest, and de Sitter's world is spherical only when the time co-ordinate is taken as $\sqrt{-1}^t$ (imaginary time). If real time is used the de Sitter universe remains open in the time direction at both ends.[2] Nevertheless, the continuous passage of time is not infinite but is purely local, and no relative movement can continue indefinitely.

World-lines in this universe necessarily diverge, so that particles initially at rest relative to one another tend to fly apart. In other words, the modification of the gravitational equations by the introduction of the cosmical term revealed in the structure of space-time what corresponds to a force of repulsion as well as that of gravitational attraction. But the repellent force becomes significant in strength only at very great distances, and at smaller distances gravity remains the dominant influence. Clearly, if this is so, there is a point at which the two are equal and balance each other in a state of equilibrium, but beyond that the force of repulsion takes over.[3] This feature of the theory, along with the slowing down of time at great distances, was taken to have been

[1] *Vide* Einstein, *Relativity*, Ch. XXXI.
[2] *Vide* d'Abro, op. cit., p. 304.
[3] Cf. Lemaître, op. cit.

confirmed later by the discovery of the red shift in the spectra of distant nebulae, interpreted in part as a movement of recession and in part as a reduction in the wave frequency of the emitted light.

By identifying the theoretical expansion with the observed rate of recession of the galaxies, it is possible to calculate the radius of curvature required by de Sitter's formula, and thence the density of matter in a static Einsteinian world which has that radius. The result turned out to be only slightly more than the density of that part of the universe which is actually observable.[1]

But as the real world is neither empty nor (apparently) static, neither Einstein's nor de Sitter's formulation can be taken to represent it adequately. Eddington suggested the view that the Einstein world represented the initial state of unstable equilibrium from which the expansion of the present world began, while de Sitter's is a limiting case of an expanding universe towards which the actual cosmos is tending. But Lemaître takes Einstein's world to be an intermediary stage, alleging that in its original state matter was extremely densely packed into a much smaller volume as a single vast, but highly unstable, atomic nucleus. This exploded, and with it space-time expanded to a condition in which the forces attained equilibrium in a world of the Einsteinian form. Subsequent gravitational condensations of matter disturbed this balance of forces so that those of repulsion overcame those of attraction and the cosmic expansion was resumed.[2]

2

The idea of a finite but unbounded whole dispenses, at least in part, with one of the most recalcitrant problems of natural philosophy that has troubled thinkers since the days of Zeno of Elea—that of infinite extension. This problem is, of course, intimately connected with that of continuity, for a continuum can be limited only by what is discontinuous with it; so the continuity of extension had of necessity to be conceived as going on for ever, and antinomies inevitably arose in the attempt to think out its implications. Now spatio-temporal extension, at least for physics, is shown to be both an unbroken continuum and a limited one. But the limit is not extraneous to the continuum, but is entailed

[1] *Vide* de Sitter, *Kosmos* (Harvard, 1932), Ch. VI.
[2] Cf. Lemaître, op. cit.

by its own structural properties. It is no external boundary and is better described as self-completion than limitation. For no defect or privation is involved: space-time is always sufficient in extent, however large the physical world may become. Its wholeness is not impaired but rather enhanced by its *'enroulement sur soi-même'*.

That this is a satisfactory solution of the problem of infinity may be called in question on two possible counts, neither of which however rests on a sound foundation. First, it may be thought that the expansion of the universe implies the availability of external space into which it may expand; and as the expansion continues indefinitely, the extra space required would have to be infinite in the old sense. But this objection rests on a mistaken conception of closed space. It is true that a Euclidean sphere in three-dimensional space has an inside and an outside, and that if it were to expand it would consume more and more of the space beyond its limiting surface. But the closed universe of relativity is not a sphere of that kind. It is a three-dimensional volume in non-Euclidean, Riemann space, of which the curvature that renders it self-contained cannot consistently be pictured as a curved Euclidean surface. The surface of a sphere in Euclidean space is no more than an analogy. Moreover, it is only the surface and not the enclosed volume of the Euclidean sphere that is the proper analogue. This self-contained Riemannian volume has no centre and no 'outside'. Its closure is a consequence of its geometrical properties and not of its exclusion of regions beyond its limits, for has has no boundary. It does not, therefore, expand into any space external to itself; but the world-lines of material bodies diverge in the time direction.

This conclusion, however, may give rise to a new objection. The time direction is along the axis of the fourth co-ordinate. If space is curved and closes in upon itself, and if it expands, is it not the fourth dimension in which the curvature and expansion both occur? And if we regard the whole four-dimensional continuum as curved, should we not then require a fifth dimension—and so on *ad infinitum*? The illigitimacy of this infinite regress and the misconception involved have been deprecated by Eddington.[1] The observable curvature of lines and surfaces which demands an extra dimension is only a pictorial analogy to the curvature of space. 'There is' says Eddington, 'no suggestion that the extra

[1] *Vide The Expanding Universe*, Ch. II, i, pp. 30 ff.

dimension is anything but a fictitious construction'. Curvature is a mathematical property of variable complexity, for the pictorial imagination of which one extra dimension is not always sufficient. But the mathematician makes no attempt to picture it. He sees it merely as a characteristic of the geometry of the space under consideration, and this involves no infinite regress of dimensionality. Curvature is, in fact, as d'Abro points out, an unfortunate and misleading name to apply to what is really no more than non-Euclideanism. It is possible, within limits, to discover curved surfaces in Euclidean space measurements on which with minute Euclidean rods show numerical relationships typical of non-Euclidean geometries. But this procedure, even when possible (which is not always the case) is arbitrary. It is equally possible to make measurements on such surfaces with non-Euclidean rods and obtain results characteristic of Euclidean plane geometry. Curvature is a relative term depending on the definition adopted of congruence. What is curved in Euclidean space may be defined as straight in Riemannian. Thus the demand for more Euclidean dimensions to accommodate the Riemannian curvature of the world is simply the illegitimate demand to regard real space as Euclidean whatever the evidence. But if our physical and astronomical investigations reveal that it is not, and in so doing constrain us to abolish infinity, without imposing bounds upon the universe, we may surely conclude that the structure of the actual world is such that it avoids the infinite regress which seems inevitably involved in the conception of Euclidean space. 'That queer quantity "infinity" is the very mischief', Eddington reflects, 'and no rational physicist should have anything to do with it.'[1]

3

The sort of infinity that goes on ceaselessly without ever becoming complete was deplored by Hegel as the endlessly finite, and he repudiated it as a 'false infinite'. True infinity, he maintained, belonged to what was complete in itself, self-dependent and self-maintaining. This is the sort of infinity possessed by the *Deus sive Substantia* of Spinoza that is *causa sui* and all-embracing, whose wholeness cannot be exhausted by the addition one to another of essentially finite modes, an aggregation which, in its attempt to match the true infinitude of God, issues in a never ending series.

[1] *New Pathways in Science* (Cambridge, 1935), p. 217.

The closed universe of modern physics does not in all respects fulfil the requirements of the so-called 'true infinite', but it is about as close a representation of it as might be expected of a purely physical whole. In this respect it contrasts sharply with the Newtonian world in absolute space and time which were both endlessly finite, and so virtually antithetical to the Hegelian Absolute. If modern philosophers scout the idea of an Absolute such as Hegel defended, they should consider whether, by so doing, they go counter to the scientific temper of their own day. Modern physics is not in need of vindication by the philosophy of Hegel, but many of Hegel's ideas do find support in the deliverances of twentieth century science, and one of these is his rejection of the 'false infinite'. Einstein has shown that infinite extension is incompatible with physical laws and is therefore factually impossible, while modern geometry has demonstrated that a closed, unbounded space, self-contained and not in the old way endless, is logically feasible. Space-time is now viewed as a continuum unbroken and limitless, yet self-contained and whole. It is the physical world: the world is not something separate from and inserted into it; and beyond it there is nothing physically real— no spatio-temporality whatever. The false notion of infinity of spatio-temporal extension, with all the antinomies implicit in it, is now seen to be the result of extending to the universe as a whole laws and conditions applicable only within a restricted and localized range.

But this new conception of the universe does not dispose of the complementary aspect of the problem of infinity—the second of the 'two famous labyrinths, in which', as Leibniz says, 'our reason often goes astray'. For a continuum, to be continuous, must also be infinitely divisible, and continuous physical description in the realm of the infinitesimal remains the unsolved problem of the quantum theory. That must be reserved for later discussion. It cannot be overlooked, for the foundation of the theory of relativity is that continuity of space-time structure which is the underlying assumption of its differential equations. The solution of this aspect of the problem also may depend on the realization that, in physics, infinity is an inadmissible quantity.[1]

[1] Cf. Schrödinger, *Science and Humanism* (Cambridge, 1952), pp. 29–39 and 53–58.

4

The theories we have been examining may conveniently be called 'relativistic' because they arise directly out of the theory of relativity and its mathematical consequences, and their authors are all physicists and mathematicians associated with the development of relativity theory—Einstein, de Sitter, Eddington and Lemaître. There are however other, competing theories and if less consideration is to be given to them, at least some reason must be shown why, at any rate for the present, it would be unsafe to seek a foundation in these hypotheses for metaphysical theory. When dealing with cosmological theories we are always at some disadvantage because, even though propounded by hard-headed scientists, and in spite of being constructed in conformity with the evidence from a wide range of scientific observations, they are unavoidably more speculative than the physical theories on which they are based. Some of those currently being advocated seem to face greater difficulties and to include more inconsistencies than do the relativistic theories.

There are two main types of cosmological theory other than those we have discussed. Neither altogether abandons the theory of relativity, but equally neither is directly deduced from it. There is, on the one hand, the hypothesis advocated by Alpher, Bethe and Gamow (and so nicknamed the $\alpha\beta\gamma$ theory); and, on the other hand, there is what has been called the 'steady-state' theory put forward by Sciama, Bondi and Hoyle. The theory of Gamow and his associates differs from the relativistic group only in detail. Whereas the latter deduces the closure of the world from the curvature introduced into space-time by matter and the cosmic expansion from forces expressed in the gravitational equation, the $\alpha\beta\gamma$ theory attributes the expansion to an original state of thermal radiation, which rapidly produces matter and eventually (after about 250 million years) gives rise to proto-galaxies, formed from cosmic gas.[1] For this theory, as for the relativists, the universe is finite in extent and in age and its history is one of continuous evolution from an assignable beginning when all matter was concentrated in a single dense mass, to the present far-flung distribution of a multitude of galaxies.

The steady-state theory, in opposition to evolutionary views,

[1] *Vide* George Gamow, 'Modern Cosmology', *The Scientific American*, Vol. 190, 3, March 1954.

alleges the spontaneous and continuous creation of matter in space and the uniformity on a large scale of the universe, both in space and in time. Matter, it is held, forms a very diffuse but universally pervasive cosmic gas, which collects under gravitational forces to form denser clouds. These in their turn coagulate into stars and galaxies, and continually recede from one another in consequence of the expansion of space. The recession is perpetual and endless throughout space and time, acceleration increasing in proportion to distance. But this is not held to be an evolutionary phenomenon beginning at a determinable date from a minimum volume, but something ubiquitous and perennial, brought about by the continuous creation of matter. It is something that has gone on through infinite time and will continue without end. Finite space and time are thus denied along with evolution, while the expansion of space and the uniform distribution of matter are maintained. This presents a sharp contrast with the relativistic theory for which uniform distribution of matter is essentially connected with space-time curvature, and that necessitates finite volume and evolutionary expansion through the gravitational law which it determines.

No judgement can here be made on the relative merits of these competing theories. One can but rely upon what the scientists themselves say, and in the scientific argument between them, objections have been raised to the $\alpha\beta\gamma$ and the steady-state theories which do not seem to affect the relativistic group. Sciama points to difficulties encountered by the $\alpha\beta\gamma$ theory in explaining the formation of certain chemical elements and in predicting the formation and distribution of the galaxies. He also objects that the theory makes arbitrary assumptions about initial conditions in order to account for later evolution according to physical laws.[1] On the other hand, it is admitted by Bondi that the steady-state theory must submit to the test of observation of the distant galaxies. Because of the time taken by their light to reach us they should, if the universe as a whole has undergone a process of change, appear younger than neighbouring galaxies; but if the world is uniform throughout space and time, as the steady-state theory contends, variations in apparent age between the galaxies would be similar at all distances.[2] Observations made by

[1] *Vide* 'Evolutionary Process in Cosmology', *The Advancement of Science*, XII, no. 45, 1955, pp. 38–42.
[2] *Vide* 'Theories of Cosmology', *The Advancement of Science*, XII, no. 45, 1955, pp. 33–8.

J. Stebbins and A. E. Whitford, however, do indicate a systematic difference in the apparent age of nebulae which varies with distance. The more remote elliptical nebulae appear redder than they should be according to calculation, and this reddening exceeds what can be explained by the Doppler effect or by absorption of light by interstellar matter (unless the density of such matter be greater than observed transparency would admit). The spiral nebulae, in a similar fashion, appear bluer than normal according as they are farther away. The consistent explanation of both these facts seems to be that, because they are now seen as they were long ago, the distant elliptical nebulae formerly had more red stars and the spiral more blue, and their difference from the nearer galaxies in these respects is due to the evolution of the latter in the intervening time. As the difference varies systematically with distance, the evolution would appear to be general and not simply local.

This evidence is supported and strengthened by the more recent discoveries of thousands of localized sources of radiation by Professor M. Ryle of Cambridge. These centres of radiation are scattered throughout the universe and their numbers increase with distance more rapidly than would be the case if their distribution were uniform. Extra-galactic sources of radio emission have been identified (by Baade in 1952) as the effects of collisions between galaxies, and their increase in number with distance has been explained on the presumption that such collisions were more frequent in the remote past, as would be expected according to certain evolutionary theories, notably those of Lemaître and Gamow. Lemaître indeed affirms the past occurrence of such collisions as a feature of an earlier stage of the world's development.[1]

Again, it has been argued that if matter were being continually and uniformly created, an old cluster of galaxies should continuously acquire more matter and so a more intense gravitational field. The effect would be cumulative until the group became infinite in size. If the same conditions obtained everywhere and always throughout infinite space and time, this must already have occurred and no expansion would anywhere be possible (as gravitational forces would exceed and overcome all others). To avoid this conclusion one would have to postulate a limit to the total mass of matter possible in a finite volume and so an

[1] *Vide* Georges Lemaître, *Hypothèse de l'Atome Primitif*, Neuchatel, 1946.

automatic restriction to the spontaneous creation of matter.[1] This would introduce into the theory an arbitrary, *ad hoc* proviso.

Once again 'that queer quantity infinity' proves to be 'the very mischief', and the argument on the strength of which the steady-state theorists have committed themselves to it may be ill-founded. It is that if the universe had been and still is evolving it is not uniform in time and in that case our local conditions, on the observation of which the relativity theory is based, would be insufficient grounds on which to decide which features were permanent and which were not. So we might find at some stage that we could not maintain the invariance of physical laws.[2] The invariance of physical laws, however, is the very foundation of the theory of relativity and observation of local conditions is not the source from which it is deduced. That serves only to confirm what the theory has been able to predict. If contrary assumptions lead us back into paradoxes arising from the assumption of infinite space and time, the theory which has this consequence must be suspect.

Hoyle, however, maintains that the steady-state theory is able to meet all these objections, and at this stage of scientific knowledge decision between the alternatives still hangs in the balance. We can therefore do no better than note the rival theories, and can rely for our present purposes only upon that type which seems at the moment to be the most consistent and best attested.

5

The physical world which the theory of relativity discloses is thus, not merely a four-dimensional continuum imbued with principles of systematic diversification, but one which is complete and self-contained, unique yet self-differentiating, a universe which, *as a whole*, constitutes just such a polyphasic unity as we attempted to describe in the last chapter. It is a single totality of which the interdependence of its properties in detail, and the mutual involvement of the laws governing the behaviour of its parts, one with another and with the character of the whole, become inescapably apparent in the theories of two great physicists: first, in

[1] Cf. G. O. Jones, J. Rotblat and G. J. Whitrow, *Atoms and the Universe*, pp. 221 ff.

[2] Cf. H. Bondi, 'Theories of Cosmology', *The Advancement of Science*, VIII, 45 (1951).

the results of Eddington's researches into the constants of nature, through which he succeeded in forging a link between relativity theory and wave mechanics, and secondly, in E. A. Milne's kinematic theory of the universe demonstrating the fundamental laws of physics as logical consequences of a minimum number of initial assumptions.

Both of these scientists have been subjected to criticism for what many regard as excessive rationalism. The charge, if it is to be made, applies more plausibly to Milne than to Eddington, for Eddington is the readier of the two to accept and use experimentally discovered quantities, though he never neglects the opportunity to point out the dependence of the so-called 'pure' experimentalist upon theory for the attainment of his experimental results. But we cannot, at this stage, make or evaluate epistemological judgements. Whether, and to what extent, science legitimately proceeds by pure deduction, or by observation and empirical generalization, or by a mixture of both—what, in fact, any of these terms actually mean—are questions I have decided to defer until the conception of the world as a whole has been set out as it emerges from the deliverances of the natural sciences. When that is before us and the place in it of man and his scientific activity can be established, we shall be in a better position to tackle the problem of knowledge. My present object is to consider how the theories we are reviewing contribute to that world picture, and we may perhaps accept, at least provisionally, Whittaker's defence of Eddington (as valid also for Milne) that it is no detraction from observation and experiment to demonstrate, after the event, that the same results can be reached by theoretical deduction. The ancient Egyptians discovered empirically the ratio of the area of a circle to the square of its radius as well as the equality of the square on the hypotenuse of a right-angled triangle to the sum of those on the other two sides long before they were theoretically demonstrated by Greek geometers.[1]

Eddington's theory draws upon the findings both of relativity and of wave mechanics, but no great harm will be done by discussing it here in anticipation of our consideration of quantum physics, for I am not attempting to expound the scientific doctrines for their own sake and need not, therefore, observe the strict order of logical dependence.

We have seen that Weyl and Eddington generalized the

[1] *Vide From Euclid to Eddington*, p. 185 f.

Riemannian geometry required by the general theory of relativity so as to include in space-time a curvature which related to the standard of length adopted in measurement. A natural standard is thus provided in the radius of curvature (or some convenient fraction of it) at the point where the measurement is made. Eddington contends that the existence of this universal standard follows immediately from Einstein's law of gravitation, $G_{ik} = \lambda g_{ik}$, without which physical determinations would be impossible because space would be featureless. 'No question can arise', he says, 'as to whether the comparison unit for reckoning of lengths and distances is a magnitude intrinsic in space, or some other physical quantity of the universe, or is an absolute standard outside the universe. For whatever embodies this comparison unit is *ipso facto* the space of physics.'[1] The cosmical constant λ is thus implicit in all physical measurement and, with it, the force of cosmical repulsion responsible for the recession of the galaxies. To this we shall return anon.

But space curvature is no more than the divergence from Euclideanism demanded by the invariance of physical laws for differing frames of reference. The radius of curvature is, therefore, a sort of distilled essence of the nature of the physical world. It is the system of physical laws informing the character of space-time, a sort of ambassador-at-large of the government of the universe. As space-time is the seat of all geometrical and physical relationships between physical entities, it is hardly surprising that the radius of its curvature serves as the natural standard of length. Determination of the size of elementary particles and their behaviour under the influences of gravitational and electrical forces will ultimately all be given in terms of this standard; and this we can now see is but another way of saying that the size and other properties of each particle are a consequence of its relation to all the rest of the universe. The position and dimensions of a particle, Eddington maintained, are interaction effects. 'The wave equation of the electron,' he writes, 'is an equation which straddles the whole of physics and describes the relation of the electron to the universe.'[2] Now, the average effects of interaction of the myriads of particles in the universe is a 'field' possessing a definite number of types of variation, or degrees of freedom. Just as the electrical field represents (and, for purposes of physical specification,

[1] *The Expanding Universe*, p. 103.
[2] *New Pathways in Science*, p. 227.

D

replaces) the interaction of myriads of electrical particles, so, Eddington argues, the interaction of 'the rest of the universe' on the particle under observation is averaged and replaced by the *metrical* field—or space.[1]

The number of degrees of freedom (*n*) by which the metrical field is characterized, for four dimensions is 10, and Eddington argues that it is equivalent to a universe with as many degrees of freedom as there are elementary particles, to the number of which he gives the symbol *N*. 'The rest of the universe', accordingly is represented in equations for quantitative attributes of individual particles by *R* (the radius of curvature) and the ratio of *n* to *N*. To each particle wave-mechanics assigns a wave-function, so *N* is the number of possible independent wave systems which the universe contains—the separate constituents of its total energy. In the closed universe, this number is limited not only by the number of degrees of freedom belonging theoretically to each particle, but also by Pauli's principle of exclusion, which forbids any orbit to be occupied by more than one particle (or, alternatively, two particles of the same kind to have the same set of quantum numbers). These facts form the basis on which Eddington is able to correlate the gravitational equations of the relativity theory, incorporating the ten degrees of freedom of the four-dimensional continuum and expressing the curvature of space, with the wave equations of the quantum theory representing elementary particles. As any measurement in relativity theory requires four entities, two to provide the relation to be measured and two to serve as a standard of comparison by reference to which the measurement is made, every measured quantity pertaining to elementary particles must be associated with a quadruple wave-function, and it follows that the total number of possible independent quadruple wave-functions would give the total number of particles in the universe.[2] This number is calculated from an equation derived from the group structure of symbols involved in such wave equations and is given in round numbers as 10^{79} electrons and the same number of protons.[3]

So it transpires that the number of particles in the universe is implicit in the curvature of space.

---

[1] *The Expanding Universe*, pp. 105–6.

[2] Cf. Eddington, *The Philosophy of Physical Science*, p. 168, and Whittaker, *From Euclid to Eddington*, p. 194.

[3] *Vide* Eddington, op. cit., p. 176 f., and Whittaker, *ibid*.

From the constant of nebular recession—the increase in velocity of the galaxies per unit distance—the radius of world curvature can be obtained by Lemaître's equation

$$V_0 = \frac{c}{R_0\sqrt{3}},$$

and from this again the mass M of the universe can be calculated by means of Einstein's equation

$$\frac{\gamma M}{c^2} = \frac{\pi R_0}{4},$$

Dividing this by the mass of the hydrogen atom, Eddington obtained a value for N agreeing with what he had found by other methods. A further corroboration arose from the study of the relation between Coulombian and non-Coulombian forces acting between protons. The latter Eddington identified with forces of interaction with the rest of the universe, and he discovered, in the pursuit of his investigation of them, a relationship between the recession constant and the range constant of non-Coulombian force between protons. So the theories of relativity and quanta, which hitherto had dealt with branches of physics seemingly little related to each other, were brought together. The cosmic and the atomic were shown to be essentially related, and, as Sir Edmund Whittaker testifies, the foundations laid of a unified theory of nature.[1]

The number of particles in the universe, N, is called the cosmical number, and Eddington used it to relate to one another and to calculate the universal constants of nature. The cosmical constant λ, involved in the gravitational equation, corresponds to the force of repulsion which drives the galaxies apart. It is also a determinant of the curvature of space, which is linked with the average density and so with the total mass of matter in the universe. This total mass is obviously the sum of the masses of the total number of particles, and the symbol M in Einstein's equation for the universe may thus be replaced by Nm_p, the product of the cosmical number and the mass of the proton. Further, on the assumption that the mass (or energy) of the electron is due to an

[1] *Vide From Euclid to Eddington*, p. 198.

interchange with the rest of the universe—is a quantity measured against the radius of curvature of the world as a standard—an equation can be constructed relating it to N and R. This quantity appears in the wave equation of the hydrogen atom, in the expression $\dfrac{mc^2}{e^2}$, as representing the movement of the electron in the electrostatic field of the nucleus, and Eddington takes this expression as equivalent to what he calls the 'adjusted natural standard of length', $\dfrac{\sqrt{N}}{R}$. The resulting equation, in conjunction with that of the Einstein universe, corroborates the value previously found for N by other means. Moreover, from the relationships so established, a modified form of the equation for the Force Constant—the ratio of electrical to gravitational forces acting between proton and electron—now becomes available in terms of N.

Essential connexions are thus demonstrated between gravitation, space-curvature and the cosmical constant, which determines the recession of the galaxies, the total mass and number of particles in the world, the energy of the electron and the electrical and gravitational forces binding proton and electron in the structure of the atom. Nor is this all.

Eddington equates his adjusted natural standard $\dfrac{\sqrt{N}}{R}$ with the mass of the electron multiplied by 136, a figure derived from the fine structure constant, which he holds to be the whole number 137, because this, he says, is the number of degrees of freedom associated with the wave-function for a pair of charges. But the use of an invariable natural standard, he avers, reduces it by one to 136.[1] Hence he deduces a quadratic equation, the two roots of which are respectively the masses of the electron and the proton. The solution gives values remarkably close to those obtained by experiment.[2]

Thus, from the constant of nebular recession, the radius of the universe is calculable; from a combination of certain essential requirements in relativity and quantum theory, the cosmical

---

[1] *Vide The Expanding Universe*, pp. 114–5.
[2] *Vide* Whittaker, op. cit., p. 200.

number is derived; so the 'adjusted natural standard' $\sqrt{N}/R$ can be evaluated and from it the mass of the electron and of the proton.

The philosophical importance of all this is summed up in Eddington's modest assessment of it: 'I only want to make vivid,' he declares, 'the wide inter-relatedness of things.' Our goal,' he had earlier remarked, 'is not to reach an ultimate conception but to complete the full circle of relationship.'[1] But this would hardly be possible unless the physical world were so constituted that the circle of relationship were in actuality complete; and this is surely what is most impressive and conspicuous about the conception of the world offered us by contemporary physics—that it is a unitary world, the contents of which, though of staggering extent, complexity and variety, are nevertheless all essentially and inextricably interwoven into a single, continuous, self-contained and unbroken fabric.

6

The same moral is taught by the theory set out in his James Scott Lecture of 1943 by E. A. Milne. He asserts that the more advanced a branch of science is, the more it relies on inference and the fewer independent appeals it makes to experiment in deducing 'diverse phenomenal laws from a few general principles'.[2] He even goes so far as to say that the process of deduction and the elimination of appeals to 'experience' can be developed to the point at which no appeals at all are made to quantitative experience, and the general principles from which the laws of phenomena are deduced are seen to be epistemological principles, such as that of operationalism. Statements such as these may be shocking to many scientists, and nowadays the majority of philosophers would think them altogether misguided. It must be especially disconcerting to the empiricist, who prizes the scientist's insistence on operationalism as one of the foundations of his own rectitude, to find it made the starting point of so thorough-going a rationalism. But antipathy to any theory can be attributed only to prejudice unless the evidence is examined, and so far as Milne succeeds in deducing otherwise accredited laws from a minimum of contingent assumptions, and so far as he obtains results that agree with experiment,

[1] *The Expanding Universe*, pp. 104–5 and 120.
[2] *Proceedings of the Royal Society of Edinburgh*, Sec. A, Vol. LXII (1943–4), p. 11.

his view is surely vindicated and deserving of respect. But the importance, for our present purpose, of success in this venture is the evidence it gives of the inter-relatedness of things—the inseparability of particular facts from one another and from the total system of fact which constitutes reality.

Milne adopts two 'rules of policy'. The first is never to introduce any elements of contingent law into the construction of the system, except with the proviso that at a later stage it can be exhibited as a logical consequence of other principles already established. The second is to define every quantitative statement in terms of actually practicable operations, the result of which could be communicated to a distant observer. This involves the ultimate resolution of all physical measures into kinematic measures, which, in the last resort, can be reduced to measures of time and length ('epoch and distance') understandable by a distant independent observer. From the rigorous necessity to observe these epistemological rules, which Milne calls 'the quintessentials of relativity', he deduces the laws of nature. He maintains that once the precise way is stated in which we become aware of other observers and of the quantitative aspects of things, it automatically becomes possible, given sufficient skill, 'to infer all the relations that exist between those quantitative aspects'; and this is what he understands by the rationality and intelligibility of the universe. In other words, what makes a coherent knowledge of the world possible is the systematic way in which its quantitative aspects are related to one another and to our means of ascertaining them.

Dealing first with the motion of a 'free particle', which is admitted to be an idealized conception, he lists the relevant data of perception as (i) those of position and velocity of the particle at the epoch in the observer's experience at which it is being considered, and (ii) similar data for every other particle in the universe. The reason for including the latter is that the presumed 'free particle' is in the presence of all the others and could be observed from any and all of them. 'The rest of the universe' is provisionally assumed (but later demonstrated) to be a system of receding nebulae which are, in turn, idealized to particles each provided with an observer. The law of motion for the free particle is then the rule of calculation by which any observer can predict his own observations of the particle's position and velocity; and it will be such that from it and from his knowledge of the motion of any other observer the rule used by that observer for obtaining *his* description of its motion can also be calculated. But as there is to be no discrimination between observers—as none is to have a privileged status—the rule for all must be the same; hence, as calculated by one observer for any other, the same result must be obtained as by simply *copying*. In short, the rule must be such that, when applied to other observers, and their predictions of the movement of the particle are calculated, it will reveal the fact that they are using the same rule of prediction.

If these conditions are to be realized the motion of the particle will be restricted in certain ways, and it is further restricted by the provision that the rest of the universe effectively exhausts all other matter in existence. It is then claimed that mathematically there is only one form of law that will satisfy all the conditions laid down, and that the motion of the particle, as a result of these restrictions, is something precise and definite.

Milne insists on the inclusion of 'the rest of the universe', which, he says, is always present, so that 'no *deduction* of the motion of a single free particle, *per se*, ignoring the rest of the universe, can be legitimate'. But it is as the theatre (and the only possible one) for other observers that he considers it; not, like Eddington, as the source of physical influences on the particle. This, of course, is necessarily so, for the particle is assumed, in the idealized conception, to be moving free of all such influences. It thus becomes evident that not even an idealization in which all extraneous influences are thought away can dispense with the rest of the universe, and the simplest idealized observable motion is still governed by relations involving the entire world. So, according to Milne, cosmology and kinematics are inseparably connected.

By this method of derivation, an equation of motion is obtained which does not coincide with Newton's form of the first law, but from it Newton's law can be recovered by a change of co-ordinates, which is effected by regraduation of clocks in a particular way. The original description of the universe assumed is inappropriate to the measures used in Newton's dynamics. It is that of an expanding universe of finite extent but infinite content (the first law is found to be independent of density). This implies a time-system extending back to an origin at which the expansion started. If the time reckoning is modified in a special manner, and with it all other derivative measures, the universe can be regarded as static and infinite in extent. In such a world Newton's law is found to apply. But, Milne explains, we could not begin with the Newtonian model, because its description involves a constant, the origin of which is not explicable until we realize the relation of the Newtonian picture to that of the expanding universe. Then it transpires that it depends on the age of the universe, from its natural zero of time, at which we make the change in the time reckoning in order to obtain a static, infinite world, and that in the expanding universe the constant in question corresponds to *curvature*.

Milne proceeds from the consideration of one free particle to the motion of two in each other's presence and that of the rest of the universe, and without empirical assumptions he is able to infer, by means of the first law of motion, the accelerations and future movement of the particles. This gives the law of gravitation, which, he says, 'is nothing but the pair of equations of two free particles in one another's presence'. So where both Newton and Eddington simply posited the law, Milne claims to have deduced it.

There are two components in the acceleration of each of two particles, one attributable to the presence of the second particle and the other to the rest of the universe. Milne proposes to regard them both as gravitational, so that the first law is as much a law of gravitation as the second. 'A "gravitational" acceleration is just an acceleration which a particle cannot help possessing.' So Newton's first and fourth laws are shown to be just two aspects of one and the same phenomenon. Milne then contrives to derive the constant of gravitation mathematically from a formula including the natural time t_o (or age of the expanding universe involved in the first law), the radius of the world taken as $R = ct_o$ (c being an arbitrary constant which is subsequently proved to be the velocity of light) and the apparent mass of the universe, obtained by filling the sphere of radius ct with matter of uniform density equal to that at the centre at time t (for which a formula is available). The constant of gravitation is thus found to depend on the age of the universe, and Milne asserts that in the Newtonian picture it 'masquerades' as a constant because the time scale has been transformed in an artificial manner. Gravitation is conceived simply as the way in which particles must move in each other's presence and that of the rest of the universe if they are to do so according to rules the same for all observers. It is the condition without which there could not be an observed universe— a sort of Kantian *a priori* principle.

The gravitational potential implied in the kinematic model of the universe contains only the positions and 'epochs' of the two particles concerned. But certain other invariants involving velocities as well as these and called by Milne 'super-potentials' give, by a process of double differentiation, equations of motion containing terms corresponding to electromagnetic forces between two charged particles in motion. Differences in detail between these equations and those of Faraday and Maxwell become conspicuous at high velocities, and, when the particles are in close proximity, are so marked that energy and angular momentum are no longer conserved. Modifications are accordingly made to the expressions used to describe the forces, and these correspond to a force which changes suddenly at the distance which proves to be the radius of the electron, and it provides conditions for a temporary, unstable, close association of two oppositely charged particles, suggesting the neutron.

In all this certain assumptions have been made attention to which yields new and spectacular results. First we accept (unavoidably) time order as given in subjective experience, where it is (contingently) one-dimensional and possesses direction away from what is later identified as the 'natural zero'. We also have to accept the contingent proposition that space has three dimensions, and we notice that unlike time space can be traversed reversibly in any direction. But space is not an object of perception, it is only a locus for perceived objects without which it does not exist. Here again we have the Leibnizian view. Perception of objects in space, however, implies some causal chain linking the perceived object with the percipient. Milne takes this to be light, giving preference to visual perception as the simplest for the construction of physical theory. Space without light, he says, is invisible darkness and is 'inimical to geometry'. It is the spreading light wave that creates space for Milne, and not, as for Einstein, the existence of matter; but so far as mass is equivalent to energy and energy manifests itself as radiation, there need be no difference in principle between the two views. As was quoted from Eddington, what extends space is 'a cause which creates intervals and geodesics'—and that is precisely what light is.

We can now construct co-ordinates from comparison of the time, on an arbitrarily running subjective clock, at which the observer (myself) momentarily uncovers a light, and that at which it momentarily reveals an object at a distance. The semi-sum of these primitive measurements is called the 'epoch', and the

D*

positive semi-difference, multiplied by the conventional constant c, the distance. We then find, when we come to measure velocities, that c is the velocity of light. So we avoid reliance upon an empirical law about the velocity of light which, if we defined distance independently of clock-readings, would be required to correlate observations by different observers in separate places. Distance co-ordinates are therefore always defined by time measures, and also for the further reason that otherwise 'epoch-at-a-distance' could not be satisfactorily defined.

A second observer at a distance can now be introduced, and methods can be determined of correlating and regraduating clocks so that they agree. The correlation of observations by both observers of events external to them both, and circumstances in which the clocks of any number of observers can be correlated and regraduated, may then be considered. Out of the first of these considerations arise Einstein's theory of relativity and the Lorentz transformations, and out of the second the possibility of dispensing with any geometrical axiom of congruence in the comparison of measurements of length. It has now become obvious why Milne gives so much importance to the reckoning of time and makes so much depend upon the graduation of clocks and the consequent time scale adopted.

Finally, Milne shows that the condition of world-wide relativity is a world-wide class of observers with mutually congruent clocks —a condition, says Milne, of the rationality of the world. A property of such a situation is that it makes possible the definition of an instant (and only one) at which all observers coincided in position and at which complete synchronization was possible. This gives us the natural zero of time. Further, the relative movement of such a class of observers results in the kinematic model of the expanding universe described earlier, from which the properties of all combinations of particles and the relations of all phenomena taking place in it follow mathematically.

7

No more is needed to make obvious the complete and thoroughgoing unity of interrelated differences which characterizes the world for these theorists. The ideas used by Milne are essentially those required by the theory of relativity, and from them he demonstrates, *more geometrico*, the essential inter-connectedness of the laws of motion and those of electrodynamics, of these again and the dimensions of the electron, of the velocity of light and the nature and measurability of space and time, and all of these with the structural scheme upon which all contemporary cosmological theories are founded.

It is apparent from the account so far given of physical theories that no physical observation can be made and no physical description given of a particle in isolation, or even of pairs of particles, or of groups, completely severed from the rest of the universe. For all observation in physics is measurement, and all description is in quantitative terms; and we have seen that all measurement involves the principle of relativity, and that all measured quantities are related explicitly or implicitly to the universe as a whole. This is brought out emphatically by Eddington and, in a different way, insistently required by Milne. The-rest-of-the-universe is a constituent of every quantitative assessment—in short, the whole is immanent in every part and determines the dimensions of the part. Whether we concern ourselves with the nature of the whole or whether we investigate the details of its constituents, we are compelled to view it as one totality, not in any absolute sense divisible, yet a totality the singleness of which is constituted by the interrelatedness of different and distinguishable components. For the disposition and movement, the interchange of influence and structural specifications, of the particular contents of the world are all mutually dependent and mutually constitutive. In Whitehead's phraseology, they enter into the real internal constitution one of another; each is ingredient in all, and all in each. They are inter-constitutive, yet in such a way as to be recognizably distinct from one another in their mutual dependence.

The universe is thus a texture of relations between parts which though distinguishable, as they must be to be related, are not merely inseparable but intrinsically interdependent. The existence and character of each is what it is because the rest of the universe, *in toto* and *in minutiis*, are what they are. Whole and part are mutually determining and no detail could be other than it is without making some difference, however slight, to all the rest. This is no mere unverifiable 'metaphysical' speculation (in the pejorative sense), but the conclusion forced upon us by scientific theories based upon scientifically ascertained facts.

If science may command any respect as a form of knowledge; if its criteria of validity are at all reliable, and if its theories have any claim to truth, then the doctrine of the independence and atomicity of facts is not simply unverifiable. It is plainly false. Nor would it be necessary to labour this point, were it not that the doctrine has been propounded by the two most influential philosophers of our time, Bertrand Russell and Ludwig Wittgenstein, and that they have been believed by a widespread and powerful following. True it is that Wittgenstein later modified his views and largely repudiated his earlier opinions, and many contemporary linguistic philosophers (who may not unjustly be considered his followers) have criticized and rejected the doctrine of logical atomism. Yet they still adhere to many of its consequences and submit to its influence in their attitude towards and practice of philosophy in a manner which would be justifiable only by means of its support.

And if, in the light of contemporary science, the doctrine of atomic facts goes by the board, the parallel doctrine of atomic propositions, with all its consequences in logical theory, may be expected to go with it. And along with these a whole host of related notions about the impossibility of necessary connection between matters of fact, the enormity of synthetic *a priori* propositions, and the analyticity of logic and mathematics will require careful re-examination. The conception of the world as a close-knit unity of systematically related and interdependent phenomena implies a very different epistemology and a very different idea of logic. But all this belongs to a separate inquiry and, so far as it can be included in this study, must come at a later stage.

CHAPTER VI

MATTER AND ENERGY

I

The theory of relativity represents fields of force as structural properties of space-time, and a field of force is the arena in which the presence of energy is detectable. Energy manifests itself in the physical world as radiation, and Einstein established its fundamental identity with mass.[1] This has since been demonstrated experimentally by the annihilation of elementary particles and their conversion into γ-rays and the reverse process of conversion of γ-rays into pairs of electrons and positrons ('pair production') as observed by Blackett and Occhialini. It is hardly surprising, therefore, that both matter and energy should appear to us in the same phenomenal forms, as particles and as waves. The universal interconnectedness of things is here again exemplified. Space-time structure, in the form of curvature of differing degrees, appears as field, and field, by what Teilhard would call 'complexification', organizes itself into material particles. The contemporary theory of matter, notwithstanding disputes and controversies still current about the concepts involved, unquestionably represents the atom as a complicated organization of fields of force describable without misrepresentation as an energy complex. This being so, an unbroken continuity between space-time, field, energy and matter is established, as a series of forms or manifestations of the real, each a more complex elaboration of its predecessor in the series. The progression is effected, to borrow again from Teilhard, by a process of self-enfoldment (*enroulement sur soi-même*) of the prior form: curvature of space gives field, the structure or complexity of the field (as we are about to find) takes the form of waves (or radiation), further complication of these, by superposition, produces wave-packets or particles, and the intricate organization of particles into a single energy system constitutes the atom.

But the state of our knowledge on these matters is at present such as to make speculation hazardous, and what conclusions we feel justified in drawing must be held with an open mind. Eddington

[1] Cf. Schrödinger, 'Our Conception of Matter', in *What is Life? and Other Scientific Essays* (New York, 1956), p. 168.

wrote in 1926, 'It would probably be wiser to nail up over the door of the new quantum theory a notice, "Structural alterations in progress—No admittance except on business", and particularly to warn the doorkeeper to keep out prying philosophers'. Certainly, even apart from its technical and mathematical intricacy, the theory presents the philosopher with serious difficulties. First, there is less agreement among scientists here on the correct interpretation to be given to the experimental results and their mathematical treatment than is the case in other branches of physics, so that it is often difficult to say what precisely may be considered as established. One must therefore guard against placing too much reliance on hypotheses that may in the near future be abandoned. Nevertheless there are some firm tendencies the direction of which is unlikely to be totally reversed, and even out of the welter of controversy, some facts emerge that can hardly be gainsaid. Upon these we may be able, by moving cautiously, to build enough to give our conception of the physical world a modicum of structural unity.

Secondly, the physical theory has been linked with epistemological opinions even by the physicists themselves, including its originators and some of its most distinguished exponents. My policy up to the present has been, as far as possible, to defer epistemological investigation until a conspectus of the world is possible and the place in it of the knowing mind is discernible; but here we are confronted with a situation in which the conception of the physical reality, in consequence of the scientists' own attempts to form it, has become infected (so to speak) by that of knowledge. To some extent this is also true of relativity, but it has been possible so far to keep the two notions more or less apart; it will not be possible to do so to the same extent in the ensuing discussion. Nevertheless, epistemological considerations will not be allowed to intrude beyond what is necessary in order to deal with the views of scientists who introduce them into their theories of matter.

2

The atomic or granular theory of matter has a long and continuous history going back to Leucippus and Democritus. It was revived at the Renaissance, when the philosophy of Epicurus became popular in the reaction against Aristotle. It was adopted by Francis

Bacon and by Newton and was taken for granted by John Locke. But no definite progress could be made towards its scientific confirmation until the science of chemistry had advanced sufficiently to clarify the idea of a chemical element and to enable experimenters to determine the exact proportions in which such elements combined with one another to form compounds. From that point on the hypothesis became practically useful for laboratory work and for making scientific predictions. The molecular structure of the elements was then inferred and the determination of atomic weights followed, leading to the construction of the periodic table in which chemical properties of the elements were correlated with their atomic weights. The study of electrical phenomena further advanced the knowledge of atomic structure, and what had hitherto been imagined as a hard, indivisible, minimal fragment of matter was discovered to be complex and to consist of an arrangement of two or more elementary particles differing in mass and size and with opposite electrical charge. So there emerged the Rutherford model of the atom as a minute solar system, with a positively charged and heavy nucleus at the centre containing protons, surrounded by negatively charged planetary electrons. The progress of atomic physics has since continued to the point at which the existence of elementary particles has been established almost by direct perception of them. The Wilson cloud chamber has revealed their tracks through space; X-ray analysis of crystals has displayed 'an admirable texture of parts' no less than the atoms themselves, while the electron microscope shadows forth individual molecules. A whole series of different kinds of elementary particles have been distinguished: hyperons, neutrons, neutrinos, positrons and mesons, besides the proton and electron. Meanwhile, the electromagnetic theory of light and the discovery of Herzian waves had led to the development of the notion of undulatory radiation covering every form of radiant energy. Planck's discovery of the quantum of action at first confused these two lines of development and later led to their union, if not yet quite to their reconciliation. First, Einstein's postulation of the photon and the granular structure of radiant energy, confirmed by the photoelectric and Compton effects, combined classical and quantum concepts in what seemed an inconsistent manner; for the quantum of light consisted of the product of its frequency (a wave property) with Planck's constant (a corpuscular quantity). Next, Bohr's application of quantum concepts to the Rutherford atom again mixed classical with quantum ideas. According to the classical view the atom ought both constantly to emit radiation continuously varying in frequency (which, in fact it does not) and, in consequence, to collapse as the energy lost by the accelerated electron causes it to fall into the nucleus and neutralize its charge (which does not happen). Bohr removed these contradictions with the help of the hypothesis that radiation was emitted only intermittently when an electron changed from one orbit to another, as the result of a change in the energy state of the atom, which occurred without traceable transition by a 'quantum jump', that took place neither in space nor in time.[1] These quantum jumps occasioned many eminent physicists, including Bohr himself, great concern, and Schrödinger spent much time and thought in attempts to evolve an interpretation which did not require them. In an effort to overcome the difficulties of the 'old quantum theory', Louis de Broglie postulated a wave theory of the electron based on Einstein's equation of energy with mass and Planck's quantum of action. This enabled him to represent the electron orbit in the atom as a stationary wave and removed some of the paradoxical aspects of Bohr's theory. The wave character of elementary particles was then experimentally confirmed by Davisson, Germer and G. P. Thomson, so that, henceforward, physicists were unable to draw any sharp distinction between wave and particle, matter and field, for, as Schrödinger has declared, 'everything—anything at all—is both particle and wave field'.[2]

But the classical notions of wave and particle are mutually incompatible. Particles are discrete and waves are continuous; particles have precise position in space, waves are spread out and have no definite spatial limits; waves are periodic, particles may be indiscriminately scattered; waves move as spherical expanding fronts from a point source, particles follow trajectories. How can

[1] Cf. Schrödinger, 'Are there Quantum Jumps?', *British Journal for the Philosophy of Science*, III (1952): 'Since intermediary states had to remain disallowed, one could not but regard the transition as instantaneous; but, on the other hand, the radiating of a coherent wave train of 3 or 4 feet length, as it can be observed in an interferometer, would use up just about the average interval between two transitions, leaving the atom no time to "be" in those stationary states, the only ones, of which the theory gave a description.' (*What is Life? and other Essays*, p. 137).

[2] 'Our Conception of Matter', op. cit., pp. 161, 165 and 170.

one and the same entity be both? Yet we must notice that even in classical physics this identity of particle and wave motion had been adumbrated. Not only had light originally been regarded as particulate, the granules being projected in straight lines as rays, but also Jacobi had represented the possible trajectories of a material point in a permanent field of force as curves orthogonal to surfaces, in exactly the same relation to one another as are rays to wave fronts. According to the Principle of Least Action of Maupertuis, the path actually followed by a particle from one point to another in a permanent field is that curve which makes the line integral of the momentum minimal. This can be derived from Jacobi's theory in a way which is identical in form with the method of reaching Fermat's Principle of Least Time determining the path of a light ray in a refracting medium. In de Broglie's wave theory these two Principles are explicitly identified. Other features of the classical doctrines have strong affinity to features in the new quantum theory and to them we shall return.

The difficulty has been overcome for the practising physicist by resort to mathematics. He has been enabled by the matrix mechanics of Heisenberg, the wave mechanics of Schrödinger and de Broglie, unified and improved in the quantum mechanics of Dirac, to predict phenomena with outstanding success. In the mathematical calculus, a function is derived, known as the ψ-function, which for certain operators gives definite quantities that may be taken as defining the physical properties of a system, whether we regard it as a wave system or as a particle. These quantities are called 'eigenvalues' of the function, which is itself an 'eigenfunction' of the operator. But the attribution of these quantities to the physical system is subject to a peculiar limitation, involved in the mathematical calculation, as well as by the inescapable conditions of experimentation. This limitation is expressed in the Principle of Uncertainty: that the precision with which the coordinates of a particle can be determined varies inversely as that with which its velocity can be determined, and *vice versa*; and this carries with it the consequence that no experimental means is available for determining whether, in the last resort, matter and energy are really particulate or undulatory,[1] for it seems that one set of quantities can be measured exactly only by regarding them as characteristic of waves, while another equally essential set of

[1] *Vide* Sir Charles G. Darwin, *The New Conceptions of Matter* (London 1931), Ch. IV.

quantities can be measured exactly only by regarding them as characteristic of particles. And all this applies equally to radiant energy and to matter. Accordingly, no firm agreement has yet been reached upon an interpretation of the mathematical treatment of the experimental data, which can offer a clear view of the actual nature of matter.

Bohr suggested that, as the uncertainty relations make it impossible for the wave and the particle pictures ever to be simultaneously applicable, they can never conflict in actuality even though they are incompatible in conception. They are both essential to the physical reality, each in a separate type of situation, and are therefore complementary concepts. This is known as the principle of complementarity, which Bohr attempted to support by drawing attention to parallel instances from other fields. Nevertheless, we are not much helped by this suggestion to form a clear and coherent notion of the nature of the fundamental physical real.

This state of affairs has induced a large and important school to adopt the position that the ψ-function is not a wave-function describing a physical entity, but only a probability function, and that the wave formation is simply a theoretical projection upon the physical situation suggested by the form which the mathematical equations usually take. These merely enable the physicist to assess the degree (or 'density') of probability with which a particle will be found experimentally in a given region at a given time. The 'objectivity' of the physical description is in this way largely repudiated. The wave function is, so it is stated, only partly a description of physical reality. It is also in part descriptive of our knowledge of it. Hence, according to this view, subject and object are indissolubly united in physical theory, and, though we may separate them provisionally in various ways and to differing extents in different situations, they can never be completely divorced.[1]

3

A whole budget of philosophical questions are contained in this interpretation, some epistemological and some metaphysical. If

[1] Cf. W. Heisenberg, *The Physicist's Conception of Nature* (London, 1958), pp. 24, 28–9, and *Physics and Philosophy* (London, 1959), Ch. III; Rosenfeld, 'Strife about Complementarity', *Science Progress*, 1953, and C. F. von Weizsäcker, *The World View of Physics* (London, 1952), pp. 181 and 200.

the waves are of probability only, they do not exist in nature, but that of which they determine the probability does, presumably, occur in reality in some way. As Schrödinger remarks, 'After all, one can speak of the probability of an event only if one believes that, occasionally, it actually occurs'.[1] What then is the ontological status of the particle to the position of which the probability function refers? Has it also a trajectory? That would seem questionable, for we have it on Heisenberg's authority that the probability function can give us no information about what actually happens between two experiments.[2] One might counter that what cannot be ascertained may nevertheless exist, but this rejoinder would be met from one quarter by the reminder that what is unobservable in principle may not be presumed in science, and from another by directing attention to interference phenomena and other experimental evidence which suggest that the only form of motion by which quanta (whether of energy or of matter) can traverse space is wave motion.[3] But the theory of relativity has dispensed with any undulatory medium, and if the waves are only waves of probability one can hardly be confident that the particle exists at all between the occasions on which its position is experimentally ascertained. In that case, what sort of continuity has the physically real? And what causal connections, if any, can link the successive appearances? Further, what are the implications for physical reality of the alleged inseparability of subject and object? Are we so soon to be committed to a form of idealism, and if so to what form?

We may begin with the last question, not in order to answer it finally, but to remove unnecessary obstacles from our path; for if at this stage we were forced to say, without qualification, that physical science gives no objective account of the real, we should have to give up the attempt to derive a theory of knowledge from the scientific conception of nature, but would be compelled to proceed directly to construct (presumably *a priori*) a theory of knowledge from which to derive the scientific conception of the world. It is essential to consider at once how far the quantum theory impels us to any such course, and immediately it is evident

[1] Op. cit., p. 174.
[2] *Physics and Philosophy*, pp. 54–5.
[3] Cf. Eddington, *The Nature of the Physical World* (Cambridge, 1948), pp. 185 ff., and Henry Margenau, *The Nature of Physical Reality* (New York, 1950), pp. 323 ff.

that the very general consensus among quantum physicists about the inseparability of subject and object is by no means the same doctrine as that of the older idealisms. The union of subject and object for the thorough-going idealist is universal in knowledge and it reduces the physical world to 'an ideal construction' within experience, but for the quantum physicist it is not intended to apply at all to the macroscopic objects. All scientific apparatus consists of macroscopic objects and, in the assessment of experimental results, the physicist relies on the classical causal laws governing their behaviour. He does not, and strictly cannot treat these as probability laws.[1] Sometimes they are alleged to be such, but where probabilities are always so great as to be indistinguishable from practical certainties, or so small as to be indistinguishable from impossibilities, such an interpretation would be otiose. If all physical events were regarded as merely probable, in the same way as the microphysical are said to be, the conception of probability, as will presently appear, would become unviable. On the other hand, by its restriction to microphysics, the assertion of the inseparability of subject and object reduces simply to the contention that the quantitative determination of certain complementary aspects of atomic phenomena are not precisely ascertainable in conjunction, but can be found only within stated limits of probability; and nothing follows necessarily from that as to the existence or non-existence of physical entities independently of the mind.

The obstacle to precise determination of conjugate quantities is always the quantum of action, for no system can either radiate or absorb energy in less than single quanta, and no measurement can be made except through some interchange of energy between the measuring instrument and the object measured. If the quantum and the property to be measured are of comparable size, as is always the case in micro-physics, any possible process of measurement will significantly interfere with the object measured. But how far are we justified in consequence in making the 'objective' event dependent upon its 'subjective' assessment?

Sir Charles Darwin considers it legitimate to hold that the particulate or undulatory character of the phenomenon, whichever is observed, is actually created by the experiment and does not exist antecedently in nature. Von Weizsacker also maintains that the experiment brings to birth what it reveals and that the mind creates what it knows. Philipp Frank goes even further, contending

[1] Cf. von Weizsäcker, op. cit., Ch. III.

that the theory with all its mathematical apparatus is no more than a device enabling us to predict the occurrence of subsequent sensuous data. Here the influence of Mach is clearly apparent, and the limitation of existence to experienced sensa is implied. But this goes too far. It is not necessary to deny that quantum physics forces on our attention some form of interdependence between subject and object in order to detect the untenability of so extreme a phenomenalistic position.

Some thinkers seem to be led astray by too rigid and extreme an interpretation of the principle of 'operationalism'—that the only scientifically admissible entities and states are those for the observation of which we can conceive the requisite experimental operations. This principle is of undoubted importance and has played a very significant part in the development of science, expecially in that of the theory of relativity; but it may be mis-interpreted with disastrous effects for epistemology. It is certainly sound teaching that to postulate entities for which there is no evidence nor any conceivable way of obtaining it is unscientific. But it is far from sound to reduce that which is observed to the bare occurrence of sense data. This leads directly to pheno-menalism, and extreme subjectivism, for which nothing at all is factual except immediately experienced sensa. Science is then reduced to the calculated prediction of their occurrence. Such a doctrine, however, we shall see later, renders any reasonable and coherent theory of scientific observation totally impossible and makes nonsense of such physiological and psychological accounts of perception as modern science offers. The whole concept of observability requires very careful analysis, a task to be under-taken at a later stage, which will reveal the fact that observation is not as simple and obvious a process as is often assumed. To understand by operationalism the subordination of rational inter-pretation to pure sense-experience (if any such thing exists) is to undermine science and deprive us of all coherent epistemology. We cannot anticipate here the reasons which lead to this conclu-sion.[1] It will be sufficient for the present to record the fact, without necessarily endorsing the opinion, that several of the foremost scientists of the age have believed the indeterminacy, which seems so unsatisfactory a feature of present-day atomic physics, to be simply an unavoidable practical limitation, and the

[1] *Vide* N. R. Hanson, *Patterns of Discovery* (Cambridge, 1958), Ch. I, my own *Nature, Mind and Modern Science*, Ch. XVI, and Chs. XIX and XX below.

more sweeping epistemological conclusions drawn from it by some of their colleagues to be unwarranted.[1]

The phenomenon created by, and observed in, an experiment is never limited to what is directly perceived by the experimenter. Much less is it true that it is limited to what is immediately sensed. The result of an experiment is always a more or less elaborate interpretation of what is perceived, and the perception itself is not innocent of all rational supplementation. The implications of any observation upon which such interpretation relies have wide ramifications and they may well include the existence of unobservables, for which, nevertheless, what is observed may legitimately count as evidence. Professor David Bohm has put forward an interpretation of quantum mechanics explicitly adopting a position of this kind. He presumes the existence of hidden variables, which, though they cannot be given values with our present knowledge and experimental techniques, can be allowed for in the mathematical formulation of physical situations, without affecting the agreement so far obtained with experimental results, yet in such a way that crucial differences arise in the range of dimensions less than 10^{-13} cm., where the current theory runs into difficulty, and which might permit, as techniques improve, of an experimental test to decide between this and the usually accepted formulation.[2] This suggestion in philosophically interesting in that it helps to clear up a serious confusion concerning the notion of probability often vitiating both scientific and philosophical thinking.

[1] Cf. Einstein, Podolsky and Rosen, 'Can Quantum Theory Descriptions be Considered Complete', *The Physical Review*, 47, 1935, pp. 777–80; Einstein, 'Quantenteorie und Wirklichkeit', *Dialectica* II, 1948; P. A. Schilpp (Ed.) *Albert Einstein, Philosopher Scientist* (Evanston, 1949); E. Schrödinger, 'Are There Quantum Jumps', *British Journal for the Philosophy of Science*, III, 1952; Mario Bunge, 'Strife about Complementarity', *B.J.P.S..*, VI, 1955; P. Feyerabend, 'The Quantum Theory of Measurement' in *Observation and Interpretation* (Körner, Ed., London, 1957); A. Landé, 'Dualism to Unity in Quantum Physics', *B.J.P.S.*, X, 1959. Milic Capek opposes views like these on the ground that the interaction involved in experimental observation is typical of all physical interaction, and he agrees with Eddington that the unascertainable quantities simply do not occur in nature. We shall see reason later to give qualified support to this contention. It does not seem possible to assent to it without qualification, but it does express at least an important half-truth. See p. 138 below.

[2] *Vide* D. Bohm, 'A suggested interpretation of Quantum Theory in terms of hidden variables', *The Physical Review*, V (1952).

4

The uncertainty principle in quantum physics, announcing the incurable inability of the scientist to determine specific quantities
pertaining to elementary phenomena beyond prescribed limits of
accuracy, has persuaded many physicists that causal laws, as
determining principles in nature, may no longer be considered
more than approximately valid; and they have been encouraged to
adopt an epistemological view advocated by many philosophers
that separates probable knowledge from certainty by a sharp
division. This attempt, however, to divorce probability from
certainty as two different and independent kinds of knowledge
rests upon a fallacy. Hume is largely responsible for the habit so
far as it exists among philosophers, but Hume's self-consistency
is preserved by his scepticism, which dissolved away certainty
altogether. Others retain certainty in the form of 'logical' and
mathematical truth, which they hold to be necessary and insusceptible of degree at the cost of making it purely tautological.
But if, with F. H. Bradley, we see in a tautology no significant
assertion whatsoever, the notion of truth is no longer applicable
to it at all. There are, however, propositions which are accounted
true because they are supported by adequate grounds or reasons,
which are logically cogent without being tautological,[1] and it is only
in relation to this sort of truth that probability has any consistent
meaning. If absolute truth is confined to tautology, and if truth
and falsity are held to be insusceptible of degree, then all probable
statements ought to be rejected as false. Otherwise, we should
have to use the word 'true' in two quite different and unrelated
senses, one applying only to tautologies, and the other to varying
degrees of probability, which, as it increases, approximates to
some quite different variety of truth. This position does not, on
the face of it, appear very satisfactory and we may postpone
further discussion of it. In order to avoid serious ambiguity in our
discourse, therefore, and to retain some intelligible meaning for the
phrase 'degree of probability', we must take it that what is meant
by saying of any assertion that it is probable, is that, under certain
conditions, within certain limitations, or with certain qualifications, it is true, in the same sense as an assertion free of such

[1] This statement anticipates later conclusions and its full justification
can be given only when the epistemological aspect of science is more
fully examined.

limitations would be true without qualification. To give a value to its probability is then to give a measure of its truth.

If p is more probable than q, there must be more grounds for believing p; and grounds are logical supports or reasons guaranteeing (in appropriate measure) the truth of the belief. If p is true without qualification, the reasons for believing it, whatever they may be, must be sufficient and unassailable. But when this is not the case, the extent to which the supporting reasons are inadequate or incomplete is the measure of its improbability; the extent to which they are cogent, of its probability. If no supporting reasons are available, no assessment of probability can be given—unless, of course, the absence of support is traceable to positive grounds for denial. Probability has meaning only in terms of the availability and evaluability of grounds.

In natural science, the only relevant grounds for the truth of factual predictions are known or discoverable laws of systematic connection. It might be held that 'direct observation' would be sufficient ground for accepting a factual proposition as true without qualification. But this is not the case. Just what it is that is being observed in any act of observation is never self-evident (despite persistent attempts on the part of empiricists to isolate the barely given), and what is directly observed can never be stated in precise terms without reference to much that falls outside the limits of the observation. Every statement of the content of an observation involves theoretical assumptions. This will have to be fully demonstrated in its proper place, and at this point must be taken on trust; but if it is accepted, then it follows that assertions about the occurrence of natural phenomena can, for science, be satisfactorily grounded only in scientific laws.

Laws referring to the occurrence of events are primarily causal, and a precise discussion of this matter would require an examination of the concept of cause. Though this may seem to be an appropriate piece to embark upon such an examination, we should soon be led by it to realize that causal connection is rather an epistemological principle than an ontological character. It will be proper therefore to reserve further discussion of it until epistemology is our primary concern. Here I shall presume, subject to possible later correction, that by a causal law, we mean simply a law of systematic interconnection between events.

Explicitly, laws may be either causal or statistical, but if they are statistical they presume causal laws, either known or undiscovered, as the basis of the statistics.[1] Otherwise, the statistics would be simply unreliable. If they give rise to *reliable* predictions, this indicates the existence of some systematic connections, or else the fulfilment of the predictions would be pure coincidence and no reliance could be placed on them. This fact is illustrated in statistical theory by the refusal of the statistician to regard more than a limited proportion of favourable cases to count as pure coincidence. Accordingly, theories in which probability is assessed in terms of frequency of occurrence are not in conflict with the position here being maintained. For frequency of occurrence may be accepted as a scientific ground for belief only if it is assumed (tacitly or openly) to result from causes systematically subject to law. The ultimate grounds for prediction are, therefore, always causal conditions, and unless causal connections are presumed to be compulsive they cannot serve as grounds. If they are compulsive, they are determining conditions, and if they are not, they are scientifically unimportant.[2]

Doubt cannot be cast on this conclusion by citing the laws of statistical mechanics as contrary evidence. Here, it might be said, correlations are established between the state of a volume of gas (or of a solid) and such conditions as pressure and temperature in terms of the average behaviour of vast multitudes of particles whose movement is (or is assumed to be) entirely random and indeterminate. But this is not the case. The tacit assumption of statistical mechanics is that the random movement of the particles is subject to the laws of ordinary mechanics. The particles concerned are usually relatively large (e.g. molecules of a gas), and there is nothing in principle to prevent the position and velocity of each from being specified, though this is impossible in practice. If it were done the subsequent movement of every particle would be, in principle, determined and predictable by the laws of mechanics. But as in practice none of the pertinent facts can be

[1] So-called 'a priori' probability, founded upon a limited number of possibilities, is no real exception; for what makes the alternatives possible, as well as what limits the number of possibilities, are causal conditions; e.g. the alternative possible outcomes of tossing a coin are limited by its shape, by the law of gravitation and the balance of forces.

[2] Provisionally, the word 'compulsive' may be taken to mean simply 'leaving (or permitting) no alternative'. It is not anthropomorphic, inspired by human social relations. On the contrary, what is meant by compulsion in reference to constraints upon human action is derived from the meaning intended here.

ascertained in detail because of their vast number and variety, advantage is taken of this multiplicity to rely on the mutual cancellation of exceptional cases and to determine and make use of averages, in lieu of sums and resultants of enormous numbers of individual cases. The statistical mechanics may be regarded in either of two ways:[1] as no more than a mathematical device for calculating the laws of thermodynamics, in which case it in no way abrogates the force of the causal laws of ordinary mechanics; or it may be regarded as logically prior to thermodynamics as the *explanation* of its laws. In that case, however, it makes sense as a reliable means of prediction, only if what is averaged is the behaviour of particles individually subject to mechanical laws, and if the probabilities estimated are consequent upon that assumption. 'The second law (of thermodynamics),' says Margenau, 'talks about probabilities *if the mechanical laws are exact.*'[2] (His italics.)

A probable event, for science, is therefore an event for which there exist, or may be presumed, some conditions upon which it follows by law. No assessment of probability is possible for an event for which there are no determining conditions. A statistical determination of frequency of occurrence can, of course, be made; but reliance upon it as a ground for prediction is a tacit assumption of the existence of determining causes, albeit unknown or even unascertainable. Indeterminacy in quantum theory can be consistently understood as the unavoidable impossibility of simultaneous determination of certain conjugate quantities within certain limits. It cannot be interpreted as the total absence of determining causes, even within those limits, as long as the events concerned are described as probable and a precise estimate of their probability is given (though it well may require modification of our idea of causation). For the implication of any such estimate is the presence of order and connection of some sort. If systematic determination is denied altogether, no grounds remain for probable prediction. More specifically, the operator of which the ψ-function is a 'proper' or 'eigenfunction' is derived from a formula expressing a physical law (e.g. the Hamiltonian operator in the case of the Schrödinger wave equation).[3] Without presuming

[1] Cf. Margenau, *The Nature of Physical Reality*, p. 282.

[2] Op. cit., p. 218. Dr. K. Mendelsohn's remark, 'The fundamental ideas of modern physics are based on the fact that truth is statistical' (*Turning Points in Physics*, Ch. III, p. 67) is, therefore, at best, very dubious.

[3] *Vide* de Broglie, *The Revolution in Physics* (London, 1954), p. 169.

to pontificate upon the issue of the scientific dispute, one may say that at least *prima facie*, Bohm is not unreasonable in proposing the existence of hidden variables (which in large measure correspond to what Margenau calls 'latent observables'[1]) whether or not their precise evaluation is possible in practice.

Philosophers following Hume dissent from all this because they make causality itself a merely probable connection. They maintain that causal laws are only and always statements based on the frequency of experienced conjunctions between events. This theory, however, depends upon the prior assumptions: (i) that the primary (and ultimately the only) source of factual knowledge is sense, and (ii) that sense-percepts are atomic, separate elements of experience between which no systematic connections are discoverable. Accordingly, for them, the scientific organization of factual knowledge can be no more than a system of general propositions each of which is a summary statement of the repetitions of experienced conjunctions, whose relative frequency is the measure of their probable future occurrence. This makes every causal law a probability statement, and the allegation that the grounds of probability statements are causal laws becomes a *hysteron proteron*. Persistence in this doctrine is the more surprising in that Hume made perfectly clear its failure to provide a basis even for a theory of probability.[2] But what is here in question is its epistemological foundation. We have already seen reason to deny the occurrence of isolable, atomic facts, and the belief in them has close connections with the doctrine of experience as constituted by atomic percepts. There is, moreover, a formidable body of evidence in the actual practice of scientists, which has yet to be examined, running directly counter to the view that scientific laws are derived from frequently conjoined sense-experiences, or are statements about the conjunction (constant or otherwise) of single, isolable events. They have a very different character and pattern.[3] Before we can decide this matter we need a satisfactory theory of perception and of the place of observation in scientific method. When we come to discuss these more directly, we shall find ample reason to contend that scientific observation itself depends more upon theory than upon the immediate deliverances of sense, and

[1] *Vide* Margenau, *The Nature of Physical Reality*, pp. 175 ff.
[2] *Vide* Hume, *Treatise of Human Nature*, Part I, Sec. VI (Selby-Bigge, p. 90).
[3] Cf. N. R. Hanson, *Patterns of Discovery*, Chs. I–IV.

that the interconnectedness of facts, of which the theory of relativity gives evidence and which we shall shortly see further supported by the quantum theory, is paralleled by and reflected in a similar interconnectedness of experience. The Humian theory of causality rests on a false foundation. But the examination of these matters belongs to another place and can be more profitably undertaken when the deliverances of the sciences have been more completely reviewed, unless we are to get bogged down in metaphysical dicussions divorced from scientific evidence. Meanwhile, it begins to become apparent that the question of causality is as much an epistemological question as a metaphysical one, and that we have become involved in it at this stage only because of the ambiguous character of some interpretations of the quantum theory.

5

If we are so ready to accept relativity as evidence of the unity of the world, why, it may be asked, should we not take the quantum theory as evidence for the discreteness of events? The answer is that, if the evidence is conclusive, it must needs be respected, but it seems as yet far from conclusive. It is not even clear what is to be considered as discrete. Are there quantum jumps? Or is the discontinuity, as Heisenberg asserts, only a discontinuity in our knowledge?[1] That would entitle us to say no more than that we do not know whether or not the physical reality is discrete.

Not all authorities agree about the occurrence of quantum jumps. Planck and Einstein were never convinced of the finality of the theory, and Schrödinger attempted to interpret the observed facts so as to eliminate discontinuous transitions. Moreover, no quantum jump is ever directly observed, but is demanded theoretically because measurements of specific properties made on subsequent occasions can never be brought nearer to each other than a minimal amount, in quantity, time, or space. As Schrödinger has expressed it, 'the postulate of continuity of description' has broken down, and if this break-down indicates a real hiatus in nature the principle of causality would be in jeopardy.[2]

---

[1] *Vide Physics and Philosophy*, p. 54.

[2] *Vide Science and Humanism* (Cambridge, 1952), pp. 26 ff. It is to be noted that Schrödinger assumes continuity of process to be a condition of causation.

The actual occurrence in nature of quantum jumps would imply a discontinuity in space and time difficult both to conceive and to accommodate in the scientific scheme. Relativity rests throughout on the presumption of a continuum, and if this could not be maintained the whole system of its reasoning would be affected. In large measure, the theory of relativity follows from a refusal to admit action at a distance, or to acknowledge any relations other than can be continuously built up from those between contiguous elements.[1] If quantum jumps occur, there is both action at a distance, for *naturam saltum non facere* can no longer be maintained, and no contiguous elements are discoverable. Consequently a new problem will arise of reconciling relativity with quantum physics—a task which cannot be evaded, because the results of the one have been incorporated into the other. Not only is the quantum of action a four-dimensional scalar, but Einstein's equation, $e = mc^2$, is the basis of de Broglie's wave equation for the electron, and Dirac, by casting this into relativistic form, invariant for the Lorentz transformations, was able to account for the anomalies of the Zeeman effect.[2]

The discontinuity involved in a quantum jump must be either a discontinuity of existence of the particle or one in space-time itself. For, if the continuous existence of the particle is postulated despite the absence of evidence of transition between its appearances on successive occasions in different places, it must somehow exist in the interim outside space-time. But that is not physically meaningful, and we must, therefore, maintain either that the particle ceases to exist in the interim between its appearances, or that between them there is a space-time gap. But a gap in space-time is inconceivable, for a non-spatio-temporal hiatus is either no hiatus in space-time at all—in which case places and times would still be contiguous and the continuity would remain unbroken— or else it is a spatio-temporal lapse, and so not a gap but a filling. Space and time, as we were told by Alexander, are extensions, and a discontinuous extension is a contradiction in terms. Discontinuity of existence of a particle, on the other hand, is conceivable only at the cost of its identity; for if the character of the particle is simple and elementary, the sole criterion of its individual self-identity is the continuity of its existence. There can thus be no difference between two distinct particles of the same kind and two

[1] Cf. quotation from Sir Edmund Whittaker on p. 60 above.
[2] *Vide* de Broglie, *The Revolution in Physics*, pp. 250 ff.

discontinuous and separate occurrences of what is allegedly 'the same' particle. This is in agreement with what quantum physicists have discovered. It has been found that while two elementary particles of the same kind are numerically distinguishable, individual identity cannot be attributed to them severally. The physical situation remains identically the same if they are interchanged, and if they are treated as different the prediction of experimental results is vitiated.

But if the individual identity of a particle is not traceable, the quest for continuous description in terms of it is surely the pursuit of an *ignis fatuus*. We shall find reason, presently, to suggest that individual identity is an inseparable correlative of structure in a complex whole, the analysis of which cannot fruitfully be pursued as a repeated subdivision into separable parts, but in which the differentiable elements are knowable concomitantly with the structural principle constituting the form of the system, and not otherwise. In this case, continuity is provided by the systematizing function and is not conditional upon endless subdivision, which only results in the repetition of a further divisible quantity. The endlessly divisible is the endlessly discontinuous. It is typified by the series of natural numbers, which is a continuum of discontinuities. Only the discrete is numerable. The truly continuous is *in*divisible and cannot be counted. The solution of the problem of infinity here seems similar in kind to its solution in relation to the universe as a whole. The structural unity of a self-contained whole may provide the key to the problem of subdivisibility as it does to boundless extension.

6

Another approach is to seek continuous description through the conception of some kind of substratum of physical existence (what Sir Charles Darwin calls a sort of 'electrical juice'). A quantum jump might then be conceived as the submergence of the particle in the substrate and its re-emergence elsewhere after a very small but finite interval of time, the concurrent disturbance of the medium being revealed as an emission of radiation. This idea is by no means at variance with the thinking of the authors of the quantum theory. Bohr's doctrine of complementarity is consistent with it. For to maintain that wave and particle are two complementary forms of appearance of a single physical reality implies some kind of substratum, events in which (in the words of Sir James Jeans) 'throw up bubbles and eddies' accessible to our observation sometimes as particles and sometimes as waves. Heisenberg entertains a similar notion. 'The physicists today', he writes, 'try to find a fundamental law of motion for matter from which all elementary particles and their properties can be derived mathematically. This fundamental equation of motion may refer either to waves of a known type, to proton and meson waves, or to waves of an essentially different character which have nothing to do with any of the known waves or elementary particles.' In the first case, one or a few sorts of fundamental particle would be disclosed as the structural unit of all others, but in the second all types of particle would 'be reduced to some universal substance which we may call energy or matter.'[1] Again he says: 'The final equation of motion for matter will probably be some quantized non-linear wave equation for a wave-field of operators that simply represents matter, not any specific kind of waves or particles. This wave equation will probably be equivalent to rather complicated sets of integral equations, which have 'Eigenvalues' and 'Eigensolutions', as the physicists call it. These Eigensolutions will finally represent the elementary particles . . .'[2]

Schrödinger's theory may be viewed as an elaboration of this conception in terms of waves and their superposition. An elastic medium can carry any number of waves at the same time, the coincidences of which either reinforce or cancel one another according to the correspondence or variance of the wave phase. Thus the superposition of two or more waves varying in phase gives rise to a group in which the waves reinforce one another in a limited region and elsewhere cancel out altogether. Such a wave-packet, as it is called, is found to obey equations of motion virtually identical with those applicable to a particle. Further, the velocity of the waves and that of the group are not necessarily the same. The group may travel faster or slower than the waves themselves.[3] For such a group, all the uncertainty relations established for quanta apply. For the group to be small the waves must be numerous

---

[1] *Physics and Philosophy*, p. 60. Cf. *Philosophical Problems of Nuclear Science* (London, 1952), p. 103.

[2] *Physics and Philosophy*, p. 68. Cf. *Philosophical Problems of Nuclear Science*, p. 105.

[3] For a particularly lucid exposition of the theory see Sir Charles G. Darwin, *The New Conceptions of Matter*, Ch. II.

and of different wave-length, but such a group tends to spread rapidly. If, on the other hand, there is a rather long train of superposed waves nearly harmonic in character, the spreading is much slower. But if the group is small, while its position is to that extent more definite, its velocity, due to its spreading, is uncertain; and if it is large, while its velocity is more uniform and ascertainable, its position is correspondingly vague.

The path of a wave-packet of this kind in a field of force bends exactly analogously to that of a ray of light in a refracting medium. In a very strong field such as is encountered in the close vicinity of an atomic nucleus, it bends round completely so as to form a circle or an ellipse. The wave-packet now becomes a stationary wave similar to the vibration of a sounding bell, round the rim of which run a group of superposed distortion waves forming a stationary wave in various modes, called the normal modes of the bell's vibration.[1] The wave-packet taking this form in association with an atomic nucleus represents a satellite electron, and its 'normal modes' are the different possible electron orbits. The nodes of the stationary wave may be represented by numbers and each mode is represented by a set of such numbers. In the same way the normal modes (or orbits) of the electron wave-packet are defined by quantum numbers.

The stationary 'states' of the Bohr atom thus become the normal (also called 'proper') modes of vibration of the wave group, and their discontinuity, though preserved, is accounted for in terms of superposition, which does not involve any ultimate discontinuity in the supposed medium. Schrödinger seeks to account for quantum jumps in terms of resonance phenomena, occurring when the difference of two proper frequencies in one system is equal to the difference between two proper frequencies in another. An exchange of energy between the two systems then ensues in which the radiated waves have a frequency equal to this difference.[2]

Superposition thus appears to offer a solution of the problem of discontinuity, for the discrete modes of vibration no more involve breaks in the substrate wave process than the harmonics of a violin string or of a tolling bell involve discontinuity in the substance of the sounding solid or in the series of wave frequencies in the gamut of musical tones. The quantum jump might be thought of as analogous to a pucker in a piece of cloth, which if

[1] *Vide* Darwin, op. cit., pp. 109 ff.
[2] *Vide* 'Are There Quantum Jumps', §§ 2 and 3.

pressed out in one place appears immediately in another without apparent continuous transition. Eddington uses this simile to explain variations in the curvature of space when a co-ordinate system is chosen so as to eliminate a gravitational field due to the presence of matter. This cannot be done without producing the appearance elsewhere of a field that was formerly absent (or weaker). It is not inconceivable that these two analogous instances of physical description have a more direct connection than is obvious at first sight.

If this were all, our immediate troubles would seem to be over, but serious difficulties remain, and other physicists have not been slow to point them out. The wave picture cannot be simply applied to the collision of particles such as are made visible in the Wilson cloud chamber and are presumed in the photo-electric, Compton and Raman effects. Two wave groups do not collide and rebound, they become superposed and merge. In applying the wave-mechanics to interactions of the collision type it is necessary to construct the wave system of each particle in a separate space, each with three dimensions of its own—or rather, for a number of particles n, to construct an abstract 'configuration space' of $3n$ dimensions. From this, as well as from the fact that the ψ-function at all times contains complex (and so partly imaginary) numbers, it appears that the ψ-wave is not a physical wave at all, but only a device for calculation. 'Schrödinger's wave mechanics', wrote Eddington, 'is not a physical theory but a dodge—and a very good dodge too.'[1]

Here again we may notice than an analogous situation existed in classical physics. In the analytical mechanics of Jacobi, a system composed of N material points requires a configuration-space of $3N$ dimensions in which the possible trajectories of the points in the system are set. These can be classified into families, each dependent on $3N$ parameters, and formed by curves orthogonal to a family of integral surfaces of Jacobi's equation. Again we have trajectories related to the corresponding surfaces as are rays to wave-fronts, but the 'waves' are in configuration-space and can be regarded only as symbolic.[2]

Schrödinger, however, is not daunted by these difficulties. He points out that two systems each in a 'pure energy state' cannot be said to interact, approach each other, or collide. Two inter-

[1] *The Nature of the Physical World* (Cambridge, 1948), p. 219.
[2] Cf. de Broglie, *The Revolution in Physics*, p. 37.

E

acting systems (or particles) should really be treated as a single system of waves different from either of the participants taken separately, and he prefers to describe such an interaction as 'a system consisting of two parts in slight coupling'.[1] The normal modes of this system, he declares, would be quite different from what the current view interprets as a partition of energy into two contributions, such as would pertain to two separate systems if they did not interact, plus a third which is conventionally called their energy of interaction. This partition Schrödinger criticizes as artificial and as leading to inexact solutions. It is, he says, 'only a mathematical artifice',[2] which may give satisfactory results in the first approximation but is liable to break down for higher approximations. In short, for Schrödinger it is the current theory that is a dodge, and not as good a dodge as it ought to be. He claims that the wave mechanics as elaborated by de Broglie and himself can account for the photo-electric and similar effects without invoking any assumption 'that the incident light beam produces at once in each of tens of thousands of electrons an exceedingly small *probability* of taking within the next split second a leap into a state of higher translational energy'.[3] Finally, he declares that physics is in sore need of the assumption of real spherical de Broglie waves to account for the actually observed interference patterns when these waves are diffracted by crystals. The error of his opponents, he thinks, is due to their trying to enumerate particles which 'avowedly lack individuality'—and we shall indeed find in this lack of individuality a valuable clue to the character of the ultimate physical reality.

A wave is not an individualized entity separable from the medium in which it occurs; it is a form of structure imposed upon the medium. It is not a static shape but a dynamic form—a form of activity or motion with a specific rhythm mathematically formulable. The activity is a process of change, a flux in which nothing is definitely identifiable except the structure, so that what has individuality is not a separable particulate entity but the identifiable pattern imposed upon the substratum of activity. It is this which moves—not a solid lump, however minute. It is this pattern that is translated from place to place, that appears, disappears and reappears, and yet retains its recognizable identity. In

---

[1] *What is Life? and Other Scientific Essays*, p. 148.
[2] *Ibid.*, p. 147.   [3] *Ibid.*, p. 145.

answer to the question, 'What *are* these corpuscles really?' Schrödinger answers '. . . at the most, it may be permissible to think of them as more or less temporary entities within the wave field, whose form (*Gestalt*), though, and structural manifold in the widest sense, ever repeating themselves in the same manner, are so clearly and sharply determined by the wave laws that many processes take place *as if* those temporary entities were substantial permanent beings.'[1] This idea is one to which we shall return.

Some physicists are satisfied neither with the probability interpretation of the ψ-function nor with the hypothesis that it represents an actual physical wave. Alfred Landé thinks it possible to adopt the particle picture as true for all phenomena and to make it consistent by showing mathematically how it is possible for streams of particles to produce appearances like interference patterns.[2] This possibility was earlier mooted by Max Born, but was not worked out in any detail. Landé now claims to be able to carry the idea further. To be completely satisfactory, this theory must demonstrate not only how particles produce wave-type phenomena but also how the orbits of electrons in the atom are susceptible of representation as the normal modes of standing waves, and in doing so it must be able to explain wave phenomena in terms of trajectories in all cases. If it succeeds, we may note, the question of discontinuity will not arise, though that of individuality of distinct particles would not have been eliminated. The settlement of the controversy must be left to the scientists. The philosopher can only record their opinions and try to form from them as clear a conception as he can of the reality that the scientific theories are intended to describe. As has already been said, the question of individuality may prove the most useful clue, and it is this which I now propose to pursue, with reference to a principle of the utmost importance and suggestiveness in quantum physics.

7

Pauli's Principle of Exclusion simply stated is that no two similar particles (e.g. electrons) may be in the same state of motion, or alternatively, they may not both have the same four quantum

---

[1] *What is Life? and Other Scientific Essays*, p. 177.

[2] A. Landé, 'Dualism to Unity in Quantum Mechanics', *B. J.P.S.* X, 37, 1959.

numbers. The mathematically equivalent statement is that all functions representing the states of two similar particles are antisymmetric. That is to say, any function representing the state of two like particles, for instance, using an abbreviated form:

$$\phi(1,2) = u(1).v(2) \quad \ldots \ldots \ldots (1)$$

must be written:

$$\phi(1,2) = u(1).v(2) - u(2).v(1) \quad \ldots (2)$$

so that if $u = v$ the function vanishes.

It follows as a corollary from this that any two composite particles each made up of two similar particles subject to the exclusion principle must be represented by a symmetric function. Further, the application of the principle is not confined to pairs of particles, but extends to assemblages of any number of a similar type, though in a more complicated fashion.

This principle manifests itself physically in surprising and penetratingly far-reaching ways. Its effect is the appearance of a 'force' between similar particles preventing them from coming together, which increases as their velocities approach parity and which is not attributable to dynamic causes.[1] Though physicists call this an 'exchange force', it is, in a way, not a force at all but simply a formal property of the mathematics expressing the states of motion of the particles, and every attempt to treat the manifestation of this property as a conventional force breaks down.[2] Nevertheless, its influence is widely exerted. It is what imposes on the electronic 'shells' of the atom a definite structure. As no two electrons may have the same set of quantum numbers, any one energy level can contain only as many electrons as there are different combinations of quantum numbers corresponding to states with that level of energy. A similar structure of shells has been posited within the nucleus, and while the arrangement of the electronic shells determines the chemical properties of the atom, that of the nucleic layers determines its physical properties. The forces holding together the atoms in 'homopolar' linkage (as in the hydrogen molecule) have been identified as 'exchange forces' due to the exclusion principle, and the hitherto mysterious forces of

[1] For detailed explanation of this see H. Margenau, 'The Exclusion Principle and its Philosophical Importance', *Philosophy of Science* 11 (1944), and *The Nature of Physical Reality*, Ch. XX, pp. 435 ff.

[2] *Vide* Margenau, op. cit.

chemical valency have now been traced to the same source.[1] The chemical valency of any element depends on the number of 'unpaired' electrons in the outer shell—that is, those unmatched by electrons with opposite spin but otherwise identical quantum numbers.

The resulting physical and chemical properties are, therefore, the characteristics of wholes, which their parts do not separately possess, but which arise in consequence of their ordered combination, and the exclusion principle proves to be one of organization and structural pattern governing the arrangement of particles upon which these new properties depend. A striking example of this is given by Margenau.[2] Two hydrogen atoms may attract one another, combine and form a molecule, but any third atom which may now approach is repelled. The mutual attraction (or, when it occurs, repulsion) between single atoms may be accounted for by ordinary dynamic laws, but the repulsion of the third by two adhering atoms is a consequence of the exclusion principle and is attributed to what is called 'saturation' of forces.

The influence of the principle makes itself felt again in the structure of crystals, directly or indirectly through atomic structure. Here again, new properties are displayed which are wholly dependent upon composition and are unforeshadowed in the parts compounded. They are not present in the single atoms but depend on the way in which they are arranged in the combination. Margenau lists ferromagnetism, optical anisotropy and electrical conductivity among these and designates them all 'co-operative phenomena'.[3] In the case of ferromagnetism in particular, Heisenberg's application of the exclusion principle to the problem showed that, because of antisymmetry, the force acting on each electron was not simply the sum of forces from all the rest. 'Heisenberg's work', writes Sir Charles Darwin, 'draws attention to the enormously important fact that the joint influences between a number of bodies cannot be estimated by simply taking them together in pairs.'[4] As a result of the operation of this principle, therefore, the properties of the ordered whole are discovered to be different

---

[1] *Vide* Margenau, *Philosophy of Science*, 11, p. 187; Whittaker, *From Euclid to Eddington*, § 64; Arthur Haas, *Quantum Chemistry* (London, 1930), pp. 31 ff.

[2] *The Nature of Physical Reality*, p. 444.

[3] *Ibid.*, pp. 437 and 445.

[4] Op. cit., p. 188.

from the sum of the properties of its parts, and a special creative significance is conferred upon structure and organization, which we shall find as we proceed to be of paramount importance.

At this point a brief digression may be tolerated to enable us to give attention to yet another example, arising out of the exclusion principle, of that inter-locking between apparently remote physical influences which signalizes the unity of the world. Eddington made use of the principle, in his comprehensive theory of the world, to demonstrate the origin of proper mass, and in so doing revealed that it was no less than the source of gravitation itself. To do this he treated the entire universe as a single system from the quantum mechanical point of view, and the particles in it as the eigenvibrations of the whole of space—'that is', says Whittaker, '. . . standing waves, represented mathematically by the surface harmonics of a hypersphere'. The occupation of any energy state is then dependent upon the saturation of all the lower states, defined as multiples of Planck's constant h, in accordance with the exclusion principle. The number of particles (N) and the radius of the Einstein universe (R) are then used to calculate the topmost energy level, and from this are derived the proper masses (or energies) of the elementary particles. It emerges, however, that as the system contains a large number of particles the uppermost levels of energy become exhausted and some particles have to be included from lower levels with a lower proper energy. Consequently, the total proper energy of a given number of particles is less than it would be if the proper energy of one particle were multiplied by that number. The difference between these two energies Eddington identifies with gravitational potential,[1] once again exemplifying the essential and fundamental inter-relations of the properties of the physical world.

Reverting now to our main theme, we must trace the connexion between the systematizing effects of the exclusion principle and yet another of its consequences. The antisymmetry imposed upon the mathematical functions which express the states of an assemblage of similar particles has the further result that particles of a similar elementary type become mutually indistinguishable as separate individuals,[2] because for either particle the same function develops for the prediction of its position or of any other particular property.

[1] *Vide* Whittaker, op. cit., pp. 199–200.
[2] *Vide* Margenau, op. cit., and also W. Pauli, *The Exclusion Principle and Quantum Mechanics* (Neuchâtel, 1947), p. 19.

As in quantum physics no particle can ever be simply located with absolute precision, when two of them share a common function in this way, it is as if they both simultaneously occupied the same region of space. The interchange of two like particles in any system is physically undetectable for no energy change can possibly accompany it. This fact is stated by E. C. Kemble as follows: 'All the physical predictions which flow out of any physically admissible wave function must be unchanged by the application to that function of any arbitrary permutation of the co-ordinates of like particles'.[1] By the exclusion principle, the particles cannot be identical in all respects; their state of motion cannot be the same. Yet for this very reason it is impossible to tell which is which. Though they must be distinct and even distinguishable, in as much as it is always possible to detect their plurality, it is never possible to identify either of them as a separate individual entity.

Some have taken this state of affairs as a corroboration of Leibniz' dictum of the identity of indiscernibles, and indeed physicists are in the habit of speaking of the 'identity' of particles of the same elementary kind. Others have adopted the opposite view that, as the particles are countable despite their indistinguishability, Leibniz' theory has been disproved. Strictly speaking, however, Leibniz' principle is not applicable here. He would not have regarded material particles as substantially real at all, but only as phenomenal. The identity of indiscernibles, for him, applied properly to immaterial monadic substances, of which clearly it cannot be denied. But surely there is some truth in both of the above contentions, though not the whole truth in either. The particles must be distinguishable so as to satisfy the exclusion principle and accordingly their plurality is detectable. What cannot be discerned is not their difference but their several identities If they were in all respects the same their state function would vanish and there could not be two particles. Nevertheless, the difference between them is not traceable to separable and assignable properties belonging to each individually, it is something pertaining to the *system* to which they belong. This is brought out incidentally by Margenau in an attempt to counter the argument that numerability is observable. 'But if number is an observable property', he asks, 'have we any right to say that two electrons in an atom do not differ in observable respects?' And he answers, 'Yes

[1] Quoted by Margenau, op. cit., *Philosophy of Science*, 11, p. 201.

indeed, for the number 2 is not the property of each electron, but of the composite system'.[1] This does not mean, however, that the system is double, but that it includes a duality in its internal constitution demanding a distinction to be made between constituents, which nevertheless cannot be recognized as separate individual existents. They exist as distinguishables *only qua* features of the system and not as separate individual entities. They are not individuals and can be termed particular *distincta* only in terms of their participation in the articulated structure of the system to which they belong. It is this structure that remains identical whether or not the particles are interchanged. They themselves are distinguishable, though similar, elements in its pattern which is indifferent to the exchange of their co-ordinates. Strictly, therefore, they have no separate existence, and when events occur which are interpreted as the separation of one or more particles from such a system, an entirely new configuration has been created and the old one has ceased to be.

This is borne out by the strong tendency among physicists today to deny the presence (e.g.) within the atomic nucleus of elementary particles as such, and to account for their observable expulsion, when it occurs, as the production of a new system by a change in the energy states concerned, whether this is brought about by impact from without or by internal strains.[2] Certainly the appearance and disappearance of the less stable particles, such as mesons, hyperons, positrons and anti-positrons, are strongly suggestive of temporary fluctuations in the equilibrium or structure of a wider energy system due to some internal stress or sudden *détente*.

What is here making itself felt is the effect of the transition from classical to quantum conceptions. The abandonment of the notion of hard, point-like, particulate constituents of matter is forced upon us by the quantum approach, and many eminent scientists have expressed the view that the explanation of physical phenomena is not to be reached by analysis of them into separable, additive entities, events and forces, but only through the recognition and study of structured totalities, which are neither simple unities nor dissectable aggregates, but are diversified wholes of distinguishable though inseparable constituents.

---

[1] Loc. cit., p. 202.
[2] Cf. Jones, Rotblat and Whitrow, *Atoms and the Universe*, p. 39.

Max Planck writes:

'Modern physics has taught us that the nature of any system cannot be discovered by dividing it into its component parts and studying each part by itself, since such a method often implies the loss of important properties of the system. We must keep our attention fixed on the whole and on the inter-connection between the parts.'[1]

And P. W. Bridgman holds the same opinion:

'We do not have a simple event A causally connected with a simple event B, but the whole background of the system in which the events occur is included in the concept and is a vital part of it. . . . The causality concept is therefore a relative one, in that it involves the whole system in which the events take place.'[2]

The same conclusion is reached by de Broglie, who states it thus:

'The particle truly has a well-defined individuality only when it is isolated. As soon as it enters into an interaction with other particles, its individuality is diminished. . . . In the cases contemplated by the new mechanics, where particles of the same nature occupy, somehow simultaneously, the same region of space, the individuality of these particles is dissipated to the vanishing point. In going progressively from cases of isolated particles without interactions to the cases just cited, the notion of the individuality of the particles is seen to grow more and more dim as the individuality of the system more strongly asserts itself. It therefore seems that the individual and the system are somewhat complementary idealizations. This, perhaps, is an idea which merits a more thorough study.'[3]

[1] *The Philosophy of Physics* (London, 1936), p. 33; cf. also pp. 66–7. See also *The Universe in the Light of Modern Physics* (London, 1937), pp. 25–6: '. . . it is impossible to obtain an adequate version of the laws for which we are looking unless the physical system is regarded *as a whole.*'

[2] *The Logic of Physics* (New York, 1927 & 1954), p. 83.

[3] *The Revolution in Physics*, p. 281. Cf. Leon Rosenfeld, 'Misunderstandings about the foundations of the Quantum Theory', in *Observation and Interpretation*, p. 42, and 'Strife about Complementarity', *Science Progress*, 1953.

E*

But isolated particles, in the strict sense, do not occur. Our study of Eddington and Milne alone has impressed that upon us. What de Broglie refers to is the particle in relative isolation, when circumstances permit it to form a miniature system on its own. Evidence that it is such a miniature system and not just a simple undifferentiated unit is evinced by the success attending its treatment as a wave-packet or superposition of waves of different wavelength. So we are brought back to Schrödinger's contention that the vehicle of individuality is form or structure (*Gestalt*), not a separate, isolable, material entity.

The two interdependent effects proceeding from Pauli's principle, its systematizing influence and its suppression of the individual identity of particles, may together form a basis for the reconciliation of the divergent interpretations of quantum mechanics. For they point to a conception of physical reality as a complex structured activity rather than as an aggregate of material points. Even those who, like Bohm and Landé, seek to retain the particle as the fundamental entity cannot insist upon strict individuation of particles and must therefore acquiesce in their dependence upon the energy system for their properties and behaviour. And this energy system is also, and equally satisfactorily, represented as a complex wave-field characterized by specific, identifiable features of structure. At the same time the supersession of the particles (as self-identical) by the system in which they are embedded is reflected in the uncertainty relations which obtrude themselves as soon as the attempt is made to treat particles as mutually independent, and it becomes impossible, when they are isolated from the system, to ascertain simultaneously the exact value of their measurable properties. Consequently the prediction of particular experimental results can be made only within specifiable limits, and the mathematical function expressing the general structure of the system is treated as a probability function. For, if particulars are not isolated and independent entities inherently possessing sharply defined properties, the attempt to determine them as such is bound to meet with only approximate success. Whenever the details of a system are dependent upon the unknown, or only partially known, ramifications of a complicated nexus, they can be discovered, if at all, only by recourse to a calculation of probabilities.

Probabilities, statistical averages, relative frequencies and the like can only be calculated on the basis of an assemblage (or, as it is sometimes called, 'Kollectiv'). They are properties, not of individual members of a group, but of the whole taken collectively. Moreover, the precise specification of the detailed characteristics and behaviour of each separate member of the assemblage does not corroborate the probability calculation but destroys it. If we know every detail, the question of probability does not arise, and knowledge only of the probability estimate tells us nothing about the behaviour of the separate members of the group, which, in particular cases may even appear to contradict it. In statistical mechanics, for instance, the condition of obtaining the required results is the assumption of random motion among the molecules of a gas, or similar assemblage of particles. Randomness, however, is just that condition of motion or arrangement attributed to the members of a collection in which their details cannot be specified individually. It is a characteristic of a collection or assemblage taken together as a whole.

But in the present case, the indeterminateness of the parameters sought shows a reciprocal interdependence and the form of the ψ-function seems to indicate that the system is one in which particulars determine one another mutually. When the formula linking them in dynamic interdependence is found, therefore, the limits of uncertainty are sharply drawn, whereas particular knowledge of each separate quantity (like velocity or energy) tends to obscure that of some other conjugate quantity. In short, knowledge of the organizing principle is more fruitful than knowledge, however exact, of isolated particular properties.

The proper interpretation of quantum mechanics, therefore, may depend upon the recognition that the physical real to which it refers is a whole or structured totality in which individuality is constituted by form, and particulate existence is only provisional, approximate, temporary and adjectival to the dynamic pattern in which it occurs.

8

The predominant example of a complex energy system is the atom. This, as we know today, is no solid morsel but a set of intricately interacting energetic elements arrayed in a volume of space immensely larger than any of its single components. If particles are all taken to be wave-packets, the atom clearly is a complex system of fields. But even if the particle picture is retained, each particulate member of the atom is associated with a field from which it cannot be sharply distinguished. In the immediate vicinity of the electron there is so enormous a voltage gradient that Born introduced a modification of electrodynamic laws to account for it. These modified laws remain valid at all distances from the electron centre however close. 'There is not really an electron here at all, not in the sense of being an infinitesimal massy particle'—so writes Professor Hanson—'it is more like a mathematical point embedded in an incredibly strong electric field.'[1] And every constituent particle of an atom similarly contributes to, and is also activated by, a field complex. Protons and electrons are not only centres of electrostatic fields characteristic of their appropriate electrical charges, but also, by virtue of their spin, they possess magnetic moments. Besides this, the nucleons are held together by cohesive forces—as yet very partially known—constituting within the nucleus a complicated field structure. This is surrounded by a high potential barrier difficult to penetrate in either direction. The complexity of this system is displayed by the facts that the protons in the nucleus, though all positively charged and so mutually repellent, are nevertheless held together by powerful forces, and that the electrons are not all simply absorbed into the nucleus by the attraction of the protons, but while some of them do form neutrons in combination with protons of the nucleus, others remain in orbit at various distances from it in successive 'shells'. These electron shells are themselves complex and the orbits in them, as we have seen, may be represented as the normal modes of vibration of standing waves around the nucleus. The behaviour of any one of the electrons, its state of motion, is dependent upon the energy state of the whole atom, which in turn is largely determined by the disposition of forces within the nucleus (though not every change in this affects the satellite electrons but only such as alter the ratio of protons to neutrons). The mutual inter-play of these fields of force, in short, makes it fair to say that the atom is a single complex system of mutually determining fields, none of which exists in isolation in the form it assumes in inter-relation with the others, but each of which is a distinguishable feature of the articulated structure of the indivisible whole.

The atom is thus a complex of fields, each of which is epitomized in (or as) a 'particle'; and this itself may be regarded as a convolution of wave formations the shape of which is governed

[1] *Patterns of Discovery*, p. 135.

by the way it is incorporated in the larger system—its interaction with the other particles constituting the atom. The unit of matter is a structure of structures, a 'complexification' of the basic pattern exhibited by waves, which is the specific form of radiant energy. But if the basic element is a wave form, upon what is it imposed? Relativity has left no justification for postulating an aether, and if there were any it would only give rise to a further demand for description and explanation of its mechanical properties. We cannot account for the nature and behaviour of subatomic entities in terms of molar substance, nor does it help to use a term, like 'aether', merely as a cloak to cover our ignorance. On the other hand, if we seek enlightenment in the theory of relativity, we must surely say that the wave, which is characteristic of the field, is a curvature or distortion in space-time itself. This, we have already observed, is precisely how relativity theory represents matter— as space-time curvature of a high degree. This curvature or distortion is revealed in the manner in which events are interlocked— in the laws of dynamics. In empty space there are, in the nature of the case, no events, and where events occur there is activity of some kind, there is something going on. This primordial activity, whatever it is, is what enfolds or distorts space-time.

As we alleged at the beginning of this chapter, the progression is unbroken from space-time to matter. It is difficult to find more appropriate words in which to describe this progression than Teilhard's. Each stage is produced by a sort of 'self-enfoldment' of the structure characterizing the prior stage, producing in unbroken series: first energy, then mass, then atoms, as successively more intricate, more closely integrated and more stable patterns of self-manifestation of the primordial process of activity, in which the continuum of events is space-time.

CHAPTER VII

WHOLENESS AND HIERARCHY

I

In outline the scientific conception of physical reality has now been traced, and the physical world has been revealed as a single, continuous whole of interconnected parts, distinguishable but interdependent both for their existence and for their character. It is not, however, a static whole—a mere spatial pattern of differentiations—but a spatio-temporal process, a dynamic totality, or a flux of energetic activity, structured both in space and in time. Again, the spatial structure is not separable from the temporal but either of them is differently disclosed according as the reference frame is (arbitrarily) chosen to effect an artificial section across space-time. The frame and the section are 'secondary' aspects, not inherent in the nature of things, but imposed by arbitrary selection to facilitate measurements for special purposes.

The differentiations and articulations within the totality depend upon its character as a whole and are governed by rules and dictated by principles of order and system which, at one and the same time, make the world what it is *in toto* and make its parts and elements what they are in particular. If 'the world divides into facts',[1] it does not fall apart into them, but is structured by them in ways determined by universally applicable laws. It is equally true to say that the facts cohere as a world, so long as we remember that the notion of simple, separable facts is strictly inadmissible. Each fact is complex, and variable with the point of view from which it is observed and described, with the co-ordinate system to which its measurable features are referred, with the probability (or wave) function from which it is elicited; nor can facts be each separately determined and only subsequently strung together into a system. The network of interrelations and the participant facts are mutually determining and concomitantly determined. That any one might be the case or not the case and all the rest remain the same, in the

---

[1] The word 'facts' here is Wittgenstein's. What a fact is needs examination for it is not obvious or self-evident. Cf. Hanson, op. cit., Ch. II.

light of contemporary scientific theory, is inconceivable.[1] Each fact is what it is because every other is as *it* is, and this interlacing is governed by pervasive laws of interdependence. Processes are linked together and interwoven inextricably, because the very distinctions that make them many are derivative from the system that they contribute to diversify. They are elements within a form or pattern which has determinate character only as a whole and bestows determinate character upon its constituents only as elements of the whole. In short, the world is a unity displaying itself in multifarious divergent yet systematically related and concomitantly varying manifestations—a polyphasic unit, the diversity of which is a proliferation from a unitary principle, adumbrated by physical science but not yet discovered.

At the risk of tiring by repetition, let me briefly summarize the scientific evidence for all this. The unifying tendency in the progress of physical theory has been continuous throughout its modern development. The work of Newton unified celestial and terrestrial mechanics by deriving the laws of both from a single formula. Clerk Maxwell did the same for geometrical optics and electrodynamics, and Einstein has combined optics, mechanics and dynamics into a single system. Whereas Newtonian mechanics tended to explain physical events in terms of particles and their mutual position, attraction, repulsion and impact, resolving the physical system into separable, apparently externally related parts, the introduction of the idea of the field fused the system into a continuum in which particles lose their prominence and the condition (or 'state') of every region is adequately expressible in terms of field structure. While classical physics conceived space as a system of interrelated points, the relation between any two of which was independent of those between any of the others, the theory of relativity abolishes simple location, makes position and length dependent upon the velocity of the co-ordinate system which is relative to that of all others, so that relations between all points in space become as interdependent as are the velocities of all co-ordinate systems. Further, while the classical mechanics separated space from time so that the relations between points were independent of those between dates, modern theory welds space and time into a single continuum in which these distinctions are made

[1] Cf. Hanson, op. cit., 'It is not merely that no exceptions have been found. We are to some extent conceptually unprepared for an exception: it would jar physics to its foundations. . . .'

only relatively and conventionally by the introduction of artificial frames and 'meshes' of reference. Field and space-time are identified in the general theory of relativity, the field of force being no more than the structural properties, or curvature, of space-time; and so far as the field depends upon the presence of matter, the structure of space-time and the existence of matter cannot be divorced. But the special theory of relativity equated matter with energy and the field is the locus of exertion of energy. So matter itself becomes continuous with field as a higher degree of space-time curvature. Empty, independent space and time have been abolished and the physical world is the space-time whole, describable throughout in terms of its geometrical properties.

Einstein, Weyl, Eddington and Milne have shown how, from a single equation, the laws of kinematics, of mechanics, of electrodynamics can all be derived, as well as the extent and form of the universe as a whole and the movement of its constituent galaxies. In all these, the size, mass and spin of elementary particles was shown by Eddington to be implicit.

Quantum theory, again, shows momentum and position to be conjugate quantities along with the properties severally associated with them, and through the exclusion principle makes the location and properties of particular particles, and indeed their very existence, dependent upon the form and organization of the system in which they occur.

Heisenberg gives testimony that the physicist's quest is for the single function from which field structure and matter alike, in all their elementary forms, will be derivative. It is, in fact, a commonplace that the aim of science is and always has been to explain the multiplicity of natural phenomena by a minimum of interrelated laws, and, if possible, to derive these from a single principle—the ultimate goal of scientific endeavour. It is no doubt an article of faith among scientists that such unification is, in the last resort, possible, but it is an article of faith essential to the very existence of science, and one amply justified by the results thus far achieved, for the actual finding of physical science is a unified world, diversified in the manner described by a multiplicity of different phenomena all related to one another through principles of order and co-ordination.

'The world', says Heisenberg, '. . . appears as a complicated tissue of events, in which connections of different kinds alternate or overlap or combine and thereby determine the texture of the whole.'[1] It is a single, continuous, self-contained space-time whole, unbounded and so unlimited by any spatio-temporal reality external to it, inclusive of all physical being, yet not endless in extent but quantitatively defined. It is moreover not static and immobile but a continuing process of self-diversifying activity operating according to intrinsic principles of self-differentiation, by which it is systematically structured in a definite manner both spatially and temporally. The general character of this diversification is what we are next to consider.

2

We have seen that each of the distinguishable entities within the space-time universe is itself complex, more or less coherently patterned and polyphasic in character, though different types of entity vary in the degree of their self-sufficiency and stability. Elementary particles are not simple, undifferentiated mass-points, but are complexities of superposed wave-formations. In conjunction they form atoms which are further complexes or systems of fields, structured and organized in accordance with precise mathematically expressible principles of order. Even at the physical level it is apparent that the series of 'complexifications' is hierarchical. Eddington declared that there could be no such thing as empty space-time because that would be equivalent to the absence of metrical field, and space-time *is* the metrical field. Accordingly, there is no space-time without structure or curvature. Increase in the degree of curvature—in the degree of complexity of structure—corresponds to a field of force or the presence of energy. The superposition of one such complexity upon others (as it were, the enfolding of space-time upon itself) gives a wave-packet or elementary particle—what might be described as a plait in space-time or a knot of energy. The interaction or interweaving of these plaited threads, produces, by further enfolding, a more complex, yet strictly ordered, system—the atom. Here, a powerfully cohesive structure of energetic fields constitutes a nucleus, and is associated and continuous with a field complexity in its immediate vicinity which bends the system of waves representing the electron into a new and self-contained pattern, or orbit, round the nucleus. This intricate field structure at the same time determines the number, disposition and orientation of the orbits of the

[1] *Physics and Philosophy*, p. 96.

satellite electrons. The order and pattern of the atom as a whole is governed by the principle of exclusion, which Eddington strove to connect with the law of gravitation. If he was right, the principle of organization in the atom is an intrinsic structural principle of space-time, and the whole series of physical forms, field, radiant energy, elementary particle and atom, is a series of phases of the self-differentiation of the primordial spatio-temporal matrix—the manifestations of its polyphasic character.

Two questions now present themselves: (i) How are we to conceive the peculiar nature of this primordial matrix? and (ii) What motivates or propels the process of self-complication which produces the hierarchical series of differentiated forms within it? The answer to both these questions is, in the end, most probably the same, and was adumbrated at the end of Chapter II.

(i) The matrix is no inert amorphous matter, for matter is a development out of it, and when it emerges it is far from inert or formless. It is not, like Aristotle's ὕλη, a mere logical *terminus a quo*, the initial limit of the *scala naturae*—though it is also that. It is a physical entity, not just a concept. Whitehead's term 'creativity' is appropriate to it, but makes no advance in clarity or precision, for it is a mere abstract noun. Yet Aristotle's concept is by no means wide of the mark. Pure matter, for him, was not discoverable in nature, but was the mere potentiality of receiving form and the mere absence of ἐνεργεία or activity. But in the modern view the physical basis is an activity already formed; it is ἐνεργεία, in some degree at least. Alexander's view that space-time is itself the matrix is defective, as we saw, so far as it suggests that it is empty and un-qualified. No merely static pattern of potential relationships is enough, and though Alexander's space-time is meant to be more than this, the kind of motion that he describes, among pure point-instants, is bodiless and obscure. The actual physical matrix is an active, efficient process; the scientist suggests that it is some kind of sea of energy, convoluted and agitated into radiation and material particles. But this is not a precise description. It is still largely metaphorical and speculative, and we must beware of deceiving ourselves with alluring conceits. Science cannot yet answer this first question definitively, and whether it will ever be able to do so remains undecided. All we can safely say is that the available evidence and the consensus of scientific opinion point to a primitive physical matrix which is some sort of activity or process actuated by principles intrinsic to itself.

Nevertheless, we can perhaps go a little further without falling into too serious error. This primal 'substance' of the world seems to be a sort of Heraclitean flux[1] out of which individualized entities emerge in the course of its own peculiar activity, as a result of its involution upon itself, which produces in it specific forms or patterns. These are themselves first constituted by systematic interrelation of processes, and secondly, by further, more complex mutual interaction, contribute to the creation of new, more potent and more significant types of entity. The principle of individuation is form, *gestalt*, structure, coherence—that which establishes systematic wholeness—a doctrine going back to Aristotle, advocated years ago by Bernard Bosanquet, and more recently by Whitehead; but since then much despised, though clearly vindicated by the findings of contemporary physics. This organizing principle is, as we saw in Chapter II, inherent in and intrinsic to the primary source and fundamental substance of the physical world, and is probably essentially characteristic of its primordial activity.

(ii) The second question, like the first, finds no precise answer in scientific theory, though science gives ample evidence of the fact that a process of self-complication has taken place and some indication that it may still be proceeding, even on the physical level. This process, moreover, while it is clearly recognizable up to the atom, has thus far scarcely begun. Ahead lie the intricacies of molecular and crystalline structure and beyond that again the multifarious complexities of living matter, where the evidence of continuing constructive and evolutionary process is massive and pronounced. It is barely conceivable that all this comes about by accident as the result of a kind of random shuffling in the primary movement of the substratum. The evidence already examined more than suggests that the primordial activity itself is of such a kind as necessarily to issue in the forms that actually emerge. The sort of connections traced by physicists between space curvature and the cosmical number, between radiation and mass, between matter and gravitation, gravitation and energy of interchange, do not appear to be fortuitous. If the more elaborate structures were the result of random shuffling, it would seem probable that the fundamental activity were simply that—a kind of Brownian movement. No doubt many thinkers would be inclined to adopt some such view, but its implication must then be faced that random

---

[1] Cf. Heisenberg, op. cit., p. 67.

shuffling is the sort of activity which, by its very nature, produces ordered arrangement, and all the recognized laws of statistics, as well as of physics, run counter to this conclusion. In fact, the habitual and natural course of scientific reasoning is to deny fortuitous coincidence wherever orderly arrangement persistently occurs.

It might be countered, on the evidence of thermodynamics, that random shuffling in large assemblages can and does result in regular and orderly concomitances. But these are average regularities, which, as a result of certain systematic connections arising (as we noted earlier) out of precise mechanical laws, are co-variant. They are not structural wholes. The second law of thermodynamics itself asserts that continued shuffling can only increase indefinitely the improbability of organized arrangement, which, if it ever arose from such activity, could do so only at fantastically rare intervals. The source of organizations in progressive sequence of increasing integrity, therefore, must be some other agency than random shuffling.

Moreover, randomness and shuffling are terms which apply to assemblages of distinct entities. If the molecules of a gas were mutually indistinguishable or merged into one another, random agitation would not differ from uniform extension, and no randomness could properly be attributed to them. If the cards in a pack were all blank, shuffling would have no significance and could make no difference to their 'order', for they could have none. As the primordial activity is prior to the emergence of elementary particles, and as elementary particles even when they emerge are not separable from the energy system in which they occur, there can be no distinguishable units to be shuffled and randomness is an inapplicable term.

Consequently, the argument which was at one time popular that, given sufficient time, random shuffling of a finite number of units can produce ordered arrangement of any stipulated type and extent, because the chances of occurrence of all possible arrangements of units are equal—this argument is specious in application to the present case. For it must be presumed that there is a finite number of separable unit entities to be shuffled, and the evidence of atomic physics gives no warrant for this presumption, but shows individuation to be secondary to system. Further, where the shuffled units are identifiable in advance, ordered arrangement in a particular case is specifiable in accordance with any arbitrarily chosen principle of organization. But if the principle of organization is prior to the descrimination of units, what produces order cannot possibly be the random shuffling of those units.

The second law of thermodynamics asserts that the total entropy of any physical system can only increase; and entropy is the measure of disorder or randomization in the system. It follows, therefore, that the fortuitous creation of order by random shuffling is contrary to physical law. By this same law, every discharge of physical energy results in an increase of entropy, and though in a limited region this process may be checked or even reversed, it can only be by means of greater increase in entropy of the surrounding region. It would seem, therefore, that any process which has the effect of increasing orderly arrangement—any integrating, systematizing process—must be actuated by something different from the physical energy hitherto observed. If there is a process which issues in a hierarchy of forms increasing in elaboration, it must be directed either by some 'force' or 'influence' other than physical energy, or else there must be a second form of physical energy different from that subject to the second law of thermodynamics.

At the same time, it is amply clear that the progressive emergence of increasingly complex structures is not incompatible with and does not violate the second law. Electrons and positrons are created from cosmic radiation without decrease in entropy; atoms are synthesized from more elementary components and the complex molecules of chemical compounds from atoms by processes in which entropy increases. The admirable structures of crystalline forms occur and grow by similar processes without occasioning any exception to the second law of thermodynamics. The reason for this may well be, as Joseph Needham has suggested,[1] that the kind of order here contemplated by the physicist is different from that involved in structural organization, whether it be in the atom and the crystal or in protoplasm and the living cell. The physicist, Needham contends, is thinking more of sorting into like types and energy groupings. Entropy for him is (in Willard Gibbs' phrase) 'mixed-up-ness' and order a separating out of different kinds of so-called 'complexions' in an assemblage of moving molecules. Needham uses the analogy of a child's nursery, where 'order' may be viewed as the sorting of bricks into

[1] *Vide* 'Evolution and Thermodynamics', in *Time the Refreshing River*, London, 1943.

boxes each containing all of one size and colour, and disorder as a confused mixture of all sizes and hues. But a different kind of organization, still involving 'mixed-up-ness', would result from building systematically arranged houses each containing different kinds of bricks. It is clear that neither type of order is the result of random shuffling, and that either should arise from it is egregiously improbable. That the second kind should result from it in a continuous succession of more highly organized forms is virtually unthinkable; but it does occur, and its efficient cause must therefore be, as we have said, either a second variety of physical energy or something which is not a form of physical energy at all.

The former suggestion is made by Teilhard, who calls the ordinary observable kind of physical energy 'tangential' and attributes the process of 'complexification' and the intensification of what he terms 'centreity' to a different kind of energy. This he calls 'radial energy'. The neologisms are not altogether felicitous, if only because of the possibility of confusion arising out of the similarity, in sound and connotation, between 'radial' and 'radiant' (which for Teilhard would be 'tangential'); and Teilhard has been fiercely attacked for his advocacy of the doctrine.[1] Yet at least this may be said in his defence, that there is clear scientific evidence of a hierarchy of complex forms as well as of some sort of tendency in physical nature, not only to produce them, but to do so in a series of increasing intricacy and elaboration. That there is in nature a rising scale of levels of integration is no new doctrine. It has been propounded, and not without justification, by Joseph Needham, J. B. S. Haldane and Sir Julian Huxley, all hard-headed scientists, as well as by philosophers with very different philosophical outlooks. But that the source of this tendency is a special kind of energy (whether physical or non-physical) remains dubious.

There are cohesive forces in nature: nuclear forces in the atom, chemical valency, molecular cohesion and the like, but apart from some degree of mystery associated with the non-dynamic character of the effects of the exclusion principle, no new or special type of physical energy seems to be involved. It is common knowledge that each form of energy is, under suitable conditions, convertible into other forms, and this is found to be the case with these examples as well. Nor do they seem to be the originating cause of increasing integration, though they contribute to it. Nevertheless

---

[1] *Vide* P. B. Medawar's critical notice of *The Phenomenon of Man* in *Mind*, LXX, 277, January 1961.

the contrast between 'exchange forces' and the more usual kinds of dynamic force does indicate some significant physical difference between influences, whatever they be, which organize and those that dissipate and randomize. The mutual repulsion of similar particles due to Pauli's principle, for instance, cannot be treated as a dynamic force and has shown itself to be an organizing influence. But it functions as such rather through its negative effect (by *excluding* like particles from a common orbit) than by any positive action.

The propensity in physical reality, therefore, evidence for which is not lacking, to diversify itself according to a unitary principle in different yet systematically related ways and thereby to produce a series of increasingly complex systems, each in itself in some degree a polyphasic unity, is one which is far from having been scientifically explained, though it has not gone altogether unnoticed by scientists. That it is not as yet explicable and remains mysterious is, of course, no reason for making appeals to equally (or more) mysterious entities of an allegedly spiritual variety. But, while some such appeals have been made, even at times by reputable scientists, and though care must be taken to avoid short cuts which result only in mystification, criticism as virulent and scornful as Professor Medawar's exceeds what is requisite and proper. It is unjustifiably obscurantist to ridicule as mysticism efforts to draw attention to and delineate important features of well-known phenomena, even if they are sometimes made in not wholly satisfactory ways.

Even in the course of his criticism of Teilhard, Medawar concedes what is essentially the crucial issue. 'Thus Teilhard's radial, spiritual or psychic energy', he writes, 'may be equated to "information" or "information content" in the sense that has been made reasonably precise by modern communication engineers'. On the question whether communication engineers have succeeded in making the sense of the phrase reasonable or precise judgement may be reserved. But, as 'information' has been defined as 'negative entropy', and as negative entropy means no less than order, the use of this language does no more than translate into different words the problem to be faced: What is it that brings into being forms of existence progressively increasing in degree of complexity and order? To equate 'information' to consciousness Medawar holds to be a 'silly little metaphysical conceit', but that consciousness is very closely related to a specially high degree of unity and order may very well be no such thing, nor is it at all clear that the meaning of 'information' can be made reasonably precise without any appeal to consciousness at all. On these points we are not yet in a position to decide. But we may observe that Professor Medawar is fully aware in the sphere of biology, of the problem towards which the notion of 'radial energy' points, for he frankly confesses that 'what we want, and what we are slowly beginning to get, is a comprehensive theory of the forms in which new genetical information comes into being. It may . . . turn out to be of the nature of nucleic acids and the chromosomal apparatus that they tend spontaneously to proffer genetical variants . . . which are more complex and more elaborate than the immediate occasion calls for.'[1] Whether such spontaneous generation of greater complexity and elaboration is more intelligible than the postulation of 'radial' energy may be left for the reader to decide.

Not only are there observable tendencies among natural objects to combine and co-ordinate which may or may not be attributable to special 'forces', but also structure and organization evidently bestow upon the composite entity greater versatility of behaviour and more significant properties than are possessed by simpler elements in relative isolation. The free electron is capable of motion, of impact with and repulsion of other particles and of uniting with and neutralizing a positron, but of little else. Once absorbed into the atom it loses its separate individuality and becomes only a distinguishable element in the more comprehensive system, which as a whole has a far wider range of properties and potentialities of action and interaction. The neutron, by itself, travels through space, collides with other particles, disrupts atomic nuclei. But when it is united with protons and other neutrons in an atomic neucleus, when it is a nucleon rather than a neutron, it shares with its companions the capacity to bind to itself satellite electrons to constitute an atom. This is able to attract and cohere with other atoms to form molecules displaying a varied repertoire of physical and chemical properties. Among these is the ability to combine further in crystalline structures which have propensities for ordered growth and reproduction. Some of the more elaborate of these structures possess the still more plastic and varied capacities that distinguish organic substances, and other less well understood combinations of these organic materials display the adaptable and versatile proclivities of living organisms. That combination

[1] *Mind*, LXX, p. 104.

and organization are associated with greater capacity and potency in the composite entity is thus undeniable.

This increased potentiality is not a simple increase in physical energy, the source of which, if it were, would be obscure. Nor is it a mere summation of the physical potentialities of the constituent parts of the composite entity. We have noted how the operation of the exclusion principle enhances the capacities of the hydrogen molecule beyond what would be a simple sum of those of its member atoms, and how in other cases 'co-operative properties' emerge in the composite whole which are not present in its components nor equivalent to any mere collection of their qualities. There is an over-plus of potency which remains to be accounted for—not a surplus of physical energy so much as new possibilities of its exercise. It is probably a mistake to think of this enhanced potentiality as energy of any kind, and as great an error to treat it as something inscrutably mysterious. Though no clear account can now be given of it, it does not necessarily follow that none could ever be found. But that this augmentation does occur and is concomitant with increased complexity and solidarity of organization is too insistently apparent to be ignored; and Teilhard's distinction between 'radial' and 'tangential' energy is therefore suggestive, if not altogether felicitous.

3

Moreover, the hierarchical sequence in which ordered complexes range themselves is of special importance. As the more elaborate complexes include and presuppose the less, it is a logical sequence; but it also occurs as a temporal one. George Gamow maintains that the initial state of the universe was one of thermal radiation, out of which matter rapidly distilled. It is generally agreed that hydrogen and helium were the first elements formed and that those with heavier and more complicated atoms arose later. The occurrence of heterogeneous combinations comes later still, and among them the formation of organic compounds is usually regarded as subsequent to that of inorganic, and the appearance of protoplasm upon earth as a relatively late occurrence in cosmological evolution. In view of its dependence for stable existence upon special environmental conditions that did not prevail in the earliest epochs, this must necessarily have been the case. Without anticipating future discussions, however, it is possible even at the physico-chemical level to discern a hierarchy of forms in which the criteria of advance are complexity, degree of organization and coherence of unification: from space-time to energy, energy to particle, particle to atom, atom to molecule and molecule to crystal. Moreover, as already observed, the advance seems constantly to result from a kind of self-enfoldment of the simpler form: if a field of force (energy) is curvature in space, matter is a higher degree of such curvature—a superposition of curvatures (what Eddington liked to call a 'pleat' in space-time)—and the atom is a convolution of fields—the bending in upon itself of the wave-packet which constituted the electron around the complication of nuclear fields. But the self-enfoldment is not simple or linear in its progression. If radiant energy is represented as a harmonic wave motion, the elementary particle is not a special kind of single wave train (though in what is known as 'a pure case' it approaches this), it is a superimposition on one another of several different waves. And there are several different kinds of elementary particle. Again, the atom is not just a group of elementary particles, but a complex of several different types. And there are not only one, but many, different kinds of atom. The same diversity of content characterizes the molecules of chemical compounds. And so each step of the scale as it ascends is not only more complex but also more comprehensive in content than its predecessor.

It would therefore be rash, in the face of the evidence, to ridicule or deny the presence, in the very matrix of physical reality, of some sort of nisus to the construction of coherent complexes, in which its potentialities are progressively more fully and fruitfully realized. Many philosophers in the past have postulated some such directive tendency. Spinoza's doctrine of the *conatus in suo esse perseverare* at once springs to mind with all its implications in his system. Bosanquet constantly asserted the existence in 'Reality' of a 'nisus to the whole'. Alexander discerned a 'nisus in space-time' which has and will continue to bear its creatures to some higher level of existence.[1] Whitehead saw reality as a continuing creative process of concrescence. To these we may add the names of Aristotle, Leibniz, Hegel, Schopenhauer and Bergson, all of whom in one way or another supported the idea of a developmental process. If it were sheer mystical fantasy it would be remarkable that so many and such varied thinkers should all have been simi-

[1] *Space, Time and Deity*, II, p. 346.

larly persuaded of its truth. But here it is recommended not on the strength of their advocacy, but in the light of the findings of contemporary science, which, though it has not uncovered the nisus itself as any kind of physical force, presents us with a gamut of evolving physical forms, that manifestly grow out of one another in increasing complexity in a manner which demands explanation in terms of some persistent tendency towards self-enfoldment, self-differentiation and self-elaboration.

The precise nature of the nisus presents a problem which may very well be insoluble at the purely physical level. As we said above, this influence is probably not a physical force of any kind, but is possibly more closely related to the polyphasic character pervasive in physical reality and intrinsic to space-time itself, by virtue of which a principle of integration and system specifies and elaborates itself in a multiplicity of different phenomena.

4

It remains to say something about the relation between whole and part in the physical universe as so far outlined. The principle of individuation we have seen to be that which organizes into a system, and the macrocosm is a self-contained, self-complete system impregnated by a principle of order that expresses and specifies itself in innumerable different ways, giving rise, within the totality, to various new individual physical entities. These are also wholes, in large measure polyphasic like the macrocosm; but in the nature of the case they can none of them be self-complete, and are all of them in varying degrees dependent upon and continuous with their surroundings. Their systematic wholeness is partial, relative and a matter of degree.[1] So far as they are microcosms they are not self-sufficient but shade off into and interrelate with other individuals on their own or on other grades of physical existence.

The electron, for instance, considered as a system of superposed waves, and taken in relative isolation, has a recognizable degree of individuality. Yet obviously it is no more than an outcrop from a substratum of vibratory activity with which it is continuous and

---

[1] 'Partial wholeness' is, of course, a contradiction in terms; but relative wholeness is not, nor is it inconceivable for something to be partially systematic, so long as the fragmentary character is not thought of as absolute and final, but as implying completion beyond the limits of the partial system.

from which it is demarcated only because the difference of phase between its constituent waves causes them to cancel one another beyond certain limits. It is like an eddy in a stream, distinguishable but not separable from its surrounding medium. The atom is more stable, more complex and more completely self-sustaining; but it too depends for its existence and its stability upon forces acting upon it from without, though to a much lesser extent, and the energy-state that determines its internal configuration is a function of energy absorbed by and radiated from it in interaction with external physical reality. It is never wholly discontinuous with the rest of the universe. Moreover, every particle that is associated with a field is, in a sense, spread out over the whole of space-time, overlapping and intertwining with the fields belonging to other particles. Because many physical forces decrease with distance very rapidly, there are macroscopic energy systems that can, for all practical and most theoretical purposes, be treated as isolated and self-contained. But none is absolutely so, short of the universe *in toto*, and if any were, the universe would not itself be a completely continuous and unbroken whole.

What then is the relationship between the polyphasic wholeness of the universe and the relative totalities, great and small that participate in it and are the particular specifications of its organizing principles? It is already apparent that this relationship is not merely one of container and content, or of aggregate and aggregated units. The physical universe is no mere bundle or collection (however large and heterogeneous) of conglomerated individuals. Its contents are systematically interrelated first by the laws inherent in the structural properties of the metrical field; secondly, as specific differentiations of an underlying matrix according to principles of specification intrinsic to its nature and activity, and, thirdly, as a range or scale of forms of increasing structural complexity, coherent integrity and variegated comprehensiveness. These three types of systematic interrelatedness are alternative versions of the same polyphasic character.

We have seen how a single geometrical formula proliferated into laws of mechanics and dynamics in the special and general theories of relativity, and how out of these the equation of energy with mass arose. Thus, by virtue of the physical laws, which are consequences of the structural properties of the metrical field, and which lace together the things and events of the physical world, there emerges the series of differentiations of the underlying matrix, energy, matter and the range of its developing forms, issuing in the hierarchical array described in the last section.

At each level in the scale the distinguishable entities are discriminated by their characteristic form or structure, and at each succeeding level this form is more coherent and complete than at the previous level. Each advance implies fuller reflection of and closer approximation to the independence and self-sufficiency of the whole in each of the entities characteristic of that level. It seems that the principles of order and wholeness immanent in the world are expressed and exemplified more adequately at each succeeding stage. This does not, of course, imply any simple, superficial resemblance between whole and part. The physical universe is not an immense solar system, but a scattering multitude of galaxies, which bears no immediate resemblance to atomic or molecular structure. Its coherence lies rather in the laws of nature that govern the relations between and the behaviour of its parts and bind it into a single, self-contained continuum. These principles of integration are manifested in the parts in progressively more adequate degrees. Elementary particles conform to natural laws, but for the most part as subject to their imposition from without. They display no very marked internal efflorescence of diversified coherence. The atom, on the other hand, contains within itself a complex system of relations regulated by laws of nuclear, electrical and magnetic forces, of quantum mechanics and of gravitation, and ordered throughout by the operation of the exclusion principle. All of these have been shown to be logically interconnected; so that the atom in itself is a system with a high degree of stability, exemplifying and expressing to a greater extent than members of the lower grades in the physical hierarchy, the principles of organization immanent in the world as a whole. Moreover, it is less dependent than lower forms upon external influences for its construction and persistence, and so is a closer approximation to the inclusive self-sufficiency of the physical universe. Molecules, though they may be more complicated and heterogeneous in content, are not always so stable and cohesive, and it may be necessary to proceed beyond the inorganic level to reach what is genuinely the next stage in the hierarchy.

It is clear that each physical form belonging to the hierarchical array is a specific variation of the substrate activity that in undifferentiated form is simple mass-energy. The photon of radiant energy, the electron, the positron, the neutrino, the meson, the neutron and the proton, are all species of a single genus, and, as Heisenberg prognosticates, may be eigensolutions of a single equation. Yet even these seem to range themselves in ascending order of complexity and stability. Again, elementary particle, atom, molecule, are specific differentiations of material particle, though now more obviously graded as combinations (though never simple aggregates). But these specifications of a single general form bear to one another yet another type of relationship not without logical significance, though it does not appear to be regularly correlated with their order in the scale. There is between them an element of opposition and contrast. Energy is active and flowing; matter is, by comparison, stable and inert. Elementary particles are opposed in charge and have opposite spin. Molecules may be homopolar or heteropolar. At this stage we can but note these oppositions, their precise importance not being clear. Later thay may fall into place in a more general scheme of systematization.

But already it is apparent that both the scalariform arrangement of physical entities and these elements of opposition, as well as their mutual relation as species of a genus, are the outcome and expression of the interlocked system of laws and principles that elaborates itself from the geometrical properties of space-time. The physical world is thus a self-contained and immensely complex spatio-temporal configuration, which generates a vast variety of specific differentiations within its own primordial activity. These are ranged in a scale of progressive elaboration and coherent wholeness, increasing in the degree of adequacy with which they express and reflect within themselves the unity of the whole. They are at once specific manifestations of universal principles of organization, successive degrees in a scale of increasing complexity and adequacy of expression of these principles, and mutually opposed and contrasted elements within a single interconnected system.

This being the general character of the physical world as revealed by physical science, contemporary philosophy, to be in harmony with science, should expound a metaphysic holistic in type, and a logic of order, system and hierarchical structure. A pluralism devoid of any overarching principle of unity would be entirely out of keeping with scientific trends, and an atomistic logic of propositions independently true or false would be irrelevant of physics.

Before pronouncing any final judgements on these matters, however, we must proceed further and pursue the course of development of physico-chemical forms into the sphere of life. The contribution of the biological sciences must next be considered, the light which it throws upon the general character of the world, and the problems which it poses for the philosopher.

PART II
THE REALM OF LIFE

CHAPTER VIII

THE RIDDLE OF LIFE

I

The line of demarcation between the living and the non-living is notoriously difficult to draw. There are entities in the border-line area which defy classification either way and there are proper-ties seemingly characteristic of living matter which are also displayed by some non-living things. Of the four typical characteristics of life none is wholly lacking in the non-living. First, specific bodily form and structure is equally characteristic of living beings and of crystals, as well as of other physical entities. Secondly, organisms grow and develop; but crystals also grow and often diversify themselves, like ice on the winter window pane, in intri-cately patterned ramifications. Thirdly, life is distinguished by metabolic change, constant flow of energy and chemical trans-formation of matter within the stable form of the living creature, but this is paralleled in the candle flame and possibly in more complicated 'open' chemical systems. Reproduction, the fourth typical property of life, though more difficult to attribute to non-living substances, is not altogether lacking in the inorganic sphere and is certainly a property of viruses, the classification of which as living has been justifiably questioned.

E. S. Russell regards as the distinguishing character of living things their adaptive and regulatory activity, variably and per-sistently directed towards a recognizable goal. 'Purposiveness' is the word that sums up these properties, but it is a word which precipitates controversy both as to its precise meaning and as to its legitimate applicability. We shall find that those features of living activity which are most significant do very strongly tempt us to describe them in this way, but its legitimacy is a matter that must be discussed later.

On the other hand, even in the case of properties shared by organic and inorganic substances, we find characteristic differences between the two spheres. Though crystals like organisms grow and maintain a specific form, the elements of their internal organization are relatively homogeneous and repetitive, whereas those of proto-plasm are highly heterogeneous and structurally variegated.

Inorganic open systems, even when stable, are neither (without human or other living interference) self-regulatory nor adaptive. Living systems, in the most fantastically complex manner, are both. These differences will provide clues to the discovery of distinctions that will enable us to trace the hierarchical scale of forms beyond the physical sphere.

2

In *What is Life?* Schrödinger suggested that non-living matter took the form of the periodic crystal while the fundamental unit of living matter was what he called an aperiodic crystal. To appreciate this antithesis a brief description of crystalline structure will help us. It will also serve to illustrate the validity of ideas already propounded, of the progression of complexly integrated material forms by an apparent process of self-enfoldment. In this progression the holistic character of successive forms becomes more evident and more arresting, subordinating detailed structure and behaviour to the principle of order governing and constituting the complete totality.

The determination of chemical affinities by the structure of electronic 'shells' in the atom, which has already been described, governs the pattern of arrangement among the atoms of the elements within compound molecules. According to the physical state of the compound, these molecules may be more or less loosely associated, but in the solid state, which rightly is the crystalline form of the substance (other forms which are apparently, or loosely called, solid, being strictly very viscous liquids), the molecules are closely interlocked, and their molecular arrangement forms a geometrical pattern often such as to make the mutual separation of individual molecules impossible. In rock-salt, for instance, the atoms of sodium and chlorine are arranged alternately in the form of a cube so that it is virtually impossible to say which atom belongs to which molecule. Thus the cubic shape of the crystal is determined almost as if it were one great continuous molecule. This, however, would not be an accurate description of it, for while the molecule is constant in weight and form, crystals of the same compound do not maintain constant weight and, within limits, vary in form. Nevertheless, the shape of the crystal is a direct consequence of molecular structure, and its determination is dependent upon the forces exerted between the electrons and nuclei of the atoms involved. The surfaces of the crystal represent planes through its three-dimensional structure (or 'leptocosm', as it has been called), in which the atoms are most densely packed and so form stable boundaries. The cleavage planes are those between which the chemical bonds are looser and the atoms more widely spaced. Altogether, in the words of Friedrich Rinne, 'its morphological symmetry is symbolic of the arrangement of its fine-structure particles'.[1]

One of the simplest and least complex in structure is the crystal of common salt, but geometrical complication of a high degree characterizes other crystalline compounds. Always, however, the complexities of form are mathematical expressions of the structure and interconnection of the constituent atoms, so that the crystal is a visible manifestation of the molecular character of the compound. Further, interchange of analogous molecules or radicals between two different compounds in a mixture may result in a mixed crystal, in the space lattice of which layers are interwoven so that the mixture cannot be sharply distinguished from a chemical compound. The interwoven crystal structure is analogous to the interlocked atoms in the compound molecule.

However involved the atomic arrangement may be it is always three-dimensionally periodic. Each structural unit is joined to its neighbours according to the laws of chemical valency, giving symmetrical structures mathematically limited to four main types. Axes of symmetry can be two-, three-, four- or six-fold but only these are possible because any others would result in surfaces with rifts or gaps between what should be the edges of geometrical solids. It is this periodicity and its geometric determination that gives to crystal forms their regularity and beauty and even where (as sometimes occurs) dissymmetry is found it is always compensated by the pairing or twinning of crystal types in various complex modes as in ortho- and laevo-Quartz, Calamine, Haematite and the like.

In short we find, answering to elements of symmetry or periodicity in the structure of the molecule, symmetry and periodicity in the form of the crystal. P. Debye and P. Sherrer have asserted that, allowing for differences of scale, 'there is no essential difference between a crystal and a chemical molecule, for both have the characteristic property of containing atoms regularly arranged'.[2]

[1] *Crystals and Fine Structure of Matter* (London, 1924), p. 26.
[2] Quoted by Rinne, op. cit., p. 41.

The physical and chemical properties of the crystal are consequences of this atomic arrangement; its solidity is the result of the forces acting between the atoms; its brittleness and the form of fracture characteristic of it depend on the atomic arrangement within it; its properties change with direction through it in consequence of the geometrical interrelation of its atoms, and the manner and rate of its decay under chemical action by other substances are determined by this same structural character—referred to by scientists as its 'stereochemical' form—which is also connected with the valency of its atoms and is an expression of the chemical bonds existing between them.[1]

Accordingly, we have in the crystal another case of advance in the scale of natural forms effected by self-enfoldment or reduplication of the form typical of the prior level. The interlocking of different varieties of atoms each with its own intrinsic structure (which itself determines the form of interlocking) constitutes the molecule and gives it its internal pattern, and this again superimposed upon itself, produces the crystal, of which the internal complexity and external, three-dimensional configuration express the physical and chemical properties of its substance.

This is not a simple matter of aggregation but the formation of a higher order totality. We have seen that physical and chemical properties are consequences of the structure as a whole, and are determined by its organizing principle of unity and not by a simple summation of the properties of its several constituents or parts. For the crystal is not only a geometrical totality. Its wholeness is manifested also in other ways. 'The kinetic unit', writes Rinne, 'for crystalline materials, is the whole crystal. In this sense it replaces as a new compound the individual molecule of gasses and liquids'. And again 'Within the crystal, affinity tensors, in the sense of valency theory, pass in and out from one structural unit to another throughout the whole structure; the crystal is, in this respect, a leptoblast'.[2] Clearly we have here a further step in an ascending series of forms of order and one in which the prefiguring of living forms is already apparent.

Moreover, in accordance with the internal affinities of its atoms and molecules, the crystal grows in determinate ways, its shape conforming to a precise and definite pattern. Broken crystals immersed in the proper medium will regenerate the portions of which

[1] Cf. Rinne, op. cit., Ch. VI.
[2] Op. cit., p. 94.

they have been deprived in their characteristic shapes, and in some cases fragments will reconstitute themselves into whole but smaller crystals. Cases even occur of separate crystals uniting and growing together to form one large crystal, not as in the case of twinning, but by a process of complete fusion known as convergent crystallization.[1] These processes are analogous to phases of living development which have sometimes been thought exclusive to life.

Evidence, therefore, is plentiful that the crystal is a polyphasic unity of a new level or order of integral complexity, midway between atomic and molecular wholes on the one hand and living organisms on the other. The principle of order regulating its form and the process of its generation is continuous with that governing the structure of atoms and molecules, as is theirs with similar organizing influences at prior levels; so that the tendency in nature to build more complete and more self-contained totalities, expressing more fully and adequately (as well as more variously) the uniting and self-specifying principle of the universe *in toto*, is here seen to persist, and that nisus towards greater self-diversified wholeness that has hitherto been stressed is further exemplified at this stage.

We must observe, however, that there is an essential difference between the processes of crystallization described above and those, *prima facie* similar to them, which occur in living development. The crystal grows and fuses in a uniform medium (a liquid state of its own substance or a solution in a uniform solvent), whereas the living entity grows and develops by an intricate process of chemical change or metabolism in an environment constituted of quite different substances, which the organism converts into those of its own body and organizes in specific ways. Moreover the augmentation of the crystal is by the continual addition of identically similar structural units, while the development and growth of the living organism is by co-operative interaction and structural interconnection of organs differing widely in character and function. L. von Bertalanffy points out that while the substance forming the crystal is single and homogeneous, there is no homogeneous substance characteristic of a growing or regenerating organism. The living thing is an organization of numerous different substances. Further, the specificity of the organism is dependent upon itself

[1] Cf. Joseph Needham, *Order and Life* (Yale, 1936), pp. 70–71, and Friedrich Rinne, op. cit., p. 133.

and its intrinsic principle of integration, whereas that of the crystal depends on the medium.'[1]

There is yet another interesting link of which mention may be made between inorganic and organic forms. Although the solid form *par excellence* is crystalline, there are more or less liquid forms in which the molecules of the substance, if suitably shaped, may be ordered in varying degrees. A crystalline substance, in the process of melting, may go through definite stages of disorganization, each corresponding to a particular kind of so-called liquid crystal or para-crystalline form. Three main types have been distinguished: (i) 'nematic', when the axes of the molecules are parallel but their centres irregularly places; (ii) 'smectic', in which the movement of the molecules with parallel axes is restricted to the horizontal plane and they are confined to a set of parallel surfaces; (iii) states in which the molecules are still further ordered though not as regularly or with the same fixity as in the solid crystal.[2]

These liquid crystals sometimes present qualities of shape and movement similar to those of living matter. But a fact even more significant, perhaps, to which Needham draws attention, is that many living systems actually are liquid crystals of one of these kinds. And there are, of course, in living systems many substances which do or can assume solid crystalline forms. In some cases, the complexity of their molecules makes their crystalline structure exceedingly intricate, but it would nevertheless be fair to say that they were periodic in the same way as inorganic crystals.

Nevertheless essential differences must be recorded. Many parts of living organisms are crystalline, but they are formed and they function in such a way as to illustrate the contrast between living and non-living activity. The shells of diatoms, the skeletons of foraminifera and radiolaria, the spicules of sponges and sea-cucumbers, as also the stiffening in the walls of plant cells, are all of them crystalline forms, some of calcite, some of silica, some of cellulose. But the shapes of these shells, skeletons and cell-wall plasterings is determined, not by the molecular structure of the

[1] L. von Bertalanffy, *Modern Theories of Development* (Oxford University Press, 1933), pp. 100–102.

[2] Cf. Joseph Needham, *Order and Life*, pp. 158 ff. and F. Rinne, 'Investigations and Considerations Concerning Para-crystallinity', contributed to Faraday Society Symposium on *Liquid Crystals and Anisotropic Melts* (London, 1933), and op. cit., p. 63.

constituent substances, but by other forces. In some cases (e.g. in sponges) spicules of silica have the same shape as others made of calcite, though the molecular structure and normal crystalline forms of these compounds are quite different. The shapes of these non-living structures in living creatures are adapted to their functions and some writers suggest that they are imposed upon them by the moulding activity of the protoplasm,[1] or by the influence of nucleoproteins in the cell, which are known to exert powerful directive influence on the growth and development of the entire organism.[2] Here the crystalline totality has become part of and is integrated into a new and more elaborate whole with a higher and less perspicuous principle of organization. The spicule, or shell, or skeleton, is a structure, shaped by a concrescence of chemical processes of a new order. This higher system is organized, not merely according to the physico-chemical laws hitherto considered, but by whatever it is that establishes the integrity and preserves the life of the organism. To this the shape of the included crystalline structures now becomes subordinate.

3

It is not the inclusion of such substances in living matter to which Schrödinger refers when he speaks of an aperiodic crystal nor even to the substances of which genes are composed, substances whose molecular structure is already far more complex than anything at the inorganic level; yet an account of the nature and properties of such structures provides evidence of a further stage in the series of complex totalities, the holistic character of which is still more apparent and ingenious than of those already described. In inorganic compounds the molecular structure is governed by valency bonds between the atoms. These, as well as other forces (such as van der Waal forces between molecules) contribute to determine the lattice formation in crystals. But the high-molecular organic compounds display a far greater complexity of internal structure involving new principles of organization. For instance the structure of cellulose involves at least three hundred disaccharid units (cellobiose), each containing twelve

[1] *Vide* A. W. D'Arcy Thompson, *Growth and Form* (Macmillan, New York, 1942), p. 679.
[2] Cf. W. T. Astbury, 'The forms of biological molecules', in *Essays on Growth and Form* (Oxford, 1945).

F*

carbon atoms in combination with oxygen and hydrogen. These form what is called a 'main valency chain' and of them forty to sixty are joined together by van der Waal forces into a larger combination known as a 'micella'. Here the combining principles permit of greater variation in numerical properties than in inorganic molecules and the formula for cellulose is written: $(C_6H_{10}O_5)_n$, the number n being unspecified. It is about three hundred, but is not fixed. Such micellae again combine in regular fashion in the cell wall of plants and so a continuous series leads us to the structure of vegetable fibres.

Two of the most important substances of which living matter is composed, proteins and nucleic acids, are compounds with molecules of extreme complexity of structure and of relatively enormous size. Protein molecules, for instance, are constituted by long chains of amino-acid residues in an intricate periodic arrangement, the complexity of which is only dimly suggested by the fact that in certain cases their molecular weights are multiples of a unit figure of 35,000. Nucleic acids are similar exceedingly complex structures. The molecule of deoxyribosenucleic acid (DNA) consists of a double helix of mononucleotides coiled round a single axis and linked horizontally by paired bases (pyrimidine or purine), by means of hydrogen bonds, and ribosenucleic acid (RNA) is similar, but with a different base (uracil in place of thymine).

Moreover the most thoroughgoing analysis of proteins and amino-acids has so far failed to reveal the secrets of their chemical properties which vary with the least alteration of position of ions or radicals in the molecular pattern, revealing once more the dependence of specific properties upon the overall structural organization. Why one protein should display enzymic activity of one sort and another of a different sort, why one enzyme should be a hormone and another with only slightly different structure a toxin, is still altogether unexplained. But it is clear that the difference is determined by the structure. In artificially synthesized polypeptides it has been found that the chemical activities of free amino-acid groups change when they become links in a peptide chain and are variously affected according to their position in the chain so that radicals normally inactive may become active when they enter the more complex combination. These facts are incontrovertible evidence for the holistic nature of the substances. The mere aggregation of the properties of the parts does not give us the specific character and activity of the whole, which clearly

depend upon the pattern of structure and principle of organization regulating the way in which the parts are combined.

Enormous molecules of this type are found to constitute what
may be the ultimate units of living matter. Such are the viruses:
in simpler cases, crystalline proteins, like the tobacco-mosaic
virus, of 40·7 million molecular weight. Such also are the genes,
series of which in determinate order make up the chromosome
fibres in the nucleus of the cell body and which determine the
hereditary characters of living things. These are what Schrödinger
calls aperiodic crystals and he describes their relation to periodic
crystals by the analogy of a tapestry and its difference from a
wallpaper. The first has coherent design without repetition, while
the pattern of the second results from the repeated recurrence
of the same formal arrangement. Such are the chromosomes and
we can now see that they are, in fact, a further step in complexity
and intricacy of organization in the scale which we have been
following from the elementary particle upward.

Here we have reached an altogether new level of development.
Not only are new aperiodic patterns of arrangement involved but
new principles of combination. These new principles of combination are, moreover, selective and directive in special ways. The
synthesis of proteins and nucleic acids requires regulation and
selection of the involved chemical processes. Chains of strictly
co-ordinated enzymic reactions are necessary; the incorporation
of the different amino-acid residues must take place at different
and precisely regulated rates, involving both temporal and spatial
organization of the system in which the reactions occur, so that
each molecular group is attached in precisely the appropriate
position and order in the chain.[1] Bertalanffy says 'The ordinary
lattice forces of crystals are in no way sufficient to account for the
amazing specificity with which elementary biological units pick
out of the building materials available just the "right ones" and
annex them just at the right places'.[2] The organization of the
system is now not simply spatial—not only a space lattice of
definite pattern—but is also temporal and governs the order of
events in a continuous process of construction involving selective-
ness between alternative chemical paths and regulation of direction and rate of reaction.

Bertalanffy suggests that another example of the operation

[1] Cf. A. I. Oparin, *The Origin of Life* (London, 1957), Ch. VI.
[2] *Problems of Life* (London, 1952), p. 29.

of special principles of attraction and combination is provided in the process of meiosis in living organisms by which, during maturation, the gametes divide. Here the number of chromosomes in the cell nucleus is halved, and just prior to the divisions in which the so-called haploid sets are segregated, those of the diploid set come together in pairs. In this pairing not only are two homologous chromosomes mutually associated, but also the homologous chrommomeres within them pair off. If by X-ray irradiation a section of one chromosome has been destroyed, a loop will form in its partner so that the remaining chrommomeres pair off correctly. The forces of attraction hitherto described are inadequate to account for this kind of pairing.

It is this selectivity and directiveness that seems specially typical of life, for indeed what we have most prominently in mind when we distinguish between the living and the non-living is not so much complexity of static structure for this may become as intricate and varied as we please without displaying any features specially typical of life. These typical features are characteristic forms of activity rather than of spatial pattern, even though that too may be a recognizable property of the living thing. Spatial form even when peculiar to living creatures, can be imitated in non-living structures without involving vitality, as in the case of colloidal and crystalline structure.[1] The essential question concerning the possibility of reproducing living forms artificially, is whether certain kinds of behaviour rather than a special degree of complexity of structure can be reproduced.

Just what form of activity is typical of living things is a question we must presently consider, but we may observe at once that where the transition from non-living to living is being investigated the relevant phenomena are phenomena of process rather than simply of spatial pattern (though that also may be involved). This is indicated by the manner in which even the elementary biological units that we have mentioned are synthesized. It is not just a matter of accretion of relatively static parts, but depends on a continuous flow of material constantly breaking down and reconstituting the giant 'molecule' concerned.[2] This Bertalanffy

[1] Cf. imitations of living forms produced artificially by M. Traube, O. Blutschli, S. Leduc, A. L. Herrera and others described by A. I. Oparin, op. cit., Ch. III.

[2] Cf. H. Blum, *Time's Arrow and Evolution* (Princeton University Press, 1955), p. 133.

maintains is the explanation of co-variant reduplication of biological units. 'Elementary biological units', he writes, 'are crystallites, which on the one hand, attach molecular groups by virtue of specific attractive forces and thus grow, but which, on the other hand, undergo catabolic processes. If such processes are present, repulsive forces must result which may lead eventually to a division of the crystallite, i.e. to its co-variant reduplication.'[1]

In other words, genes and chromosomes and similar bodies within the living system maintain themselves in being, as does the whole system, by a process of metabolic activity, and it is the character of such activity that must next be discussed.

4

The relevant conception here is that of an open system in a steady state. A system that is relatively isolated from its surroundings and in which only those substances already present can react chemically is called a closed (or enclosed) system. In such a system an equilibrium may be attained in which reactions balance each other and entropy is always either maintained (if the reactions are reversible) or increased (if they are not). An open system, in contrast, is one in which material and energy exchanges are continuously taking place between the substances within the system and those of its surroundings, so that there is a continuous flow of material through it. If in spite of this flow the substances within the system are maintained in, or steadily approach, constant relations and proportions, it is said to be in (or to approximate to) a steady or stationary state. Such a system may be capable of numerous different stationary states and may change from one to another in response to external changes.

Within an open system entropy production is minimal and may in certain circumstances even decrease. 'The second law of thermodynamics applies only to closed systems', Bertalanffy declares, 'it does not define the steady state.'[2] This, of course, is true only

[1] Op. cit., p. 30. He supports his view by the evidence of results obtained in investigations of the utilization of radio-active phosphorous by nucleo-proteins. The use of the term 'catabolic' is no longer common. Bertalanffy may here be referring to activity such as that of lysosomes, reversing constructive processes in the cell.

[2] Cf. Bertalanffy, op. cit., pp. 126–7; Oparin, op. cit., Ch. VII, and J. W. S. Pringle, in *Symposia of the Society for Experimental Biology*, 7, 1 (1953).

within limits, for the maintenance of a steady state in such a system constantly increases entropy in the environment. It is possible only as long as free energy is supplied to the system from outside, whether as heat or in some other form. The continuous supply of energy for the maintenance of one or more chemical reactions in a system is, however, a contingency the probability of which decreases with the complexity of the reactions involved. As entropy is the measure of disorder and as the more disorderly is always the more probable the minimization of entropy is always less probable than its maximization. The existence of open systems in a steady state, therefore, is less probable than that of systems, in which entropy constantly increases. Their breakdown is more probable than their formation and elaboration. Any process which tends towards the production, maintenance and evolution of open systems, even though in its details the second law of thermodynamics is never violated, is a process running counter to expectation according to thermodynamic principles. It is a process in the direction of the improbable and implies a *nisus* in the direction of concrescence and coherence. It is presumably to this that Schrödinger refers when he says that events occurring in living processes are 'guided by a "mechanism" entirely different from the "probability mechanism" of physics'.[1]

A nisus against the physically more probable, a capacity to produce and maintain among substances, arrangements and reactions which are thermodynamically improbable, seems to be the distinguishing character of life. This is clearly apparent in the maintenance within the cell of its heterogeneous chemical structure in opposition to the normal thermodynamic tendency to uniform distribution of substances in solution. The unicellular organism contains a large number of different substances in solution, proteins, nucleic acids, sugars, salts, not just intermixed but segregated from one another in determinate ways by means as yet unexplained. In so small a volume the work needed to counteract the normal processes of diffusion is considerable, and a constant supply of free energy is thus in demand.[2] It is provided, for the

[1] *What is Life?* p. 77.
[2] Cf. R. S. Lillie, *General Biology and Philosophy of Organism* (Chicago, 1945), p. 33: 'Diffusion is the manifestation or effect of the random thermal motions of molecules; therefore, it is always *down* a concentration gradient. It is a dissipative process, making for uniformity of distribution; hence it tends to break down any organization based on local differences

most part, by the chemical processes of metabolism; but that is itself a highly organized system of reactions displaying a similarly improbable character.

The capacity somehow to maintain order and system in physico-chemical conditions which ordinarily tend to dissipate and destroy them presupposes some influence able to mobilize and direct the available free energy in such a way as to build up organized structure in higher and more complicated forms than those at the physical level which we have already considered.[1] That there is some such influence at work in living processes is clearly evident from the facts, but what precisely it may be, and how precisely it functions, are matters not yet scientifically understood. We shall find, however, that its exercise is always consequent upon the presence of ordered structure of some degree and its effect is the production of further and more highly organized systems. It corresponds closely, therefore, to the much criticized 'radial energy' of Pierre Teilhard.

The difference which we are trying here to determine is that between open systems which are simply physico-chemical and systems which, though they are physico-chemical open systems, are also properly held to be living systems. At this stage the best way to approach the question of the distinction between life and inorganic processes would be to take systems that are unquestionably alive and consider what characteristics they have which those lack which are unquestionable non-living. As an example of the latter we may take A. I. Oparin's description of the type of chemical reactions that might be presumed as leading up to the prebiotic synthesis of complicated organic compounds. He writes as follows:

of concentration or composition. As a constant factor, present in all fluid systems, it acts in opposition to the most characteristic physical activity of living protoplasm, the building-up of complexly differentiated structure from dissolved molecules.'

[1] Cf. Lillie, op. cit., pp. 85–6: 'Physically considered, the usual living cell is a minute droplet of solution separated by a diffusion-proof membrane from another solution, the aqueous environment. ... Its chemical and structural elements are arranged in a constant manner which is highly "improbable" in the physical sense of the word. ... There is here illustrated a general natural condition, namely, a tendency for complex types of order to pass automatically into a less ordered state—*unless* some active counter-process is maintained which prevents or compensates this tendency.'

'It may now be taken as an established fact that in such simple reactions occurring in the gaseous phase as the oxidation of the lower hydrocarbons or other similar reactions which took place in the primaeval atmosphere, an essential part was played by the free radicals which were initially brought into being by the action of radiations or electric discharges and perpetuated in the course of chain reactions. For example, the passage of an electric discharge through water vapour leads to the formation of hydroxyl radicals which can oxidize hydrocarbons according to the following scheme:

$$H_2O - - - - \rightarrow OH + H \text{ the initiation of the chain}$$
$$M_1 + OH \; - \rightarrow H_2O + R \qquad \} \text{ the continuation of the}$$
$$R + O_2 \; - - \rightarrow M_2 + OH \text{ etc.} \qquad \} \text{ chain}$$

a particular example is:

$$CH_4 + OH- \rightarrow CH_3 + H_2O$$
$$CH_3 + O_2 \; - \rightarrow HCHO + OH \text{ etc.}$$

Thus, it is a peculiarity of chain reactions that a large number of short cycles of reactions can be carried out by means of alternating active foci, free atoms or elements, when the sequence of cycles is initiated by a reaction giving rise to any of the active particles. . . . If a larger number of radicals is formed at the end of the cycle than were present at the beginning, there will be a branching of chains . . . and the rate of progress will quickly increase. Conversely, if the number of radicals is less at the end of the cycle than at the beginning, the chains will be broken and the reaction will get slower or stop.'[1]

Oparin goes on to emphasize the fact that chain reactions forming the basis for biological metabolism are different in principle from the above, both intrinsically and in their manner of branching. But all we need to observe at this point is that the purely chemical reaction goes on automatically so long as favourable conditions persist and ceases if they do not. The living system in contrast is internally variable in multiform, complex and interconnected ways so as to adjust to the variation of external circumstances. The entire system of any complete organism, even if known, would be too vastly complicated to describe as an example, but we can easily

[1] Op cit., pp. 335-6.

illustrate this adaptive variability by confining ourselves to one factor within it.

In mammalian metabolism the process of cell respiration is of great importance and is dependent upon the presence of oxygen in the blood. Oxygen is carried by the red corpuscles (erythrocytes) and supplied to the tissues by their circulation through the body. It is thus important for the maintenance of the system that their number and density should be adequate but not excessive. Their normal density is about 5 million per cubic millimetre but they can be increased by production from the bone marrow or reduced through destruction by the macrophages of the lymphatic glands. If the oxygen supply to the organism is decreased, as (for instance) at high altitudes, the number of erythrocytes is automatically increased (this is known as hypertrophy of the erythron). The same effect is brought about by obstruction of the trachea, and by heart defects which slow down the blood circulation so tending to reduce the oxygen supply. On the other hand, if from any cause the oxygen supply is increased, a process of reduction of the number of erythrocytes immediately begins. Again, if, through bleeding the erythron becomes attenuated, or if by transfusion it is enriched, the normal number is rapidly restored by the automatic adjustment of processes in the organism. The spleen acts as a store of erythrocytes, and when blood is lost through haemorrhage a muscle in the spleen contracts and squeezes red corpuscles out into the bloodstream. When the erythron becomes too rich the number of red corpuscles is reduced by phagocytosis. It has been found that both these processes of adjustment become more rapid and efficient if frequently repeated.

Here, then, is one of the thousand possible examples that could have been given of a complex process of self-adjustment in the organism to changes of circumstance which tend to destroy or to upset the system of its internal working. A non-living chemical system, though open and steady, which depended for its continuance on a supply of oxygen would simply slow down and eventually dissipate if that supply were withheld. The living system also slows down and in extreme cases dies, but not *simply*. Its retardation is neither immediate nor directly proportional to the reduction of supply, but proceeds more slowly, because modifications within the system tend to counteract the oxygen scarcity by making better use of what is available. Again if the non-living system is movable it does not tend to approach sources of supply or to avoid regions of dearth, whereas if the living creature is capable of locomotion it will move away from regions where the supply is poor and 'seek out' sources of supply. The unicellular animal, *Paramoecium*, for instance, when oxygen is reduced in the water in which it lives will move away from the area of deficiency and will adhere to a bubble, where the supply is richer. Likewise, *Arcella* (a shelled rhizopod) which lives near the bottom of ponds, when the water is deprived of dissolved oxygen, secretes a bubble which floats it up nearer the surface where the supply is more plentiful.[1]

Whereas non-living chemical processes take place in accordance with an available supply of free energy that is fortuitous and independent of the processes it activates, a living organism actively pursues and accumulates energy supplies. The physico-chemical processes within it synthesize and store the substances which provide energy, and the rate of their breakdown is regulated so as to release it in quantities appropriate to the requirements and the systematic interrelation of those processes themselves, and to the needs of the total system for self-maintenance. There is some principle of spontaneous activity preserving the structure and integrity of the system which is evident in every specifically living process studied by the biologist—metabolism, growth, reproduction or development. It is a principle itself unaccounted for by any purely physico-chemical law as yet known, and all that can be said of it at the present time seems to be that it is incident upon a certain relatively high degree of complex and integrated organization of matter, below which its characteristic effects are not observed.

It would then seem to be the case that purely chemo-physical open systems, to which we have no inclination to ascribe life, include processes of chemical and physical change which are continuous so long as external conditions remain constant and appropriate to their propagation, but which become attenuated and cease when the relevant external conditions change. On the other hand, in a living system, the processes are habitually modified in a manner which adapts them to changing external conditions (over a comparatively wide range of variations), by selection between possible alternatives, or adjustment of the relative rates of reaction and the mutual proportions of the products,

---

[1] All the above examples are taken from E. S. Russell, *The Directiveness of Organic Activities* (Cambridge University Press, 1945).

so that the system persists in a steady state despite continual changes of external conditions.[1] This is nothing more or less than the manifestation of that capacity already observed for producing orderly arrangements thermodynamically relatively improbable.

It does not mean, however, that the living system includes anything more or other than chemico-physical processes, but it does imply that life is not merely a more complicated case of what is already contained in the non-living. Though the living organism is a specially complicated open physico-chemical system in (or approximating to) a steady state, the mere complication in itself of physico-chemical properties, is not all that is involved in the adaptive and directive character of organization which enables the system to respond to environmental changes so as to maintain itself in being, as recognizably the same system.

Let us consider more closely the special character of a system of this kind. It is one which external changes in a wide range of variation do not dissipate or destroy, not because it is fixed and unaffected by them, but because the processes within it are plastic and variable and change, in reaction to environmental alterations and correlatively to one another, in such a way as always to maintain among themselves similar relationships and, among their most essential products, constant quantitative proportions. Only between essential products must be proportions be maintained, for many substances produced by the internal processes are instrumental to the maintenance of the proper proportions of the essential substances, and the variation and mutual adjustment of the former may result in an altered proportion among themselves such that decrease in one compensates (and is compensated by) increase in another, with the final effect of producing the same quantitative relations between essential ingredients or essential processes as obtained before the change occurred.

Such a system is one which varies its structure and activity always relevantly to a constant and overruling pattern of organization. The variations and changes of form are all and always mutually regulated so as to preserve an interrelationship of parts governed by a single and constant principle of order. Its unity and individuality are thus determined and constituted by this central principle, and is, in view of its relevant variability, polyphasic.

[1] Cf. Schrödinger, *What is Life?* §§ 56, 57.

The variations of its self-manifestation, however, are primarily variations of activity rather than of quantitative interrelation or spatio-temporal position. It does of course display differences in structural form correlative to, resultant from, and in many ways expressive of, the modifications of its activity; which, in view of their subservice of an overruling principle of order may now be termed 'functional'. In short, the relevant variations are primarily variations in functioning, to which structure becomes secondary and instrumental. It is in fact the spatial manifestation of functional processes.[1] Though the effect of this relevant variation is to keep in being the functional totality in spite of environmental changes which would otherwise destroy it, nevertheless, the environment is not wholly foreign or hostile to it, for the substances and sources of energy which are available in its surroundings are selectively used by the system to maintain itself. The variation of its internal activity, while always relevant to the overriding principle of organization, is also relevant to the outside world as it impinges on the system and affects its internal activity. But when in the ordinary course chemical and thermodynamic requirements would dictate reactions which would disintegrate and break up the system, conditions obtain within it such as to bring about compensating reactions to counteract these effects.

5

That living systems answer to this description, there is a vast mass of evidence to assure us, and there will be frequent occasion to appeal to it in the sequel. Here we are attempting to isolate that special character which will justify our distinguishing a system as alive from others which, though steady and open, are merely physico-chemical. It will be convenient to have a single term to apply to this special character by which we intend to identify life, and for this purpose I propose to use the word 'auturgy', now rarely seen, to indicate the capacity of the living system to 'work upon itself' and spontaneously to adjust its own internal processes to external conditions so as to maintain its systematic coherence. I shall call an organization of chemical processes auturgic the interrelations of which are regulated according to an overriding principle of order in such a way as to

[1] Cf. J. S. Haldane, *Organism and Environment* (Yale, 1917), pp. 102–4.

maintain the system in being as an integral whole despite variations in external conditions. The activity of an auturgic system is
regulated so as to maintain a steady state, and the system is
nothing more nor less than the active processes, mutually adjusted within it, that constitute this steady state. The various
phases and aspects of these constitutive processes are in consequence mutually ends and means. Anything less than a system
of this kind fails to qualify as an example of life.

This is the conception of life and its distinction from the non-
living held by Oparin who writes:

'. . . living things differ fundamentally from all such [physico-
chemical] open systems in the orderly regulation of their metabolism and the "purposefulness" of their internal structure. Not
only are the many tens and hundreds of thousands of chemical
reactions which occur in protoplasm, and which together constitute
metabolism, strictly co-ordinated with one another in time, harmoniously composed into a single series of processes which constantly repeat themselves, but the whole series is directed towards
a single goal, towards the uninterrupted self-preservation and
self-reproduction of the living system as a whole in accordance
with the conditions of the surrounding medium.'

'Purposefulness', he explains, is not the 'fulfilment of some higher
design', but adaptation of organization to the maintenance and
reproduction of the system as a whole.[1] It is what we are calling
'auturgy'.

It is to be noticed that an auturgic system is a new phase and
represents a higher type and order of polyphasic unity similar in
general character to those we discerned at the physical level, yet
exceeding them in stability and versatility. Even at the physical
level we found relevant variation of phenomena governed by an
overriding principle of order. But these variations were confined
to spatio-temporal and quantitative relationships subject to laws
which, while they expressed the principles of systematic articulation within the totality concerned, and governed the occurrence
and non-occurrence of subordinate wholes within it, showed no
special tendency to maintain these subordinate entities in being.
Hence elementary particles are annihilated and converted into
γ-rays in accordance with laws determining the behaviour of the

[1] *The Origin of Life*, pp. 349–50.

energy field and the conversion of one form of energy into another. Similar laws govern the radioactive breakdown of atoms, or their combination into molecules in suitable circumstances. In all such cases we have concomitant variation of behaviour the principles of which the laws express. But at this level the laws appear external to the subordinating totalities and govern their behaviour and form, as it were, from without to the extent that the subordinate wholes cannot so behave as to *utilize* the physical principles of change to create conditions favourable to their own persistence in being. Only at the level of life is the concomitant variation of parts and processes regulated so as to maintain the specific system in being when the external physico-chemical conditions tend to be unfavourable to its persistence. Only at this stage in the series of mounting complexifications does the polyphasic unity express its character in the form of specific self-maintenance, against the stream of physico-chemical and thermodynamic probability. And it does so, not by eliminating or abolishing physico-chemical and thermodynamic laws, but by using them (it is difficult if at all possible to find a more neutral term) in internal readjustment to counteract unfavourable conditions and sustain its own identity.

For example, whereas a crystal disintegrates if heated, or dissolves if placed in an unsaturated solution, a living thing when the external temperature rises adjusts its internal physiological activity to maintain its own temperature at a constant level or moves away into cooler surroundings. If it comes into contact with a substance tending to damage its own, it forms a protective covering or, if it can, takes evasive action. So the plant respires more on hot days than on cool, reducing the temperature in its own vicinity. The mammal perspires with a similar result and moves into the shade. The slime-mould in conditions of drought, divides itself into capsules which it surrounds with a hardened shell of its own substance. The oyster protects its flesh from intrusive grit by encasing it in a pearly covering. The extent and efficacy of such adaptability is, of course, limited, but its presence is marked and the distinction of living from non-living things in terms of this capacity seems both valid and useful.

The tendency in the nature of things, noted earlier, towards integration in wholes of increasing order and stability here manifests itself as the production of greater unified complexity and at the same time as maintenance of itself by means of such increased articulated unification. Hitherto the articulation was primarily structural, determining processes of change, but now we have wholes of interlinked and mutually affecting processes of change which are structured, not only spatially, but temporally so as to maintain themselves as wholes. It is as if, by self-enfoldment, polyphasic unification itself had achieved the capacity to counteract the disintegrating tendency of thermodynamic deterioration, and without any violation of the second law, to conduct functional systems *upstream* in the tide of entropy towards less rather than more probable structural correlations. It is this capacity that signalizes the emergence of life and marks the living system as a new and higher phase in the scale of polyphasic unification.

For the self-preservation of a system by adaptive response to external circumstances, two conditions are needed. First, the constant renewal of substances within the system, and secondly, the maintenance of constancy despite external changes, in what has come to be called the 'internal environment'. The renewal of substances if it proceeds at a rate exceeding that of their utilization of breakdown may result either in growth and increase in the size of the system or in its reduplication. Reproduction, which Oparin brackets with self-preservation as the goal of the series of reactions occurring within the organism, may be no more than an extension of the process of self-maintenance. The second condition— constancy of the internal environment—involves at some stage, some kind of homeostatic mechanism, an interrelation of processes such that certain properties are kept at a constant intensity and certain substances in constant quantity. The necessity of these two features of self-maintenance must be borne in mind in any discussion of the conditions of existence, of generation and of evolution of living organisms.

The necessity for organization of internal processes so as to counteract inimical changes in the environment, gives the internal changes the character of responses to external conditions. By so reacting to the outside world the living system constitutes a kind of reflection of it, not in the sense of copying or reduplicating it, but as correlative reactivity to it. Its own activity is unified as a system, but, as we have said, not in isolation from or disregard of its surround, and it is, in consequence, organically continuous with its environment.[1] By the integration of its own activity as a self-maintaining system, it becomes, in consequence, a focus of unity for the immediate environment shading off into the more

[1] Cf. J. S. Haldane, op. cit.

remote. In this respect it is similar to the physical entities examined earlier, but its method of reflecting and unifying its world is different. For it does not simply register the effects of external forces but reacts to them by means of internal adjustments. In a later stage of development this characteristic becomes highly important as the emergence of consciousness, and even before that it marks the living organism as a totality of greater comprehensiveness and more sensitive coherence.

In conclusion, then, we may summarize the answer that is being suggested to the question what the living system involves over and above mere complexity of physico-chemical processes. In particular it seems to be a new type of organization more fully and successfully exerting the general tendency of things in nature which was noticed earlier—the tendency to form and elaborate wholes of ever-increasing stability and integration. The source of this nisus we have not so far been able to decide but we have traced it back to the polyphasic character of the real, manifested even in the metrical properties of the space-time continuum. At the level of life a new phase of integrated wholeness is achieved—the auturgic phase—in which the organization of the totality is such that it can actively maintain itself by adjustment to variations of external conditions which would otherwise tend to destroy it.

CHAPTER IX

BIOCHEMISTRY, NATURAL SELECTION AND THE ORIGIN OF LIFE

I

Biologists today almost without exception assume that life evolved from non-living matter, a probability suggested by the difficulty of finding a dividing line between organic and inorganic matter which has already been observed and discussed. In these days there are no supporters among scientists of the idea of special creation to account for the appearance of life on earth, and the theory of 'seeding'—of the influx of spores from outer space—apart from its own internal difficulties, does not solve the problem of the origin of life, but only removes the scene of its occurrence from the confines of the earth. The questions to be faced, therefore, are how it is possible for inorganic physico-chemical activity to result in the formation of organic substances, of protoplasm and the proliferation of living forms; how non-self-reproductive chemico-physical systems can give rise to self reproducing organisms; how non-auturgic processes can issue in self-maintaining adaptive and ultimately in purposive activity.

In a philosophical investigation such as the present, any direct discussion of the scientific problem would be out of place. It is for scientists alone to discover and assess the evidence and evaluate the probabilities of processes by which living forms originally came into existence. We shall mainly be interested in the light thrown by their findings on the relationship between the levels of life and the non-living, and on the nature of the evolutionary process as such, first as a transition from the mere physico-chemical to the living and, secondly, as a process of elaboration of living species. The intimate connection between these two aspects of evolution has been rightly stressed by Harold F. Blum in the following passage:

'A discussion of this subject may properly begin with an examination of essential properties of modern cells, as a starting point for extrapolation back toward the primitive systems from which those cells have arisen. If we proceed in this way we remain always aware that there are certain functional properties that had to emerge—whether simultaneously or in sequence—in order for systems to come into being from which the present living organisms could have evolved. . . . What we really seek to know is how there came into being a particular kind of self-replicating system which contained those properties that have made possible the evolution of living systems in their present complexity; systems that could be subject to natural selection—I use the term carefully, in the sense of modern Darwinism. Looked at in this way, the problem of the origin of life and the problem of organic evolution are not separable; understanding the one depends on understanding the other.'[1]

This rule is of first importance—that in seeking to understand processes of origination and development, we should constantly bear in mind the type of functional properties that must be presupposed if the evolution of contemporary forms was to be possible, and we shall have occasion to refer to it again when dealing with later developments.

2

There is general agreement among astrophysicists, geologists, and biochemists that high-energy organic compounds (hydrocarbons and the like) could have been synthesized abiogenically in the primitive earth and its atmosphere. It is clear that prior to the appearance of life, chemical processes must progressively have changed as the physical conditions on and above the earth's surface altered; and the combination of elements, possible in different ways in different physical conditions, would have resulted in changing sequences of chemical reactions. Again it is plausible, that where the supply of substances required by different reactions is limited, those which proceeded fastest would produce the greater quantities of their end-products. Further, the formation of aromatic substances with disc-shaped molecules would give, in certain concentrations, collections of these molecules in ordered series due to the ease with which discs fit together in parallel planes.[2] So the formation of polymers might in suitable circum-

---

[1] 'On the Origin of Self-replicating Systems', in *Rhythmic and Synthetic Processes of Growth*, Ed. Dorothea Rudnick (Princeton University Press, 1957), p. 155.

[2] Cf. Melvin Calvin, 'Chemical Evolution and the Origin of Life', *The American Scientist*, Vol. 44, 3 (1956), pp. 248–63.

stances be facilitated. In this way, some of the more complicated compounds and organic substances, may very well have been formed abiogenically, especially when we take into account the effect of ultra-violet radiation, electrical discharges and other sources of extraneous energy.

These high-energy compounds might have been used by the first organisms as a source of energy for the synthesis of more complex substances essential in the constitution of protoplasm, such as proteins and nucleic acids, but their abiogenic synthesis is not enough to account for the origin of those organisms themselves. When, as must soon have happened, the supply of organic compounds became exhausted, organisms could only survive if they could synthesize such high-energy compounds for themselves or derive them from other organisms which had acquired that capacity. This, however, involves chemo- or photo-autotrophy, neither of which are simple processes, and which, it is now generally believed, must have arisen subsequently to heterotrophic organisms. Both in chemo- and photo-autotrophy the synthesis of hydrocarbons and carbohydrates takes place in the course of a complex metabolic cycle involving special catalysts.

As chlorophyll plays a major role in photosynthesis, the appearance on the scene of this highly complex compound is itself one of the factors to be explained. H. Gaffron thinks it feasible that chlorophyll could have been synthesized abiogenically,[1] but the process of photosynthesis, the details of which are only gradually being discovered, proves to be exceedingly complex—something much more than chlorophyll alone can bring about. It depends on the breaking of a chemical bond in the molecule of water, and that needs more energy than can be provided by a chlorophyll molecule after absorption of a single quantum of light. What is further required seems to be a complicated process known as cyclic photophosphorylation, which needs more than chlorophyll for its successful accomplishment.[2] Moreover, Gaffron remarks that 'this

[1] *Vide* 'Photosynthesis and the Origin of Life' in *Rhythmic and Synthetic Processes in Growth*, Ed. Dorothea Rudnick (Princeton University Press, 1957).

[2] *Vide* A. L. Lehninger, 'How Cells Transform Energy', *Scientific American*, Vol. 205, No. 3, 1961. The absorbed photon raises an electron to a higher state of energy than normal, and this is passed from one to another of a series of 'carrier' substances in a circuit, losing energy as it goes and forming *en route* a molecule of ATP by attaching a phosphate group to a molecule of ADP. Thus energy is accumulated for further

astounding and highly improbable result comes about only in co-operation with other rather complex metabolic reactions, which in turn have been seen to occur independently in living cells devoid of chlorophyll and showing no photosynthesis of any kind.'[1]

In other words what has to be explained is the emergence of an organized metabolic system, and the origin of any such system, because it involves the activity of enzymes, presents, as we are about to find, a peculiarly intractable problem. What must here be emphasized is that again and again in accounts of research into and thinking about the beginnings of life, the importance and necessity of the whole integrated system and the impossibility of assembling it piecemeal in a simple additive process are forced upon the attention of the scientist. The type of property that must be presumed to make possible the emergence of life is that which has already been adumbrated in quantum physics. It is that type of property which is holistically determined by the structural principle of the system to which the properties belong.

The known enzymes are all proteins, so that the synthesis of proteins and of similar high-molecular compounds is one of the chief hurdles to be surmounted in a theory of the origin of life. It is now generally accepted that amino-acids, and possibly nucleotides, could have been formed abiogenically, but the more highly complex substances of greater molecular weight present a less tractable problem. Yet before the appearance of so intricately organized a structure as that of protoplasm can be considered, the question must be faced how the macromolecules of proteins and nucleic acids can have been synthesized.

Considerable discussion and speculation still surround this topic. The problem is largely one of energetics, for the linkage of peptides in the polypeptide chain, which constitutes a protein, requires a long series of endergonic reactions (i.e. reactions for which free energy must be supplied from external sources), and if sufficient energy for this purpose is released all at once it is liable to produce explosive or thermal conditions in which the protein

reactions including the reduction of triphosphopyridine nucleotide (TPN) which can effect the dissociation of the water molecule and reduce CO^2 to carbohydrate with the release of oxygen. This cyclical series of reactions has been found to depend upon an intricate arrangement of substances within the chloroplasts of the living cell, where the chlorophyll molecules themselves are stacked in orderly structures ('grana') and the specialized electron carriers are also lodged.

[1] Op. cit., p. 130.

molecule ceases to be stable. It must therefore be provided in small instalments, each sufficient to produce a single dipeptide linkage. These instalments must occur in a series which will make possible the formation of a chain with as many as 50,000 links not simply in haphazard sequence, but in a definite order, with a regular pattern of distribution of the different amino-acids concerned. Futher, only the left-hand form of the amino-acids is included (except in the case of glycine, which is optically inactive), whereas amino-acids synthesized *in vitro* occur in racemic mixture, the separation from which of the l-forms and d-forms makes its own demands on the supply of energy and requires some process of discrimination hitherto undiscovered.[1]

In living organisms these and other essential macro-molecular substances are synthesized stepwise, using successive small transfers of energy from the breakdown of certain high-energy compounds (among which ATP is one of the most important). This is effected in the course of intricately ordered processes, with precise mutual interrelation both in space and in time, regulated by the help of catalysts, each performing a highly limited and specific role. The catalysts are themselves proteins, so the problem to be solved is how so complexly organized a process for the synthesis of high-molecular compounds could have developed before the existence of such compounds themselves. As yet no other method of their synthesis is known and no other method is easy to conceive. Sidney W. Fox has recently produced a protenoid substance by thermal polymerization of amino-acids[2] but, interesting and exciting though his experimental results may be, it is as yet too soon to foretell their precise significance. What is, however, relevant is that the protenoid thus synthesized is of relatively low molecular weight and Fox refers to N. W. Pirie's suggestion that proteins of higher molecular weight developed only after the emergence of the first organisms.[3] It is these higher molecular proteins that are important because the enzymes belong to this class and it is generally acknowledged that the synthesis of complex molecules essential to the functioning of living

---

[1] The 'template theory' (see below) for the formation of protein molecules is currently favoured, but it does not explain the original formation of the template.

[2] *Vide* 'How did Life Begin', *Science*, Vol. 132, no. 3421 (1960).

[3] *Vide* N. W. Pirie in J. D. Bernal, *The Physical Basis of Life* (London, 1951).

substance requires the structurally ordered metabolic processes in which these enzymes play an indispensable part.

Once again the structured whole, both as spatially patterned and as temporally ordered, asserts itself as logically prior to the existence of its constituents, and it may well be the case that the problem of origins is insoluble if the process is conceived as additive, and, like that of complementarity in physics, it may remain enigmatic until the holistic nature of the phenomena is fully recognized and better understood.

Two main methods of approach have been made to this problem of origin. One depends on the conception of autocatalysis of complex molecules and the other envisages the evolution by natural selection of metabolisms which can synthesize them from other materials. The first view is held by A. Dauvillier, and is presented by N. H. Horowitz[1] and by Blum[2] as a possible explanation of some factors (though not all) contributing to the origin of life. Oparin, however, offers a different hypothesis. He rejects the notion of a self-replicating molecule on the ground that autocatalysis (as most biochemists nowadays agree) never occurs by direct reproduction of a molecule[3] (not even in the case of viruses) but always requires a complicated cycle of reactions including the action of large numbers of highly specific enzymes,[4] most of which are associated with formed elements of the cell, giving them a special character different from that observed in simple aqueous solutions of these same enzymes when isolated from the cell. Moreover they are not arranged at random but are lodged in special structures (e.g. plastids, mitochondria, ribosomes) in different spatial relations within the cell. In short, the pre-existence of the whole spatio-temporal structure of living protoplasm with its metabolic processes is, in his view, a prior condition of the synthesis of proteins.[5] To regard metabolism as a later

---

[1] 'On the Evolution of Biochemical Synthesis', *Proc. Acad. Nat. Sci.* (U.S.) (1945), 31.

[2] *Time's Arrow and Evolution*, Ch. X.   [3] *The Origin of Life*, Ch. VI.

[4] Cf. *ibid.*, p. 263: 'The chemically individual proteins which have been isolated do not arise of themselves by the "division" of molecules nor by simple automatic autocatalysis. We can, in fact, only observe the production of proteins in living bodies, and this process requires harmonious participation of a series of systems including many different protein-enzymes.' Cf. also Hinshelwood in *Progress in Biophysics*, 5, 1 (1955).

[5] Cf., *ibid.*, pp. 268–70.

development than autocatalysis would thus be a *hysteron proteron*. He believes that metabolism must first have arisen by natural selection of chain reactions in open systems occurring in multiple complex coacervates—colloidal complexes of which protoplasm is, in fact, a highly intricate and convoluted example.

Blum, however, emphasizes the fact that the Darwinian conception of natural selection presumes the existence of a self-reproductive system, which repeats itself, not always exactly, but with occasional minor variations, some at least of which are themselves self-replicating.[1] These latter variations are called 'mutants' and the process of their production, 'mutation'. If a mutant is such that it can survive after an environmental change unfavourable to the persistence of the original system, it will continue in existence and will mlutiply itself while the original from which it derived will be eliminated. In short, it will be naturally selected. The presupposition of natural selection, therefore, is the existence of self-replicating systems capable of producing self-replicating mutants. Now Oparin proposes a process of natural selection prior to self-reproduction by which self-reproducing systems are brought into existence,[2] so that his theory also seems to commit a *hysteron proteron*.

In fact, the whole problem bristles with difficulties. If the hypothesis of a self-reproducing molecule is adopted the only plausible form of it, for proteins (and nucleic acids), seems to be that which includes the notion of a template on which the new molecule is constructed from the several radicals and chemical groups which compose it. But the template must be an already synthesized molecule and how this could originally come into being remains obscure; yet that is the nodal issue. On the other hand, if this hypothesis is rejected on the ground that enzymes 'could not have arisen by the action of selection on their separate isolated molecules',[3] it seems equally inept to suggest, as Oparin does, that their activity, by increasing reaction rates within coacervate systems, could have effected the evolution of such systems *towards* the 'purposefulness' of structure characterizing living things; for that structure (as his next paragraph implies) is prerequisite to their synthesis.

[1] *Vide*, H. F. Blum, *Time's Arrow and Evolution* (*passim*) and 'The Origin of Self-replicating Systems', in *Rhythmic and Synthetic Processes of Growth*.

[2] *Ibid.*, p. 360.   [3] Oparin, op. cit., p. 373.

Epitomized, the problem seems to be that the origin of life presupposes the synthesis of enzymes, and that requires an integrated metabolic system spatio-temporally organized; but any such system presupposes the activity of enzymes in a protoplasm already formed. The dilemma of the hen and the egg apparently, goes back to the very beginnings of life. The problem is not one that can be solved by any arm-chair philosophizing and its solution must await the results of further scientific research, but from the discussion of it by scientists, certain factors emerge which support conclusions of great philosophical significance about the nature of life and evolution.

3

(i) The first and most important of these conclusions is that the persistent outcome of the biologists' investigations is the priority and indispensability, for any conception of living matter and its activity, of an integrated dynamic system of reciprocating and mutually sustaining processes, that can be understood only as a whole, parts of which can be explained only in terms of its totality and the generation of which is always holistic and never simply piecemeal summation. It is a complex of processes which are all physico-chemical, but, in virtue of its integration, its activity and products transcend those of processes occurring below the organismic level.

The dominance of the whole over the sum of the parts through internal organization has already been illustrated by the dependence upon molecular structure of the various properties of protein substances. Not only is the order of sequence of amino-acids a determining factor, but also their three-dimensional arrangement within the chain is of the utmost importance. The side chains and terminal groups have specialized chemical affinities and potentialities which are effective not only in reactions with other substances (external to the chain) but also in the formation of internal linkages which produce orderly convolutions in the polymer and unify it into an intricately interwoven, three-dimensional structure with a definitely ordered internal architecture. Nor is the structure of the protein molecule a simple consequence of known physico-chemical forces. 'Direct investigation of the structure of corpuscular proteins by diffraction of X-rays and infra-red rays shows that this structure is, in fact, far more complicated than any of the schemes drawn up on the basis of general physico-chemical considerations.'[1]

Still more impressive, however, is the holistic character of biosynthetic processes. Every biosynthesis of complex organic substances is a system of processes most delicately adjusted to one another. The energy required for the synthesis of proteins and nucleic acids, for instance, is derived mainly from the breakdown of carbohydrates, in the prior synthesis of which numerous protein enzymes have already played an indispensable part in precisely co-ordinated series of reactions. The enzyme system is itself intricately and complexly organized, each enzyme performing a highly specific function supplementary to others in the system, accelerating finely specialized reactions just to the right extent at just the required place and time. In the course of these processes high-energy compounds such as ATP, that are needed to effect endergonic reactions, are produced by means not yet fully understood. These compounds give up their energy in just the right parcels, precisely when needed to bind together groups and residues into polymers—a step-by-step process for which the total energy required, if all released at once would destroy the most important substances involved in the reaction. Further the rates of the various reactions contributing to the process are regulated in definite relation to one another by the specific activity of the enzymes involved, so that exactly the proper proportions of the resulting compounds are provided as and where they are required to maintain the flow of reactions and to take part in other processes upon which the life of the organism depends. The occurrence of none of these processes is significant as and when it takes place, and none is at all intelligible, except by reference to the total structure and sequence of the entire system which it subserves and in which its interrelation with the other processes is determined.

Again the inclusion of the processes within the organic system modifies the effects of physico-chemical laws and the transmutations are not governed solely by thermodynamic possibilities. To quote Oparin again:

'In living things . . . these reactions are strictly co-ordinated in respect of their velocities so that they form a long chain of processes in which one reaction follows the other in strictly determined

[1] Oparin, op. cit., p. 257.

G

sequence. As a result of this, it is a general rule that *not all the transformations which are thermodynamically possible in the organism actually occur there*' (my italics).[1]

Instances multiply themselves as one continues to investigate biological phenomena. It is hardly necessary to recite a long catalogue of examples. One final reference may be made to the striking evidence provided in the discovery by Vlés and Gex, when examining the sea urchin's egg in the ultraviolet spectrometer, that the normal absorption curve for proteins was not obtainable so long as the cell was alive, but only after it had been killed. This should be sufficient to justify our taking the point as established that in the sphere of life the whole determines the properties and activities of the parts to an extent even more marked and more decisive than is displayed at any prior level of physico-chemical organization.

(ii) Secondly, the existence of such an integrated system is prior to, not the product of, natural selection. Evolution by natural selection presumes variations in the progeny from some parental stock and the selection of the variants which are better adapted to environmental conditions. The so-called 'chemical evolution' briefly described above (on page 186) could result at most in the accumulation of a limited number of organic substances, not the complex metabolic processes required for 'generation' and self-reproduction, without which (Blum must surely be right) no 'natural selection' can properly be said to occur at all. That is possible, as he insists, for no structure less complicated than proteins and nucleic acids—highly organized totalities with very specialized internal arrangement. Blum assumes that these complex molecules are capable of self-reproduction and their structure is such that, if they were, minor modifications of them could occur and could be treated as mutants. These, according to Horowitz's hypothesis, would be selected for survival if they could (as their forebears could not) catalyze the synthesis of compounds essential for their own composition which were becoming scarce in the environment. But this auto-catalysis is (as already noted) far from being a simple matter and involves a whole cycle of chemical reactions pursuing determinate 'paths' among a whole series of chemical substances. Even Horowitz's hypothesis of the evolution of auto-catalysis, therefore, is not the description of a

[1] Op. cit., p. 197.

succession of accretions, but of the step-wise modification of an already existing open system, which must be presumed already in some measure to be self-maintaining.

There is no real alternative to conceiving natural selection as operative upon organic systems. If the stage prior to selection is just a concatenation of chemical reactions, and no more, and if some accidental modification of any of its products should occur, the result would be a new direction or order in the series of chemical reactions. What could give either of these alternatives (the old series of reactions or the new) any advantage for 'survival'? Let us consider for a moment the Horowitz-Blum schematic model for the synthesis of proteins.[1] It is assumed that substance X is heterotrophically synthesized from A and B. Accidental modification of the process gives rise to a new form of X (X_1) which can catalyse the synthesis of A from C and D. The course of reactions which first ran thus:

$$A + B \rightarrow X$$

now becomes

$$X_1 + C + D \rightarrow A + B \rightarrow X$$

If A now becomes exhausted in the environment, the first reaction becomes impossible without X_1, but future reactions could still produce, with the help of X_1, either X or X_1 or both, so long as the supply of B, C and D is available. X_1 would thus not have been 'selected' because the production of both X and X_1 is equally possible so long as A can be synthesized from C and D. Meanwhile, there would be constant danger of the accidental elimination of X_1, and so of the whole process, unless there is some guarantee that the reaction of A with B will continue to give an adequate supply of appropriate mutants, and this is far from probable. The only plausible assumption is that the whole system is self-reproducing and that once the mutation of $A + B \rightarrow X$ has occurred, only X_1 can be produced and in no other way than by the entire, self-contained and self-reproducing system, $X_1 + C + D \rightarrow A + B \rightarrow X_1$; and that would suggest that the $A + B$ part of the system has been modified by its association with the part, $X_1 + C + D$, so that in this context it can no longer produce X. Further, the A so produced (by catalytic activity of X_1) would not

[1] Cf. Blum, op. cit., p. 195.

be made freely available to combine with B under the catalytic action of any residual X. But this would be to admit that $X_1 + C + D \rightarrow A + B \rightarrow X_1$ is not just a cycle of chemical reactions, but an organic system with inseparable and unisolable components; and again we have support for the contention that natural selection can be exerted only upon the system as a whole.

The prerequisite for natural selection, therefore, is an already existing whole, not less than a self-replicating protein molecule, which itself requires for its genesis a complex cycle of chemical reactions (a sort of inchoate metabolism), and this is found to presuppose an already existing organization of living matter. Ordered totality is thus logically prior to natural selection.

(iii) The third philosophical inference supported by the scientific evidence is the improbability of the processes essential to the emergence of life and the consequent error of believing that they could have arisen by sheer chance in the course of a chaos of purely random changes. It is largely for this reason that Oparin refuses to concede the possibility of abiogenic autocatalysis of molecules as large and complicated as those of proteins and nucleic acids. He emphasizes the improbability of its occurrence by pointing to the facts that the free energies of the bonds in the polypeptide chain are different between different amino-acid residues, and that the incorporation of different amino-acids into the chains proceeds at different rates affecting their arrangement. These different rates are regulated not only by inherent chemical properties of the combining groups but by the action of specific catalysts. Similar conditions also govern the arrangement and combinations of nucleotides in nucleic acid molecules.[1] But, more than this, Oparin points to the specificity of proteins themselves and their performance of definite and mutually complementary functions in the metabolic processes of protoplasm. This, he says, precludes their fortuitous synthesis prior to, and independently of, that metabolic system. The idea that they could be so synthesized, he holds, is as ridiculous as Empedocles' doctrine that limbs and organs first came into being separately and were later joined together into complete living bodies.

'From the present-day Darwinian point of view, the falsity and

---

[1] Evidence has been found (and Oparin refers to it) that nucleic acids are concerned in the synthesis of proteins and again that protein enzymes are instrumental in the synthesis of nucleic acids.

absurdity of hypotheses of this sort are obvious. Any particular organ can arise and become perfected only by the evolutionary development of the organism as a single whole. The definite, complicated structures of eyes and hands are only adapted to the purpose of fulfilling those functions which these organs carry out in the whole organism. The effect of natural selection is, there-fore, only exerted on them as parts of the whole living thing. . . . The same applies to the catalytic powers of enzymes. . . .'[1]

The points that have so far been made may now be summarized:

(1) On the biological level we are concerned from the beginning with functional organic totalities, the elements of which are basically chemical processes, not just in fortuitous sequence or loose juxtaposition, but mutually determined and interdependent so as to maintain and reproduce the integrity of the system.

(2) It now seems established that the transition from the in-organic interplay of chemical reactions to the organic totality that constitutes life cannot be effected by natural selection in the biological sense of the phrase, so long as the former is purely random and fortuitous. How it could have taken place remains obscure, but it may be safe to assume some intermediary stage of quasi-auturgic organization upon which a semblance of natural selection could operate. If physico-chemical wholes are polyphasic the operation within and upon them of a nisus to more complex forms of order could quite conceivably effect the transition. But that it should occur by so-called natural selection of chance variations in an incoherent chaos of chemical processes is entirely unsupported by evidence.

(3) On the other hand, the ordered coherence of any system that can plausibly be regarded as alive is so intricate and complex that its occurrence by mere chance concatination of non-living processes is not credible. Whatever brought life into being must have been a principle running counter to the thermodynamic tendency to-wards increasing disorder. The activity of a principle of this kind need not violate the laws of thermodynamics and could even utilize and rely upon them to produce its effects.

Though the actual method of transition from the non-living physico-chemical sphere to the living is still unknown, it is never-theless clear and demonstrable that a continuous scale exists of types of whole, with a continuous series of degrees of complex

[1] Op. cit., pp. 260-1.

integration, extending from the waves of radiant energy, through the corpuscular, chemical and crystalline forms of matter, to the living. Moreover, the hierarchical structure of this scale extends into the biological sphere, for the living organism is not just a system of chemical substances or a more complicated crystalline structure, it is a dynamic organization of chemical reactions, each presupposing all the forms prior to it in the scale. As the atom is a system of fields, the molecule a system of atoms, and the crystal a system of molecules, so the organism is a system of chemical processes involving all of these—processes promoting and sustaining one another in definite ways which maintain the system, and reproduce the substances reacting within it, as well as their order of mutual interrelationships.

That this dynamic system should be auturgic seems a natural consequence of the extension of the scale, for that type of organization is all that could give coherence and significance to a system of chemical processes. If it were not self-maintaining it would not be a recognizably coherent whole, but at best an equilibrium of concurrent reactions. It is the reciprocal sustaining effect of the processes within the system that gives it that integral character, which is constitutive of its organism and is instrumental to its self-maintenance. The transition from the non-organic to the organic, from the non-auturgic to the auturgic may be a natural inevitable step in the 'complexification' and 'self-enfoldment' of existent forms. If the general principle of this progression were understood the explanation of this particular transition would no doubt be forthcoming. But scientists cannot trace the precise mode of transition from any one level in the hierarchy to the next above it with complete understanding and certainty, and if their success in doing so is greater below the level of life than it is from the inorganic to the living, that is hardly surprising, in view of the overwhelming complexity of living structure and activity. The secret may, nevertheless, lie in the principle (whatever it is) of diversified wholeness and the nisus which it instils towards increasingly complex and coherent unity, which we have found operative in all the forms of reality so far examined as an unbroken thread uniting the scale.

CHAPTER X

ORGANIC ACTIVITY

I

The *scala naturae* has led us from energy to matter, from elementary particle to atom, from atom to molecule and thence to the crystal. At the next stage, that of life, the unit of auturgic, dynamic wholeness is the cell. Here is Sir Charles Sherrington's description:

'The cell is a unit life. . . . The cell is not a polyphasic chemico-physical system merely. Many a mere drop of complex jelly could be that. The cell is a polyphasic chemical system which is integratively organized. Hence there comes about that it can answer to what is described as "life". . . .

'It is dynamic. It is energy-cycles, suites of oxidation and reduction, concatenation of ferment-actions. . . . We seem to watch battalions of specific catalysts, like Maxwell's "demons", lined up, each waiting, stop-watch in hand, for its moment to play the part assigned to it. Yet each step is understandable chemistry.'[1]

This description in a manner sums up all we have said in the last two chapters about life, its distinction from the non-living and the transition between them. Here we have self-enfoldment upon self-enfoldment; complex molecules compounded into polypeptide and polynucleotide chains forming and reforming, reacting with other similarly extravagant and convoluted molecules, shedding and absorbing energy at the bidding of an array of varied and intensely specific catalysts. Here we have a bewildering advance in complexification resulting in fantastic new properties and propensities.

The cell (apart from bacteria, which seem almost to be the counterpart in miniature of cells) is the smallest living organism, related by continuous evolutionary development to ourselves. It is a self-maintaining system of chemical processes, the distinguishing character of which is its specifically auturgic form of organiza-

[1] *Man on His Nature* (Cambridge University Press, 1951), pp. 66 and 70.

tion. It is no *mere* aggregate of chemical compounds or of synthetic processes in equilibrium (though, of course, it is both), but is a systematically structured, organized and temporally ordered web of chemical interaction regulating itself for self-maintenance and displaying an (as yet) scientifically inexplicable nisus towards order and elaboration of coherent structure that runs counter to thermodynamic probability. This nisus forbids it to remain a mere cell and, as by an inner necessity, conducts the natural hierarchy, through the process of living development, to further self-enfoldments, greater complexification and more prolific versatility of performance.

The argument of this chapter is, in outline, to be (i) that a condition of self-maintenance is renewal of substance and a consequence of that is growth, (ii) that growth compatible with self-maintenance necessitates reproduction and differentiation, (iii) that reproduction and differentiation together issue in development, and (iv) that the course of living development is a unified totality marked by relevant variation in changing conditions—a polyphasic unity at a new and higher level. These points will be treated successively in the following sections.

2

Constant renewal by synthesis of essential substances constituting the system was one of the conditions of the self-maintenance of an open chemical system which was noted in Chapter VIII. This, in certain circumstances, results in growth. Any set of synthetic processes is liable to produce an accumulation of compounds unless the rate of their breakdown exceeds that of their synthesis, and an open, self-regulating system is especially suited to effect this augmentation of its own substance. Once the system has attained a degree of coherence comparable with cell organization, however, simple accumulation is not only uncharacteristic, but is inimical to it. If material increase continues beyond a certain limit the structure may become unstable and fall apart. Surface tensions or the strength of containing membranes will prove insufficient to hold it together and, if it is to survive, it will need some kind of rigid support to keep it intact. Again, volume increases as the cube of the linear dimensions, whereas area increases only as the square. Accordingly, functions upon which the maintenance of the system depends and which can be carried out only on surfaces (e.g. intake of oxygen) are liable to become deficient as bulk increases. Further, Julius Sachs came to the conclusion that there is an optimal size within which metabolic processes can be efficiently carried out, so that even a multiplication of undifferentiated cells, mutually dependent for their internal metabolic transformations, is by itself detrimental to efficient self-maintenance. Increase in size, therefore, endangers the persistence of the system, unless some form of adjustment or adaptation can be made to the new situation it creates. Two such forms of adjustment are available and both are adopted either separately or together. First, the organism may split up into smaller systems similarly organized, initiating by so doing the process of reproduction. Secondly, it may differentiate its substance so that different parts perform different functions ministering to its self-maintenance. Preservation of the system along with increase in size, therefore, requires as its condition either reproduction or differentiation and elaboration of structure,[1] which prove to be necessary aspects of the auturgic character of the living organism. Mere growth in size could be simple increase in quantity of the products of metabolism, but if it were, reproduction and differentiation of function would be necessary for the survival of the system as a living organism and are thus aspects of the self-maintaining process and a logical manifestation of the tendency towards elaboration of systematic order.

But sheer accumulation of chemical substances is never the mark of a living system. Even when it occurs, it is invariably adapted to the requirements of self-maintenance. The quantities of synthesized materials are delicately regulated and balanced; compounds which have supplied energy in the course of their breakdown are either rebuilt in the cycles of metabolic activity or, if no longer usable, are ejected from the system, and those which have vital functions to perform are integrated into it. Any simple accumulation is in the service of such functions, as in the storage of carbohydrates in fatty tissues or of erythrocytes in the spleen. Similarly, as noted earlier, the crystalline silicious skeletons of diatoms and radiolaria, the calcite shells of foraminifera and the spicules of sponges, though true crystals, are not just crystalline accumulations growing according to the demands of molecular pattern. Their shape is not determined according to the normal crystalline structure of the materials, but in intricate patterns

[1] Cf. J. T. Bonner, *Morphogenesis*, pp. 15 ff.

G*

according to the functional needs of the organism. If accumulation of substance is not subordinated to any such functions it marks the breakdown of organization and in critical cases may be lethal.

Growth is never simply continuous accretion. It is strictly regulated to comply with the demands of organic and dynamic wholeness, according to a structural pattern. The rates of growth of various portions of the body of an organism are so regulated as to maintain proper proportions in size necessary for efficient functioning. For example, deer shed their antlers each winter and regenerate them in the spring. The initial rate of growth of the new antlers is faster each year but gradually decreases to stop when there is a precise relationship between the weight of the antler and the body weight of the deer.[1] This ratio is maintained constant from year to year, and has obvious importance for balance, strength and the efficient use of its antlers in combat by the deer. As the tennis player suits the weight of his racquet to his own size and strength, so the weight of the deer's antlers are adjusted to its size and strength. Transplantation experiments have shown that the eyes of certain amphibians, transplanted to hosts of the same species but of different ages, grow at different rates, according as they are too big or too small in relation to their hosts, until the disproportion has been rectified.[2]

Illustrations of this principle are ubiquitous in biology. Growth is regulated to maintain the system in innumerable ways. As weight increases in proportion to volume and the strength of its supports is dependent on the area of their cross-section, the means of support must become relatively thicker. Thus the leg-bones of mammals are proportionately shorter and stouter as the animal becomes larger and heavier.[3] The stalks of mushrooms are similarly related to the weight of their caps and the girth of trees to their height. Again respiring tissues increase in volume whereas the quantity of gas exchange depends on the area of surface; accordingly, as organisms increase in size their respiratory organs are of corresponding complexity. Another example is found in the young sponge, which

---

[1] Cf. J. S. Huxley, *Problems in Relative Growth*, London, 1932.

[2] *Vide* V. C. Twitty, 'Size-controlling factors', *Growth Symposium* 4, 1940; Bonner, op. cit., p. 141.

[3] 'An exception proving the rule is the hippopotamus whose comparatively thin legs are explicable by its aquatic way of life—its weight being partially supported by the water.'

being small and having few flagellated collar cells, would not be able to eject water to a sufficient distance to prevent its being sucked in over and over again, the small organism, however, has an osculum chimney that is relatively enormous and so prevents this repetition. As the sponge grows and the number and size of its flagellated collar cells increase, the added velocity they give to the water expel it to a distance sufficient to dispense with so disproportionate a ventpipe, which relative to the growing size of the sponge becomes insignificant.[1]

Explanations of these differential rates of growth have been suggested in terms of chemical gradients and the influence of hormones as well as of the operation of the genes, and Bonner declares that if we understood more fully the mechanisms by which growth is controlled we should 'not be so bothered by the wholeness of the organism'.

As a comment upon the psychology of scientists, this remark is perspicacious. Scientists in the main are very apt to allow themselves to be distracted from the comprehensive structure of their object by the mechanical details of its working parts. It is the old story of the wood and the trees; and usually the excitement and the triumph of discovery attending the disclosure of the mechanics of minute and recondite processes diverts attention from the way in which these processes fit together and are mutually interwoven. The 'mechanics' of the interweaving, the source and origin of the overall pattern is then apt to be forgotten. It no longer seems important and the demand for its elucidation is neglected. But such neglect is to be deplored because 'the wholeness of the organism' is its major distinguishing character as a living entity, and we undoubtedly ought to 'be bothered by' it. However well the mechanics of control were known the harmony of the processes and pattern of the product would still require explanation. Bonner himself asks for the cause of the distribution and total pattern of metabolic gradients[2] and confesses that, 'there is a general theory to cover every aspect of the control of growth save one, and that is the problem of the *configuration within the whole organism*'.[3] We must, therefore, above all 'be bothered by the wholeness of the organism' if we are to find any satisfactory scientific account of its biological character. And it is this whole-

[1] Examples from Bonner, op. cit.
[2] Op. cit., p. 133.
[3] *Ibid.*, p. 147 (His italics).

ness that repeatedly impresses itself upon us and incessantly reveals itself in the regulation of processes of growth. It manifests itself in the uncanny precision with which specific form is maintained by the organism—what Noll referred to as 'morphaesthesia'. 'Again and again', writes Bonner, 'at every turn, with every new example, we are faced with the fact that developmental processes are controlled and regulated within living organisms in a spatial configuration that respects the whole. . . .'[1]

3

Accordingly, it is the auturgy of the organism, the systematic self-maintenance of the organized totality, that expresses itself in and through growth. Constant renewal of its substance is a condition of this, but accumulation of vital material must of necessity, to meet the needs of survival imposed upon it by mere geometry, issue either in division and reduplication of the organism (to prevent excessive and destructive accumulations), or in diversification of function and of structure to support and adapt to the increased bulk; and growth forthwith is regulated subject to the demands of structure and function. That both the alternatives, reproduction and differentiation, should in fact occur, separately and in conjunction, is wholly in accordance with the logic of the situation; whichever eventuates and how being a matter which local and particular circumstances would determine.

In minute organisms like bacteria and Protozoa chemical interactions requisite to the continuance of the system take place at the interface between the system and the medium in which it lives. With growth the ratio of surface to volume changes and the proper relations between chemical processes is maintained by division of the organism, on achieving a critical size, into two similar organisms. The process of fission is not entirely simple (in some Protozoa it is remarkably complex) and probably any explanation purely in terms of geometrical proportions would be far from complete. Nevertheless, the sort of proportional change naturally brought about by growth would make some kind of reproduction by fission necessary in the absence of differentiation of some other kind—for reproduction by simple fission is differentiation of a sort, if only through replication and multiplicity, and for bacteria and Protozoa it is obviously a means of prolonging

[1] Examples from Bonner, pp. 114–15.

the existence of the living system and of preserving its form of organization. It is thus essentially a process of self-maintenance.

The relatively simple method of binary fission is in some cases complicated by the fragmentation of the organism into numerous offspring, and the method of reproduction by division is not confined to the simplest of organisms. Sea-anemonies sometimes reproduce by splitting in half and some annelid worms shed their tails, which, developing new heads, become separate individuals. A kindred type of reproduction in colonial forms (like hydroid polyps) is budding, and all these methods of asexual reproduction are recognized by the biologist as forms or modifications of growth. 'It is evident', write Wells and Huxley, ' . . . that reproduction is essentially nothing more than a special type of growth. It is growth accompanied by detachment. A bit of the parent body is split off: a piece of living substance, instead of growing on as a part, grows into a new whole.'[1]

Though a sufficient condition for differentiation, growth is obviously not a necessary condition, for any system displaying the characteristics of life must already be highly differentiated. Even the simplest living entities, bacteria and one-celled animalcules, are internally far from homogeneous. The single cell is a complicated system of interacting substances and includes manifest differences between nucleus and cytoplasm, as well as specialized bodies (Golgi bodies, mitochondria, ribosomes and the like). Unicellular organisms possess organelles and are variously structured according to species. So long as the organism is alive its internal processes and overt activity are persistently constructive. The single system displays a palpable effort towards proliferation and diversification, and these are both concomitant with growth. Reproduction by division may reasonably be viewed as a form of differentiation inasmuch as it also produces multiplicity and variety out of what was originally less diversified unity. Yet at some stage conditions must have favoured the survival of organisms whose cells, after division, remained in association or (like the slime moulds, *Acrasiaceae*) mobilized to form conglomerations after a term of separate existence.

Forms of colonial organisms, however, present a new phase of differentiation. They are, as it were, alternative ways of solving the problem of growth. The slime moulds execute different vital functions in different phases of their life cycle, first feeding and

[1] *The Science of Life* (London, 1938), p. 502.

multiplying in separation and then fruiting and reproducing in conjoint and associative activity. Colonial forms, like the hydroid polyp, though constituted of originally identical cells, differentiate their form and function in association in the most diverse fashion. *Hydractinia*, for example, is thus described by Bonner:

'It forms a mat on the mollusc shells inhabited by hermit crabs. From the mat, which is largely a tangle of stolons, arise zooids . . . and these vary in their structure. There are those which closely resemble *Hydra*, which are feeding polyps; there are protective polyps which have no mouths or tentacles but instead have mace-like knobs which stud their tips; another type of protective polyp which lacks apical knobs will often be found specifically along the edge of the colony; and finally there are the male polyps and the female polyps which carry the sperm and the eggs.'[1]

Yet all these varied forms co-operate in systematic and co-ordinated fashion to maintain the life of the colony as a whole. All the differences are expressions of, and are determined by, the one principle of order and unity that constitutes the whole. The life of the organism as an integrated system is the unity to which all these different phases and functions are variously relevant. They are the facets and manifestations of the polyphasic unity, raised to a new level of complexity.

So growth and differentiation co-operate auturgically to maintain the system. The source of differentiation, which is always more improbable than simple aggregation, could hardly have been mere random variation; still less is the precisely appropriate variation sufficiently probable to be adequately explained by pure chance. Growth and differentiation are continuous with metabolism, and all are aspects of the ceaseless living activity of the organism. The general effect of this activity is construction and maintenance of its own intricately diversified system of organization, in itself a highly improbable structure needing constant effort and absorption of energy for its maintenance. Destruction of the organization is death, and once the organism is deprived of life by whatever means, the processes of self-maintenance cease, the nisus against probability is reversed and, even though the same chemical substances may still be present, the physico-chemical processes which ensue tend towards disorder and the increase of

[1] *Morphogenesis*, p. 266.

entropy in a direction opposite to that which typifies life.[1] The accretion of protoplasm which growth represents, if it followed the most probable course, would simply choke out the life of the organism by increasing its size incompatibly with vital functions; but by adopting the less probable course of functional differentiation and adaptation, the system maintains itself in being and its various structures and processes are co-ordinated by the unifying principle of its individual wholeness. It is the life of the organism which demands the mutually supporting interplay of functions; and if this life is to be preserved, the organism cannot grow indefinitely without either fission or internal specialization. So the course of evolution tends in the main[2] towards increasing complexity in the interplay of specialized organs and functions and the organization of living things becomes progressively more elaborate.

4

The process of diversification soon arrives at a stage in which one of the functions separated from the rest and reserved for a segregated group of cells is reproduction itself. To preserve its order and system the organism must somehow keep at bay the everthreatening tide of entropy. For this the increasing complexity of its metabolism seems not to be sufficient and some means of constant renewal and refreshment is required. How this rejuvenation is effected is unknown, yet it evidently occurs. The mere division of the organism can hardly result in rejuvenation without some further factor and whatever that additional factor may be it seems to be especially present in the replication of the special cells which, in more complex forms, are set aside to perform the function of reproduction. This specialization is evident in colonial organisms, such as *Obelia*, which though they consist of polyps living and thriving in concert, growing and budding and enlarging the colony by the production of new hydranths, also produce blastostyles, which do not feed but absorb the vital juices of the feeding colony and concentrate on the production of new organisms, free-swimming medusae, which when fully developed break away to found new colonies. So also the sponge,

[1] Cf. Lillie, op. cit., pp. 85–6, and von Bertalanffy, *Modern Theories of Development*, pp. 32–5.
[2] There are exceptions, which however have exceptional explanations. See below, pp. 251 and 273.

though it grows and reticulates in a compact colonial mass, produces its 'gemmules', segregated and enclosed masses of renewed and reproductive cells, which regenerate new sponges on the decay of the old. Yet, like so many other lowly and relatively unindividualized creatures, it also adopts a sexual form of reproduction resulting in free-swimming larvae.

The evolution of sexual methods may be connected with the need for metabolic rejuvenation, for these involve, first fission of the cells in the gonad from which the gametes arise, and then fusion of the male and female gametes to form the zygote. Fusion, known as 'conjugation', also occurs between protozoans, and apparently has rejuvenating effects. This is not the same as sexual reproduction, though it has comparable features. There is an exchange of genetic material, and in some species (e.g. *Paramoecium*) the new combined organism redivides after the merging and redistribution of nuclear substance. *Paramoecium* carries, besides its ordinary (macro-) nucleus a second (micro-) nucleus which appears to be some kind of reserve of genetic material. It can reproduce for many hundreds of generations without conjugation, but when this occurs, a stage is reached in which (it is found) the macro-nucleus disintegrates while the micro-nucleus grows, divides and reconstitutes both macro- and micro-nuclei in the daughter organisms. But over and above this, the mixture of heritable material from different organisms provides a greater range of variations and enriches the possibilities for selection. It has been suggested, therefore, that sexual reproduction has developed in the interests of the evolutionary process, and if this were the case, the differentiation of sexual forms would seem to be auturgic, for it would then be a method of self-maintenance and of increasing and improving the adaptability through which the principle of polyphasic unity in the organism expressed its nisus towards self-elaboration.

It is clear that the segregation of reproductive cells, whether they be spores or gemmules or gametes, imposes on the organism the necessity of development from the single cell stage in which it is comparatively undifferentiated, to the more elaborate and diversified condition of the mature organism. Thus in the life of the single creature the process of differentiation from the single cell to the multicellular form which has characterized the evolutionary process must be repeated. The theory that in embryogenesis we witness a measure of recapitulation of the evolutionary process, by which the species came into existence, though now out of fashion, is no incredible speculation, for it would be a natural result of the process of growth and of consequent differentiation. So we are led to consider development as a natural manifestation of the general tendency of living systems to maintain themselves in varying conditions—conditions in significant measure created by their own activity of self-maintenance through metabolism, growth and self-diversification. There are two kinds of development, of which embryonic is the primary form and regeneration is the more obviously a form of self-maintenance. But what is manifest in both is the dominance of the whole and its constitutive principle of organization over every phase of the process, the immanence of the whole in the part, and the regulation of the morphological process by the structural pattern of the total organism.

Embryonic development may be regarded as the first main episode in a longer process of maturation, which may in some cases (insects, for instance) involve several distinct periods (e.g. larval, pupal and adult). Different biologists analyse the developmental process differently. P. Weiss[1] distinguishes four aspects: tactical displacements, internal organization, histological differentiation and growth. Waddington[2] distinguishes three: segregation or regionalization, by which different parts of an embryo become specialized in form and function, histogenesis or the gradual change in character of any one particular region, and morphogenesis or the moulding of the particular part into a specific form. These aspects may constitute relatively independent processes going on separately or together or they may be simultaneous and mutually interdependent.

That a complex substance should change its form with time is neither mysterious nor remarkable, for this is the effect of all chemical interaction; that such change should affect the shape of its agglomerations is no more surprising; but that chemical changes and alterations of shape should be regulated and ordered to a definite and precisely repeated plan demands explanation more difficult to come by. The process of segregation or regionalization (sometimes called 'determination') may be effected either early in the process, as in so-called 'mosaic' eggs, by the separation within the fertilized ovum of various chemical substances. Or the

[1] *Entwicklungsphysiologie der Tiere* (1930).
[2] *The Strategy of the Genes* (New York, 1957).

determination of different potentialities may occur at a later stage after the cell has segmented and multiplied many times, so that the differentiation is between different cells and not internal to any one. In mosaic eggs, different substances are segregated after fertilization during a phase in which the cytoplasm is in a highly fluid state. Then, when the segregation is completed the protoplasm becomes suddenly viscous fixing the position of the segregated substances. Their mutual disposition is thus established before the first cleavage, so that subsequent segmentation largely effects the separation of substances which become different tissues and organs.[1] This process of differentiation in the egg is one which obviously must require energy. It runs directly counter to the disordering tendency of normal diffusion which results in uniform mixture. It is not due simply to gravity, for before fertilization the substances later separated are more uniformly distributed throughout the egg. Their separation, moreover, is precisely the kind of order—sorting out into like kinds—the dissipation of which is measured by entropy. The moment of increased viscosity undoubtedly marks the operation of some definite (as yet unknown) physico-chemical cause;[2] but what determines that it should occur just at the right time, neither before the separation is complete, nor after the fluidity of the protoplasm might have permitted subsequent diffusion? What directs the chemical substances into their proper positions? What stimulates cell division precisely when it is appropriate to distribute the segregated substances? These are the relevant questions and they could be properly answered only by reference to the total systematic plan of the life of the organism, its anatomical structure, the physiological functions of its parts, the temporal pattern of its life cycle which the processes contribute to constitute—in short, the establishment and maintenance of a specific ordered totality of high complexity.

5

In regulative development the presiding influence of the whole and its organizing principle is patent throughout. The holistic principle persistently asserts itself in the process, so that cells normally destined to become one kind of tissue or organ can develop into

[1] Cf. Bonner, op. cit., pp. 235-8 and Conklin, E. G. (1931) in *Journal of Experimental Zoology*, 60, pp. 1-119.

[2] Some kind of crystallization or gellation has been suggested.

something quite different if, through damage or distortion, the normal process of embryonic development is disturbed so as to threaten the integrity of the organic pattern. Thus the blastomeres of the first cleavage of the egg can develop either into complementary halves of the embryo (if left in conjunction) or, if separated, each into a complete organism. Selected groups of cells constituting even smaller fractions of the whole, if cut off at the blastula stage can reconstitute themselves into a whole embryo. Within limits, cells already to some extent differentiated, when they are separated from the rest, may undergo some degree of de-differentiation and reorganization to effect this result. The same nisus towards wholeness is seen in partial phases of ontogenesis. Fragments of the eye-cup, at a certain stage of development, will if separated from the rest form complete but diminutive eyes perfect in shape and structure.

The slime mould, *Dictyostelium*, displays a phase of development in which separate amoeboid cells collect together to form a single mass, migrate in concert, like a minute slug, and proceed to develop into a delicately stalked sporangium. Though in the earlier phases all the cells are indistinguishably the same, in the last phase there is distinct differentiation, some becoming large and vacuolated with a cellulose sheath to form the pedestal and stalk, and others becoming encapsulated spores. Which cells are to become the stalk cells and which are to become the spores seems to depend entirely on the order in which they enter the aggregation, and if part of the migrating mass is cut away, the remaining cells regulate so as to form a normal sporangium.

But quite apart from the regulation of development when its proper course has been disturbed, the normal process of embryogenesis in the higher species of animal is the automatic generation from a single cell of an intricately integrated totality of a complexity that staggers the imagination, and one in which every detail is governed by the whole to which it belongs and the requirements of its subsequent self-maintenance. The fertilized egg by innumerable divisions gives rise to million upon million of new cells modified in form and character beyond any recognizable likeness to itself. These cells are specified and differentiated in multiple ways and relatively few retain any likeness to the original cell or its capacity for reproducing the entire system. The first group of daughter cells resemble one another but at the end of the process of embryogenesis they have proliferated into liver cells, nerve cells, muscle cells, epidermis, erythrocytes, phagocytes and hundreds of other mutually remote varieties. Sherrington creates for us the bewildering picture:

'The cells of the various parts of the systematized assembly assume special shapes, octagonal, stellate, threadlike or what not. They, as the case may require, pour out cement which binds, or fluid in which they shall move free. Some will have changed their stuff and become rigid bone or, harder still, the enamel of a tooth; some become fluid, so to flow along tubes too fine for the eye to see. Some become clear as glass, some opaque as stone, some colourless, some red, some black. Some become factories of a furious chemistry, some become inert as death. Some become engines of mechanical pull, some scaffoldings of static support. Some a system transmitting electrical signs. It might serve as a text for democracy. It is as if the life of each one of all those millions has understood its special part. Thus arises the new integral individual to be.'[1]

Not only does this proliferation and diversification of cells occur, but they all take their appointed places within the system, they regiment themselves in proper formation and position to constitute organs interconnected to perform mutually sustaining functions. Sherrington quotes E. G. Drury's description of the spectacle as seen in a motion-picture taken through a microscope: 'Team-work by cell-masses. Chalky spicules of bone-in-the-making shot across the screen, as if labourers were raising scaffold poles. The scene suggested purposive behaviour by cells, and still more by colonies of cells arranged as tissues and organs.'[2]

The notes of the theme-song of the whole developmental process are variety, integration, system, structure, interdependence of whole and parts. The product is a patterned unity expressing itself in a vast variety of co-operating structures, and even the process of its generation is a unified whole in which every phase still figures forth the totality.

The course of the development is threefold. First there is repeated division of the egg-cell into a group of cells all with similar potentialities. Then there is a segregation into sub-

[1] *Man on his Nature*, pp. 94-5.
[2] *'Psyche and Physiologists', and other Essays on Sensation* (London, 1938), p. 4.

ordinate groups each determined to produce its own special tissue, limb or organ. Within each of these subordinate regions the same process continues of initial equipotentiality within the limits of the regional determination and subsequent irreversible specialization. Finally all the separately developing specialized regions are linked together and coherently co-ordinated by the formation of nervous and vascular systems enabling the whole polity of organic functions to minister to the health and efficiency of one another and of the whole. The entire developmental process is a polyphasic system spread out in time, governed throughout by the unifying principle of the organism that is developing.

6

Though in this stupendous diversification the reproductive cells are segregated and are the only ones that retain the full capacity to reproduce the total organism, there are others which always possess in some measure the same creative potentiality; so that if certain limbs or organs are damaged or removed they can, from these cells be regenerated. The same character of regulation by the whole is displayed in such regenerative processes and the same potency in cells to vary their function and products to meet the changing needs of the organism. The healing of wounds is the simplest example and, as described by Russell, is marked by the activity of the cells bordering the lesion which spread out, thinly at first, to cover the wound. Cell division takes place in the peripheral zone and more cells migrate to increase the cover until the density of the new membrane is sufficient. In the case of burns, cell-division occurs in the zone of spreading between the burned cells and the cuticle, not in the peripheral zone. What is remarkable here is that in the earlier phases of the process, before new cuticle has formed to cover the healing wound, the epidermal cells, migrating to replace lost tissue, form a layer thicker than is eventually needed, but thin out by cell degeneration after the cuticle has been reformed. The nisus is towards the normal density and distribution and the norm is set by the demands of organic integrity in the body as a whole. But the process is varied to meet the momentary need as the exigency of the situation demands in the interests of self-maintenance, so that the norm is reached, not directly, but by means adapted to the changing circumstances of internal and external environment.

A further fact to be explained is that cells normally fixed and sedentary suddenly migrate to form protective covering and new tissue. Clearly, the excision of the portion that causes the wound gives room for movement. It has also been suggested, that the cells are activated chemically by the products of protein degradation issuing from the damaged tissue. For the manner of their spreading no real explanation has yet been proposed beyond the postulation of a tendency in some organic structures, when they move, to follow along flat surfaces. The name given to this tendency is 'thigmotaxis'. The absence of continuity where the epidermis has been burned or cut away may also stimulate the surrounding cells to reach out and move into the space left by those that have been destroyed until continuity has been re-established. But all these speculations rightly or wrongly suggest a kind of sensitivity in the cell, which, dependent though it may be upon chemical and physical factors, implies some sort of rudimentary or inchoate consciousness. What, in purely chemical or mechanical terms, is sensitivity to and stimulation by protein degradation products, such that it produces movement in the right direction? How, in such terms, can the absence of continuity stimulate movement? Is 'thigmotaxis' anything intelligible without the tacit assumption of some sort of tactile sensation? It would be preposterous to suggest that the cells are aware of their surroundings and know what they are doing, and a more credible explanation is surely conceivable, but it can hardly be denied that every detail of the processes and movements here involved are somehow informed by, and directed in accordance with, the total situation and the systematic structure of the organism.

Flatworms cut even into quite small pieces grow new heads and tails by reorganizing their substance and no matter at what angle they are cut will remodel themselves to become properly proportioned creatures.[1] The ascidian, *Clavellina* when mutilated degenerates and then by reorganizing its substance reconstitutes a new, perfect but smaller ascidian. Here and in other animals it has been shown that the regeneration is effected by reserve cells (blastema) which have remained embryonic and relatively undifferentiated. They move to the site of regeneration from other parts of the organism and become differentiated to effect the growth of the new parts, once more as if they knew what was

---

[1] If the cut is very close to the head, a double head results, but no tail.

happening, were aware of what was required of them, and could discover where their activity was most needed.[1]

Here again there is first general potency and then progressive determination of the cells, a fact which displays itself in many cases of limb-regeneration in amphibians and other animals where the restoration is effected by the cells of the stump; and the new limb is always characteristic of these even when the stump is a transplant that has been experimentally amputated and differs from its host. For all this explanations have been sought, often with considerable success, in terms of chemical organizers; but such explanations do not detract from the holistic nature of the phenomena (as the name 'organizers' implies), for the plan of organization, the distribution of 'organizers' and the manner of their operation are all systematically related to constitute an integrated whole. When 'determination' occurs, it is in the required pattern and once it has occurred the pattern is retained, even when 'determined' parts are experimentally transferred to other parts of the organism. The freak effects are no more than an artificial displacement of the structure of the whole which is still asserting itself in the distortion.

A similar manifestation of regenerative regulation in somewhat different circumstances occurs in the unicellular *Stylonychia*, one of the most elaborately differentiated of Protozoa. If starved, this little animal shrinks in size continually rearranging its substance to maintain its organization and the correct relations and proportions between its parts. But perhaps the most spectacular of all such feats is that performed by sponges and by hydra. These organisms may be forced through fine muslin so that their cells become separated from one another. The separated cells will then connect and adhere together to reconstitute the complete animal. It is not clear in such instances whether the cells are equipotential (each capable of performing any of the varied functions required in the normal organism) or if different cells collect together according to their specific types and then move into the position where their function has to be performed. In either case the directing influence of the whole is apparent.

Such self-regulating systems were called by Driesch equipotential systems in which any unit constituent has equal potentiality to become either the whole or any part of the whole de-

[1] *Vide* Bertalanffy, *Modern Theories of Development*, pp. 168 ff.

veloped creature. This kind of system clearly exemplifies further, at a higher degree of elaboration, a unity which is polyphasically differentiated, which asserts itself through different yet complementary phases mutually dependent and supporting, which is organized both in space and in time. The principle of unity and order in the organism governs the temporal process of development in such a way that it can be varied in varying circumstances to produce the same final result, just as the organism maintains its own life in different ways to suit different conditions. The creature and its development are but two aspects of one unity displaying and expressing its identity in a repertoire of different forms which, however diverse, are nevertheless always appropriate to the demands of its immanent architectonic. That the details of any developmental process are physico-chemical reactions proceeding in accordance with physico-chemical laws is virtually undeniable, but this fact does not affect the polyphasic and holistic character of the organism, of its generation and of its life-history. The various explanatory scientific theories which are currently favoured abjure vitalism and the entelechies of Driesch, and rightly so; but they all acknowledge the holistic nature of the *explicandum*. Biologists are in broad agreement that the special character of their object and the central issue for elucidation is organization; and the patent facts before us and the only ones relevant to our present thesis give evidence of a continuing process of increasing organization, occurring in such a way as strongly to suggest an immanent nisus in the direction of more diversified and more integral wholeness, despite and even with the help of the thermodynamic shuffling, increasing entropy, to which the process runs counter.

CHAPTER XI

HOMEOSTASIS AND RELEVANT VARIATION

After renewal of substance (issuing in growth, reproduction, differentiation and development), the second condition of the self-maintenance of an open system is homeostasis—the constancy of certain essential internal conditions characterizing the specific steady state of its processes. The holism of the organism and its auturgy are markedly displayed in this property. The subordination of particular parts and processes to a governing principle of order, and the plasticity of structure and of internal relationships within the system, permitting adjustments relevant to this central principle, are all impressively illustrated in the versatility with which homeostasis is sustained. The more complex the organism the more conspicuous these characteristics become, and complexity itself we have seen to be the outcome of self-adjustment in growth, through differentiation, to the demands of viability.

Even unicellular animals maintain a steady supply of needed substances by regulating their behaviour appropriately. *Amoeba* keeps its water content constant by continually ejecting the surplus from its contractile vacuole to counteract osmotic absorption due to the dissolved substances in its own protoplasm. *Arcella* and *Paramoecium* move with the oxygen supply to keep it adequate. But for the most part conditions to which the lowlier creatures have to adjust are those of their immediate external surrounding which is usually water. As we go up the phylogenetic scale there is a progressive domestication of the external environment and the formation within the anatomy of the organism of what Claude Bernard called '*le milieu intérieur*'.[1] Maintenance of the living system thus comes to depend upon the constancy with which favourable conditions persist in the internal environment, and the means by which this constancy is achieved and retained illustrate impressively the organic wholeness that has been emphasized in other connections.

Though homeostasis (a term adopted by W. B. Cannon) applies

[1] Reptiles preserve in their bloodstream the same saline constitution as the primeval seas in which the earlier aquatic orders lived and our own mammalian blood, by descent from them, has a similar salinity.

properly only to the constancy of the internal environment and to the maintenance in a steady state of some dynamic equilibrium, it may without undue distortion be used also of the maintenance of nomality in the structure of living bodies the material of which is almost wholly and constantly in a state of flux. A not unsuitable example of this type of auturgy is provided by the acquisition and disposal of nematocysts by the Tubellarian Rhabdocoele, *Microstoma*.[1] Evenly distributed over its epidermis, this creature has nematocysts, lashing and penetrating threads which are released by prey brushing against them. These nematocysts are not originally part of the body of *Microstoma* but are acquired by the ingestion of *Hydroids*. Microstoma, at considerable risk to itself, will attack *Hydra*, paralyse it by means of a secretion, devour it and digest all the soft parts. The cnidoblasts carrying nematocysts are passed from the endoderm to the mesoderm, each by one of the mesenchyme cells, which transports it to the ectoderm. Each cell acts apparently independently and carries its cnidoblast to the surface in such a way as to produce a uniform distribution over the skin of properly oriented nematocysts. The movement of the carrier cells is thus controlled and directed in accordance with the over-all pattern and functional organization of the creature.

More than this, however, if *Microstoma* is sufficiently provided with nematocysts, it will not attack *Hydra*, unless starved of other food. Then it digests the soft parts and rejects the nematocysts. Yet it will attack even if otherwise well nourished if its supply of nematocysts is inadequate. Obviously its behaviour is governed by the state of the system and ministers to it so as to maintain a normal arrangement and restore it when disturbed.

Kepner and his co-workers experimented with *Microstoma* and the green Hydra (*Chlorohydra viridissima*) which has four kinds of nematocysts, two of the stinging type and two which serve only to hold the prey. They found that though all were taken into the mesoderm of *Microstoma* the holding type were then rejected while the penetrating type were transferred to the ectoderm. For a creature without tentacles, Kepner remarks, the adhesive type of nematocyst would be only a hindrance.[2] These rejected nemato-

---

[1] *Vide* L. H. Hyman, *The Invertebrates*, Vol. II (McGraw Hill Co., New York, 1951), pp. 71–72, and E. S. Russell, *The Directiveness of Organic Activity*, pp. 23–27.

[2] W. A. Kepner, W. C. Gregory and R. Porter, *Zool. Anz.*, CXXI, pp. 114–24 (1938), quoted by E. S. Russell, op. cit.

cysts are digested by phagocytic parenchyma cells, and even the penetrants, when the epidermis is fully stocked, will be ejected by the endoderm. The norm is respected in all circumstances.

The regulations of multiple processes by different methods to produce the same end result is here unmistakable, providing a remarkable instance of the auturgic adjustment of the organism to external and internal needs. It is an adaptation not simply self-activated but variable in a manner obviously directed by the integrating principle of the organism, which adjusts each particular phase and movement so as to mesh with every other in accordance with the pattern of the whole.

The most spectacular examples, however, of control of physiological processes for homeostasis occur in the mammalian body. Here the blood and the lymph constitute the internal environment in which the body cells live, and the blood-contents of water, oxygen, sugar, salt, protein and fat as well as neutrality between acid and alkali, are all regulated within strict limits by the most intricate and delicate interplay of mutually adjusted processes. In the case of protein, fat and calcium this is done largely by storage of surplus, and release of stored material in times of dearth. The control of other factors is more complex and ingenious. The means of attaining the required condition vary with the circumstances relevantly to the body's need and the failure of one device is compensated by resort to another.

Loss of water through perspiration, breathing, urination or haemorrhage is compensated by drawing upon stores in the skin, muscles and connective tissue depriving the salivary (among other) glands of their supply. This produces unpleasant dryness in the mouth and larynx which, as thirst, stimulates the animal to drink and restore the supply of water to the body. Loss of water from the tissues also stimulates the secretion of pituitrin which has an anti-diuretic effect and so checks the output of water through the kidneys. With excessive intake of water, on the other hand, the secretion of pituitrin is inhibited and expulsion through the kidneys proportionately increased. If, however, the posterior lobe of the pituitary body is excised and water is consequently lost through excessive diuresis, thirst is greatly increased and the loss of water is compensated by drinking abnormally large quantities of liquid.

What is most notable is that in all these variations of intake and output the water content of the blood remains virtually unchanged.

Uncompensated loss of water for as long as three days makes scarcely any perceptible difference to the blood content. On the other hand excessive intake, to the amount of a quart an hour for six hours, though accompanied by a greatly increased output through the kidneys, has been found to cause no appreciable dilution of the blood.

In the maintenance of the oxygen supply through respiration and blood circulation, Cannon lists no fewer than fourteen contributory and interdependent processes. Strenuous muscular activity burns up glucose and produces lactic acid so creating an 'oxygen debt' and an excess of carbon dioxide. To meet this, first, the innervation initiating the activity also excites deeper respiration, which is then automatically kept up, during and after the activity, through the stimulation of the respiratory centres in the brain by the excess of carbon dioxide. Vasomotor nerves contract the blood vessels of the stomach and intestine increasing the flow of blood to the heart, brain and muscles. The contraction of the muscles massages the veins running through them and so accelerates the blood-flow to the heart. Simultaneously the diaphragm presses down on the contents of the abdomen and releases pressure in the cavity of the thorax, so venous blood from the legs is pressed upwards while that from the arms and upper parts of the body is drawn inwards. In these ways the blood overcharged with carbon dioxide and lactic acid is rushed to the heart and lungs for ventilation. Meanwhile, the heart-stroke is increased by the stimulation of increasing pressure of the venous blood and so expels the aerated blood more strongly and efficiently into the arteries. Further, the influence of the vagus nerve upon the heart is inhibited increasing the rate of its beat, which is further stimulated by the secretion into the bloodstream of adrenin through stimulation of the sympathetic nervous system. At the same time the adrenin relaxes the muscles of the bronchial tubes permitting the easier passage of air and facilitating deeper breathing. The same activity of the sympathetico-adrenal system dilates the capillaries and arterioles and increases the blood pressure. It also raises the temperature which speeds up combustion and oxidation processes as the passage of the oxygenated blood is accelerated. The consumption of oxygen in the lymph leaves a higher diffusion gradient for absorption, while more vigorous respiration heightens the oxygen pressure in the lungs and expels the carbon dioxide from the haemoglobin in which oxygen has been depleted in circulation.

Meanwhile (in many animals) the spleen also contracts enriching the blood with extra red corpuscles better to absorb the larger supplies of oxygen.

The homeostasis of blood sugar is maintained by a similar complex of delicately adjusted processes, involving the secretion of insulin from the pancreas when sugar is excessive to facilitate its conversion to glycogen and storage in the liver and elsewhere.

Another equally involved system for homeostasis is that by which body temperature is kept regulated in homoiothermic animals, by changes in the basic metabolic rate, as a result of secretion from the thyroid and pituitary glands. Accompanying these changes is an elaborate organization of processes to counteract excessive heat or cold. Increased evaporation of sweat from the skin and (through panting) from the respiratory tract reduces temperature when heat is excessive. Increased blood-sugar and speedier heart beat stimulated by sympathetico-adrenal action, and automatic muscular activity in shivering, generate heat when the temperature falls too low. All this is dependent upon a highly sensitive thermostat, the nature and working of which is not known, apparently lodged in the diencephelon (the central portion of the brain), which is stimulated by temperature changes of the blood as well as by impulses from the tactile nerve-endings in the skin.

There is no need to go into further detail nor to enumerate further examples. Those we have mentioned, though typical, are far from exhaustive, but they are sufficient evidence of a widespread, complex and highly efficient, capacity for self-adjustment to changing external conditions. In every case, if the usual resource fails or is put out of action, there is automatic variation of the method of re-establishing optimal conditions. The maintenance of blood pressure in the mammalian body is a striking case in point. In the first instance this is effected by the vaso-motor centre in the medulla oblongata, if that is injured subsidiary brain centres take over, if they in turn are eliminated the sympathetic ganglia stimulate the vessels and heart to the requisite changes, and if they are excluded the vascular wall, itself sensitive to pressure changes, makes the necessary adjustments.[1]

It is in fact by relying on this capacity of the organism to substitute one device for another that experimenters have been able to discover the great range of possibilities at its disposal.

[1] *Vide* Cannon, op. cit., p. 219.

For, by severing or altogether removing essential nervous connections to special organs they have eliminated in turn certain of
the normal adjustive processes and have been able to observe the
compensation made by the organism for this loss and the alternatives brought into play. So Cannon by depriving the heart of
nervous connections was able to observe the effect on its action of
adrenal and other glandular secretions, the effects of which often
reduplicate and can be substituted for those directly produced
by the sympathetic nervous system. Likewise by removing the
sympathetic ganglia and their nerve processes which activate so
many of the physiological reactions to cold, he was able to observe
the substitution of shivering for these reactions, for the maintenance of body temperature. Richter and Eckert in the same
manner observed the increased activity and efficiency of nest-
building in rats when their physiological capacity to regulate
body temperature was impaired by removal of the hypophysis and
consequent depression of their basic metabolism with general
reduction of other activities.[1] Here behavioural adjustment takes
the place of the physiological which it normally supplements. It
is, in fact, sometimes difficult to draw any sharp distinction between behaviour and physiological activity.

The significance of homeostasis is that it maintains some
condition—temperature, water content, oxygen supply, salinity,
or the like—at a level which makes possible the persistence of the
organic system of the living being. The dynamic order of chemical
interactions, which constitute the life of the organism is in
delicate equilibrium—'our stability is but balance'—and an
equilibrium which is actually very unstable and is easily upset.
'Our bodies' writes Cannon, 'are made of extraordinarily unstable
material.'[2] Our nerves and organs are sensitive to very minute
stimulations only recently rivalled by scientific instruments. The
cells of the brain disintegrate if deprived of blood for so short a
time as seven or eight minutes, and electric shock or brief deprivation of oxygen may so damage vital tissues that life is irrevo-
cably destroyed. The stability requisite for viability in the
changing conditions of the external environment is achieved,
in consequence, only by rapid, sensitive and delicate modifications
of internal processes, so as to keep the conditions constant within

[1] Cf. Cannon, *The Wisdom of the Body*, pp. 261–65; and Richter and
Eckert, *Proc. Ass. Res. Nerv. Ment. Dis.*, XVII, pp. 561–71.
[2] Op. cit., p. 19.

the narrow limits of which the unstable materials and equilibria can be maintained. These conditions therefore constitute a set of norms, in accordance with which the interplay of processes is regulated. At the same time the very instability and sensitivity of the materials is used to modify processes so as to compensate for inimical external changes. 'By an apparent contradiction,' writes Charles Richet, 'it [the living being] maintains its stability only if it is excitable and capable of modifying itself according to external stimuli and adjusting its response to the stimulation. In a sense, it is stable because it is modifiable—the slight instability is the necessary condition for the true stability of the organism.'[1]

The essence of the living entity is thus revealed as organization. It is a system of chemical processes, but their basal chemical character is subordinated to their function in the subservice of norms which maintain the system. It is their *functional* character which is paramount. And they are functional both in the sense of sub-serving an end and in the mathematical sense (not wholly dissociated from the first) of varying concomitantly and proportionately with the variation of other processes (or quantities of material) in the system. This is what I have consistently called relevant variation and it marks the organism as a polyphasic unity at its characteristically high level of complexity and integration— a polyphasic unity which is at the same time auturgic or self-maintaining.

The contributory processes, as has been said, are physico-chemical and the means by which they are mutually adjusted and subordinated to norms, though still very imperfectly understood, are almost undoubtedly mechanical, in the loose sense of that word in which we speak of chemical 'mechanisms'. The maintenance of homeostasis is nowadays traced to the principle of negative-feed-back and its incorporation in what are known as servo-mechanisms—the term immediately reveals the functional character of the process. Negative feed-back is an arrangement whereby a proportion of the output of energy from a mechanical or electrical system is fed back to adjust the input so that the work will be done at a constant rate. Such devices are common and may be more or less complex. That numerous devices of this sort exist in the working of the living body is nowadays accepted without question, and it is obvious that they are of superlative complexity and are most intricately interdependent. At times, however, two quite un-

---

[1] Quoted by Cannon, op. cit., p. 21.

warranted inferences are drawn from this admission. The first is that there is no essential difference between a living and a non-living system because many non-living systems include feed-back mechanisms. To this point we shall have to return, but may here observe that apart from human artifacts no such non-living systems are known. Known non-living machines have been deliberately constructed to serve human purposes and are therefore teleological in character. It is solely for this reason that they contain servo-mechanisms. Any attempt to assimilate living organisms to such devices gives by implication a teleological account of living processes, and presupposes a designer, like a human being, who deliberately constructs mechanisms to serve preconceived purposes. Whether or not this is a desirable or legitimate method of explanation is a discussion reserved for a later chapter.

The critical consideration, for our present purpose, is that servo-mechanisms are always by their nature functional and minister to norms which they do not and cannot themselves determine. The norm is set for non-living servo-mechanisms by man, and in living organisms it depends upon the nature and structure of the system to be maintained. The feed-back mechanism in living physiology is subordinate and integral to this. Accordingly, the existence of feed-back is always a sure sign of auturgic wholeness and integral, polyphasic organization. For the present this is all that we need stress, though we shall later return to a discussion of the whole question of mechanism and teleology.

Among scientists today there is an influential body of opinion opposed to any suggestion of teleological explanation in biology or elsewhere, and accordingly a second unwarranted conclusion is sometimes drawn from the discovery of servo-mechanisms in the organism, namely, that this whole and astoundingly complicated system of mutually supplementary processes could have developed by a series of random and accidental changes from non-living physico-chemical activity. Some discussion of the plausibility of this suggestion has already been undertaken and we shall return to it later. A very little reflection upon the character of living activity makes the hypothesis of chance concatenation seem implausible in the extreme. 'When we consider the extreme instability of our bodily structure,' writes Cannon, 'its readiness for disturbance by the slightest application of external forces and the rapid onset of its decomposition as soon as favouring circumstances are withdrawn, its persistence through many decades seems almost miraculous.'[1] It is surely colossally improbable that the extraordinary organization of functions that assures its stability should have occurred by accident. As E. S. Russell says: 'It seems, indeed, fantastically improbable that the complex and self-maintaining organization of even the simplest living things can be built up by the free play of inorganic forces as we conceive them; there must be in life some different principle at work, even though we can form no adequate conception of what it is.'[2]

This is the essential point. The very high degree of improbability of a cumulative series of accidents issuing in so delicately adjusted an auturgic system as a living entity, rules out of court the view that it could be the result of the interplay of purely inorganic forces. The laws of physics as at present known forbid it, for they assure us that the trend of inorganic activity is always towards the most probable state, and that is in the direction of increasing disorder. To account for life, therefore, we need, in addition to known physico-chemical laws, 'some different principle', some sort of 'radial energy', some nisus to order and wholeness, which can transcend thermodynamics. Whatever this principle turns out to be, it is not necessarily confined to life— the evidence is rather to the contrary. For we have already seen its influence in the physical realm building up, by repeated self-enfoldments, a continuous series of polyphasic unities. And this only strengthens the case for presuming the existence of a positive, constructive, ordering nisus in nature, and weakens the hypothesis that in the sphere of life all phenomena can be explained in terms of random shuffling and natural selection. This hypothesis is commonly associated with the theory of evolution and can be most profitably discussed in that context.

[1] Op. cit., p. 20.
[2] *The Directiveness of Organic Activities*, pp. 7–8.

H

CHAPTER XII

EVOLUTION

I

How has this immense organized complexity of life developed and what is its source? The theory of evolution is now established beyond question, but some controversy still persists over the 'how' and the 'whence'. There can be no serious dispute over the main fact, revealed in the fossil record and by other evidence, that there have been major trends, and not much doubt about what they were. Life has evidently progressed from the relatively simple to the fantastically complex, from the lowly and minute to the larger and more elaborate, growth imposing the necessity of greater complexity. It has evolved from single celled creatures to metazoan and colonial types; from the less to the more completely individuated; from the aquatic to the terrestrial and aerial; from the poikilothermic to the homoiothermic; from the instinctive to the intelligent, a progressive internalization and increasing auturgic control of the immediate conditions of living. That there has been such progress is not seriously disputed by scientists, but, as G. G. Simpson points out, the line of development has been neither straight nor single. It seems rather to have been a ramification and radiation of types at different stages along a zigzag course; yet through and amidst all this the major trends are distinctly recognizable. Moreover, unicellular and colonial organisms, aquatic, poikilothermic and numerous relatively 'primitive' forms still persist, and are not really primitive in that they are themselves products of evolution stretching back through lost and largely unknown genealogies. In several different ways past forms are preserved and carried on into present developments, sometimes as separate organisms and species that have been evolved along lines of their own, sometimes as subordinate and possibly vestigial components incorporated in more highly organized animals. With some exceptions (to which we may later advert) the progress has been one of complexification, but always as the correlative and concomitant of integration. It has been a progress of increasingly elaborate polyphasic unification of differences.

For our present purpose there is no need to describe in detail either the forms which have so emerged or the precise course and order of changes. What is more important is to examine the currently accepted theories of the 'forces' and influences which have brought about the successive changes and the laws (if there are any) which govern their course.

2

The predominant theory of evolution at the present time has been called neo-Darwinian. It is the Darwinian theory modified by the incorporation of Mendelism. Briefly, its tenets are as follows. Offspring differ from their parents by small variations, some of which are the result simply of recombination of genes and others the result of mutation. During their life-time off-spring may acquire new characteristics different from those of either parent, but these are not heritable and are not passed on to progeny. Variations resulting from recombination do not always (especially in animals) produce new species, but those resulting from mutation may. Whether they do or not depends upon the viability of the mutant. If the mutation is favourable it will persist and may, in the competition for survival oust some or all of the older forms. If it is unfavourable it will be eliminated, as the result of this same competition. This is the effect of natural selection. New forms may be better adapted to different environmental conditions or different ways of life and so may persist and proliferate in new habitats, or by changing their habits in the old, without undue disturbance of the older forms. Alternatively the new forms may compete with the old and in the course of time may come to replace them. There are several different kinds of selection, environmental, sexual, intra-uterine, intraspecific and interspecific; each has different effects and the effects of one type of selection may counteract those of another. Consequently the products of natural selection may be very diverse, but selection by itself cannot produce specific changes. Only mutation can do that. Present-day knowledge of the cause of mutation is only partial, but it is presumed to occur for the most part in a random fashion and to have no connection with or necessary bearing upon environmental conditions. Whether positive or negative its adaptive value is held to be entirely fortuitous. Thus mutation alone is not regarded as the source of adaptive or directional change; adaptation is attributed solely to natural selection, while selection alone is incapable of giving rise to new specific forms.[1]

That the minimal basis of the evolutionary process is what is here outlined, there is a vast mass of incontrovertible evidence to assure us. That mutations do occur, and do occur randomly, has been fully confirmed by experimental evidence, though the actual causes of their occurrence are not all known and it cannot positively be asserted that all mutations are the effect of purely random causes. Further, the reproduction rate within a species and the observed fact that populations remain relatively constant makes natural selection inevitable, and the evidence is too massive to give room for serious doubt that these are the primary causes of specific differences and of directional changes, though, as we shall shortly see, significant questions must be faced concerning the meaning of selection, concerning that which is selected and what determines the selection made. The short answer to this last question, 'survival value', is far from precise and requires careful examination and analysis. Nevertheless, mutation and natural selection can be made to account for the known facts without any appeal to postulated entities such as the Bergsonian *élan vital* or Drieschian entelechies. This is the prevailing scientific view; the supporting evidence is plentiful and familiar and it has been convincingly marshalled by such writers as R. A. Fisher, J. B. S. Haldane, Julian Huxley, and G. G. Simpson.[2]

If this were all there were to evolution we should have to conceive the whole efflorescence of living forms with their myriad, minute, delicate, interlaced and often (in detail) inexplicable adaptations and mutual adjustments as the cumulative effect of selection from purely random changes. Scientists often write as if this were all, and as if this finally settled the question of mechanism and vitalism so far as evolution is concerned. But, though the dispute about mechanism and vitalism in undoubtedly obsolete today, this is not because it has been finally settled in favour of either side, but because both terms have lost their

[1] Cf. J. Huxley, *Evolution, The Modern Synthesis* (London, 1942), Ch. 2, i; G. G. Simpson, *The Meaning of Evolution* (Yale, 1949), Ch. XIV; Wells and Huxley, *The Science of Life*, Chs. XXI–XXIV.

[2] R. A. Fisher, *The Genetical Theory of Natural Selection* (London, 1932), et al.; J. B. S. Haldane, *The Causes of Evolution* (Oxford, 1930), et al.; Julian Huxley, *Evolution, the Modern Synthesis* (London, 1942), *Evolution in Action* (New York, 1953), et al.; G. G. Simpson, *The Meaning of Evolution* (Yale, 1949), etc.

original significance and the issue no longer arises—at least, not in its old form. Nor is it established that a complete and adequate account has been (or indeed can be) given of evolution purely in terms of fortuitous random mutations plus inevitable, blind natural selection. To cover the facts such an account must be very significantly supplemented and the key terms qualified in important ways. The scientists themselves have shown how far this is necessary, though their arguments and attitudes seem at times to ignore the force of their own theories and the evidence by which they support them.

Let us, for a moment, consider the implications of the bare unqualified doctrine that evolution is effected simply by chance mutation and natural selection: that the fantastic complexity of structure and activity in the higher plants and animals has been produced in this way. The conception is of a sort of random shuffling that throws up accidental patterns of structure and function, some of which conform to environmental conditions so that they can persist and others do not. There are, of course, presumed to be some of intermediate viability which can survive with more or less difficulty—in fact a continuous scale of 'fitness' giving the more adapted the better chance, not only of longevity but of reproduction. These are accordingly selected, for not all can possibly survive and those which are eliminated are the relatively less viable. The conception of the evolutionary process is of cumulative accidental change continuously selected for adaptive improvement. Let us repeat that the occurrence of selection of this kind is undeniable. It has been experimentally and observationally established that the very slightest adaptive advantage of one phenotype over another—so slight as to be virtually undetectable in any one generation—will have marked effects on a population in a sequence of generations. Nevertheless it is hard to believe that this account is sufficient.

As an aid to the imagination we may consider a crude but perhaps, instructive model, which is not a true analogue of the actual process of evolution, but which is quite closely similar to the kind of process suggested by some contemporary theorists. Suppose we have a large number (say, several thousands) of pieces of jig-saw, of which 500 fit together to form a picture, but the rest are odd and do not fit in shape, or conflict with the pictorial pattern, or both. Suppose that they are all shuffled in a revolving drum, and that, at intervals, on the release of a spring, 500 pieces are spilled out into a frame. The chances that any one such emission would give the picture are so remote as to be altogether inconsiderable. Let us assume, however, that whenever, on such an occasion, any two pieces fit together correctly they are glued in position and, along with the rest, are returned to the drum as one. (Strictly this would not correspond to biological process, for not all mutations are advantageous.) What are the chances that by this method the puzzle could be completely assembled? And how many emissions (corresponding to generations in a given population) would be needed to produce the completed picture? If the answers were mathematically estimated, the first would undoubtedly be extremely small and the second an enormously large number.

As jig-saws go, a 500-piece puzzle is a fairly complicated example, but in comparison with the most elementary of living organisms, it is the extreme of simplicity. If the probability of the construction of a jig-saw picture by mere chance collocation of parts is so small as to require an astronomically long series of chance arrangements, the time needed to produce, by a comparable process, even the most primitive of modern organisms would exceed the age of the earth. Certainly the 2000 million years estimated by scientists as the period during which man has actually evolved from the first beginnings of life would seem totally inadequate.

In the first place, to be consistent, the theory must assert that nothing except accidental change and selection have guided the development of life, from its original emergence from non-life right up to the evolution of contemporary organisms, including man. And this indeed is a position adopted by extremists of the neo-Darwinian school. But we have already found this hypothesis not only implausible as an explanation of the origins of life, but, if Blum is to be followed, incoherent and circular.

What has to emerge from the inorganic world to qualify as a living thing must be an auturgic open system—that is, one which maintains itself in being, through a wide range of variation in external conditions, by automatic adjustive modification of its internal processes and structure, yet always subject to a recognizable principle of organization. Without such a system there is no life and so nothing to evolve. The presumption of its existence must be made before we can speak of mutation or selection or even of accidental change. For where no such system exists all change is on the same footing. Only if there is such a system can changes within it be classified according as they are brought about by the operation of the governing principle of order or independently of it. The latter are then regarded as accidental, for by 'accidental' nobody would wish to suggest that the change is uncaused.

Neo-Darwinism tacitly assumes this, but ignores it, and reasons as if chance mutations and the weeding out of the unviable by natural selection were the only principles affecting the course of development, and as if the whole story of evolution could be told in these terms.

If this were strictly the case we should have to assume that the emergence of life had been *simply* a complication of inorganic chemical change (we have argued above that it is not), and that subsequent mutations were just accidental alterations in a complicated system of chemical reactions. On that assumption, the notion of survival value becomes unintelligible for no set of merely chemical reactions, however complex, has any better survival value than any other. Whatever results from change is a complex of chemical reactions and unless we can recognize in it a unique principle of organization we cannot sensibly speak of survival at all. Consequently selection also loses its meaning for without a coherent system as the basis of mutation there would be nothing to select.

The least intelligible assumption for evolution is a complex, self-replicating chemical system tending to greater complexity. The Darwinian will then maintain that it evolves as the result of accidental changes within it of such a kind as to give it some advantage in the process of self-maintenance; but, without this assumption that the system is auturgic (i.e. self-maintaining), the contention would be incredible. For in a non-auturgic system accidental change would tend towards disintegration. Mere shuffling increases disorder and produces no tendency towards greater and more integrated complexity. The laws of chance and probability, therefore, militate against the hypothesis.

It might be objected that self-replication multiplies the chances of accidental changes occurring in the direction of greater integration. But if no auturgy is presumed there would be less chance of changes favourable to replicating than to non-replicating systems, for purely chemical self-replicating systems are more easily liable to break down as a result of accidental change. Coherent structure must be presupposed as a basis for evolution; and more than that, a coherent structure which reproduces itself and which automatically adapts itself, within a limited but relatively wide range, to environmental alteration. In other words, inherent adaptability is an indispensable prerequisite to evolution; so that, however much may be effected by random mutation and natural selection, they cannot be the only determining principles in the evolutionary process.

Once the assumption of auturgy is made, however, any fortuitous change which is assimilable by the system may be a means to further integration and self-maintenance, for it can be incorporated into the system and used to adapt to new conditions. But only on this condition is there any considerable likelihood that fortuitous changes will result in closer organization and better adaptation to environment. Without it, we should have to believe that all the astonishingly complicated internal and external adjustments enabling modern organisms to withstand inimical environmental pressures, protecting the delicately poised systems of their metabolism and physiological functioning from disturbing influences, and enabling them to perform highly complicated feats of constructive behaviour, are simply the outcome of a long series of accidental changes *in a non-auturgic medium*. It is surely obvious that the vast improbability of such a result would make the theory that imposed this belief upon us as unscientific as the belief in miracles.

If the effect of selection is, as it must be, purely discriminatory between more and less viable, preserving the first and eliminating the second, the origin of all heritable change must be mutation; and if mutation is random and unaffected by selection, whatever changes have occurred, would have occurred whether or not selection operated. Selection however would restrict the number and type of possible mutants (for eliminated forms could no longer mutate). Accordingly, as T. H. Morgan and L. T. Hogben have pointed out,[1] if no selection had occurred all the known forms of life would still have appeared, as well as an enormous number of others. It would follow that selection has contributed nothing to the actual result of evolution, which would have occurred in any case. It has merely restricted it to forms viable in a limited environment by eliminating the unfit. Accordingly, we should have to say that present-day living organisms are the products purely and simply of random mutations and the equally random shuffling

[1] L. T. Hogben, *The Nature of Living Matter* (London, 1931), p. 181; T. H. Morgan, *The Scientific Basis of Evolution* (London, 1932), p. 130.

of genes in the genome, and that natural selection has simply prevented the survival of countless others. But if this were so, the incredibly complicated and superbly well-adjusted mechanisms of the mammalian body (as but one example) must have been assembled by pure and uninfluenced chance, *within a period of less than 3000 million* years, an improbability which cannot reasonably be entertained.

'To produce such adapted types by chance recombination in the absence of selection would require a total assemblage of organisms that would more than fill the universe and overrun astronomical time.'[1] This is Huxley's admission; and if the effect of selection is purely negative then chance mutation and combination is the only source of change. Selection could easily reduce the size of the assemblage of organisms to one which could be accommodated, even on so limited an area as the surface of the earth, but it could not limit the requisite *time* needed for the occurrence by chance of so vast a number of precisely and minutely adapted modifications.

Because the great majority of mutations are unfavourable, the odds against the production *without* selection of an animal such as a horse, by the accidental accumulation of favourable mutations, each of which has arisen by pure chance, is estimated by Huxley (following Muller) to be of the order of one in $(10^3)^{10^6}$—one in a thousand to the millionth power,[2]—and that, he concedes, is tantamount to impossibility. What difference then is made by natural selection? How does it function (in the words of R. A. Fisher) as a 'mechanism for generating an exceedingly high degree of improbability'?[3] It eliminates the less viable forms, but, if variation is always only accidental, this cannot increase (and might even decrease) the chances of further favourable mutations. It will confine their occurrence to forms already in some measure adapted but this is only because unviable forms do not remain to harbour mutations of any kind. This elimination does not increase the absolute number or the frequency of mutation either favourable or unfavourable. So the occurrence of mutation, the frequency of its being advantageous and the rate of accumulation of favourable mutations are not accelerated by the elimination of the unfit.[4]

---

[1] *Evolution, the Modern Synthesis*, p. 475.
[2] *Evolution in Action* (New York, 1953), pp. 41–2.
[3] 'The Bearing of Genetics on the Theory of Evolution', *Sci. Prog.* 27.
[4] Some argue that this would not be true if there were selection for
H*

The effect, as Huxley puts it, is to convert a rare favourable mutant within a few hundred generations into the prevailing form.[1] It certainly decreases the rarity of the form, but does not affect the mutation rate nor the proportion of beneficial to injurious mutations. Whatever eventuates in the now normal form would equally have occurred within it, if selection had not eliminated the less viable forms, so long, that is, as we assume that all forms (*per impossibile*) could survive, which is precisely the assumption made by Morgan and Hogben. At least, this would be the case if the operation of selection were purely negative and if no other influence co-operated with it but accidental mutation. Huxley writes as if natural selection supplied a positive influence, but he never explains how it does so and his detailed descriptions of it always give it the role simply of eliminating what is relatively harmful and preserving what is comparatively favourable.[2] 'But' (in the words of Professor Waddington) 'to suppose that the evolution of the wonderfully adapted biological mechanisms has depended only on selection out of a haphazard set of variations, each produced by blind chance, is like suggesting that if we went on throwing bricks together into heaps we should eventually be able to choose ourselves the most desirable house.'[3]

There is, however, ample evidence of a positive influence to which we shall presently turn and which must modify significantly the crude account of evolution simply as chance mutation and natural selection. Before examining this evidence let us briefly consider a few examples of the sort of coherently integrated systems that the evolutionary process must produce.

3

The 'argument from improbability' which we are here discussing was pressed by Bergson in conjunction with the evolution of the vertebrate and cephalopod eye on the ground that the necessary

inherent variation. The notion is, however, dubious. If variation is always purely accidental, what selective advantage is provided by variation for its own sake? The argument is surely presupposing that all accidental variation is favourable (else it could not be selected); and not only is that false, but if it were true selection would not occur.

[1] Loc. cit.

[2] Cf. *The Science of Life*, Ch. XXI–XXIV; *Evolution, passim; Evolution in Action*, Ch. 2.

[3] *The Strategy of the Genes*, pp. 6–7.

changes were all interdependent and that none of them in isolation would be advantageous, while the probability of their all occurring together was too remote to merit consideration. Haldane, Simpson and others have since shown that the piecemeal development from a pigment spot to the light-concentrating, image-forming photo-receptors of insects, cephalopods and vertebrates is entirely feasible and even to be expected on the assumption of natural selection. What seems to have been overlooked however is that, while this piecemeal development might well be feasible and advantageous at each step, and though each more efficient and better adapted modification would naturally be selected, the origin of each suitable change is assumed to be pure chance. What has to be envisaged, therefore, is the probability, not of the entire object-forming, colour-sensitive and immensely complex eye-mechanism appearing at one stroke, but of the successive chance occurrences of small modifications which will serially transmute a pigment spot into a collection of light sensitive cells, such a collection into a retinal basin, and covering skin into a lens, as well as produce all the myriad devices and adjustments of neural, muscular and glandular structure and activity that go to focus, direct and protect the sensitive organ, to say nothing of the engrams and neural structures basal to its effective use. The necessary mutations could certainly occur, and they could occur successively, but the probability of the merely fortuitous occur-rence of any one of them is exceedingly small and that they should occur one by one in *the right order*, even if interspersed with disadvantageous modifications, is less probable still. Even though not impossible, the degree of improbability of the series taken as a whole must surely necessitate a time scale beyond any that is actually applicable and even beyond any that has been available. Consider, for instance, the development of a lens. If this occurred before the sensitized cells had appeared, it would be futile. If it appeared afterwards but in the wrong place, it would be useless. What actually does happen in the ontogenetic process is that the eye-cup itself generates a lens by causing the skin opposite to it to become transparent. The development and functioning of tear glands where there was no conjunctiva or no regularly sweeping eyelid, would be simply disadvantageous. Such unadapted modifications would, if they occurred, be eliminated, and once the genes producing them had been bred out the chances of their recurrence later when they would constitute an improvement would be reduced. Clearly something more than *random* change is needed to explain what has actually occurred.

Moreover it is not merely the structure and functioning of the eye that is to be developed, but also and concomitantly the adjustment of nervous connections enabling the creature to interpret the deliverances of vision and the complex feed-back mechanisms that will keep the eye trained on a moving object and will co-ordinate limb and eye movement with vision. The vast improbability of such a system's being assembled by a series of small accidental accretions or modifications is quite as impressive as Bergson maintained. In fact the whole implicit conception of development as an additive process is belied by the facts, which are by no means as simple and straightforward as the unqualified doctrine of selection of chance mutations would have us believe.

'When two or more steps are necessary,' Huxley writes, 'it becomes inconceivable that they shall have originated simultaneously. The first mutation must have been spread through the population by selection before the second could be combined with it, the combination of the first two in turn selected before the third could be added, and so on with each successive step. The improbability of an origin in which selection had not played a part becomes larger with each step. . . . The improbability is therefore enormous that such progressive adaptations can have arisen without the operation of some agency which can gradually accumulate and combine a number of contributory changes.'[1]

Huxley appears to consider that selection is somehow a sufficient agency of accumulation and combination of changes. But the crucial questions are how selection operates to combine, and what it contributes to increase the probability of occurrence of the successive steps in the right order. It does indeed make each favourable change prevalent in the population, and as new mutations occur it is obvious that unless they are eliminated they will accumulate. But selection does nothing to bring about succeeding changes, whether good or bad. They must be attributed to pure chance. Equally, it must be by chance that any new modification is harmonious or integrable with earlier features. The systems actually produced, however, are so highly integrated and so exceedingly complicated that the chance accumulation of the necessary changes is too improbable to be seriously contempla-

[1] *Evolution*, p. 474.

ted and the manner of such a process of accumulation is too incoherent credibly to issue in the result achieved.

Consider for a moment the evolution of the human brain. This has developed by stages from what in fish and amphibia are relatively little more than large ganglionic structures. In man, the neural connections in the brain-stem and midbrain are found to constitute a highly intricate network of neurones on successive levels: (a) integrating the local activity of each level, (b) connecting different levels of complicated integrating neural systems and (c) transmitting impulses upward to the cortex and downward from it. The delicate complexity of this system is further augmented and expanded in the cortex, where three corresponding reticulations have been distinguished.[1] The complexity of this system is extreme. Are we to believe that it developed as a series of haphazard, accidental changes, uninfluenced by any positive integrating trend and accomplished simply by the elimination (due to natural selection) of additions that did not happen to function harmoniously in the system? Are we to imagine that in this haphazard fashion a highly efficient system of integration and connection was generated supplying impulses to, and inter-relating, 10^{10} cortical cells to carry out minutely adjusted functions in ways that as yet baffle the best and most ingenious of our scientists?

Other products of evolution are still more difficult to attribute to accumulation of chance modifications. These are cases of adaptation involving at once anatomical structure, physiological functioning and overt behaviour, not only in one individual but co-operatively in several.

(i) Descriptions already given of homeostatic mechanisms are sufficient evidence of the complex and delicate interplay of structure and function. A mutation affecting any aspect of either must relevantly affect some fact in the other for the system to work. If some mutation modified an organ so as to produce insulin, it (or another mutation) must at the same time modify another organ to convert sugar to glycogen and store it in that form. If a nerve system is so connected to the peripheral blood vessels as to dilate them on the appropriate stimulus, there must also be some arrangement for restricting the blood flow to the intestines, so that over-exerted muscles may be adequately served. If adrenal

[1] Cf. *Reticular Formation of the Brain*, Eds. Jasper, Proctor, Knighton, Noshay, and Costello (Boston and Toronto, 1958).

glands are developed manufacturing adrenin, some nervous control mechanism is needed to insure its secretion at the appropriate times. When one considers that the appropriateness of the occasion is often determined by perception (e.g. in fear and rage, when adjustments preparatory to efficient physical exercise are automatically made on the perception of an object evaluated as dangerous or obstructive—itself a complex disposition) attribution of the development of the entire system to accidental mutations becomes almost ludicrous.

(ii) (a) in protective colouration, selection plays an obvious and predominant part. Yet even industrial melanism in moths, the classic example of natural selection, depends in part on the behaviour of the moths. The dark variety are as vulnerable on unblackened patches of bark as are the light on the smoky background. It is found that each variety preferentially chooses a background of its own colour on which to settle, where it is protected.[1] Similarly it was found by Popham that water-boatmen (*Corixidae*) become restless when confined to surroundings in which the background colour differs markedly from their own, and seek to move to safer regions.[2] The moth, *Venusia Veniculata*, lives on a tree lilly with longitudinally veined leaves. The moth's wings are marked with lines running perpendicular to its body, and it rests at night on a dead leaf so oriented that its own markings coincide with those of the leaf. Its antennae, which in the normal position would destroy the camouflage, are tucked away under the forewings. When disturbed, Cornes reports, it settles down again, 'after a few compass-like vacillations', in the right position.[3]

A number of similarly striking examples of behaviour directed to the optimal use of coloration, both protective and aposematic, is given by Tinbergen, such as the adoption of positions by birds, fish, and caterpillars with counter-shading which will bring the darker side uppermost to offset the effect of illumination from above. The fish, *Synodontis batensoda* in particular, which has reversed countershading, frequently swims upside down. Pine hawk-moth caterpillars adopt positions among pine needles which bring the direction of their longitudinal stripes into alignment with the pine needles, except in the case of individuals of the last

[1] Cf. Kettlewell, *Nature* (1955).
[2] E. J. Popham, *Proc. Zool. Soc. Lond.* III (1941).
[3] J. J. S. Cornes, 'Attitude and Concealing Coloration', *Nature*, 140 (1937); cited by Huxley.

instar where the pattern is broken up. These align themselves with the twig and not with the needles. Species with a brown head lie with the head at the base of the needles where there is a brown sheaf, whereas others that have green heads do not.[1]

In all these cases the selected mutations must affect behaviour as well as coloration or else they would lose a large part of their beneficial effects. The probability of a single change producing so well co-ordinated a result in so many different cases is infinitesimal. A series of changes each producing one of the co-ordinated elements, is still less probable, particularly as they would then singly give little or no advantage for survival and might well be eliminated by selection.

(b) The adaptation of organs for toilet well exemplifies the co-ordination of anatomical development with habits which have no direct connection with the primary function of the organs used. The rough tongue of the cat acts as a currycomb (though not the primary function of a tongue). The teeth of lemurs are modified to serve as a comb to clean out the animals' fur and, concomitantly, the base of the tongue is abnormally enlarged more efficiently to clean the teeth. In some marsupials, which use the syndactylous digits of their hind feet almost solely as toilet instruments, the size and shape of the claws are correlated with the length and type of the fur they are used to clean.[2] Such adaptation, as Huxley says, 'is concerned with a function: the function may be carried out by different organs or combinations of organs in different forms; and the organs show different degrees of structural modification correlated with efficiency in carrying out the function'.[3] Mutations affecting the genetic control of behaviour must either themselves correspondingly affect the shape of a set of organs normally performing quite different functions, or depend upon other mutations which suitably modify these organs without affecting the efficiency of their normal use; and this must occur before selection can operate, for one change without the others would have no selective advantage. In either case the diversity of the factors which have to be integrated is such as to make the improbability of the requisite combination excessive.

The cuckoo's habit of laying its eggs in other birds' nests must, on the theory under consideration, be the result of one or

---

[1] *Vide* N. Tinbergen, *A Study of Instinct* (Oxford, 1951), pp. 164–7.
[2] Huxley, *Evolution*, p. 423.   [3] *Ibid.*, p. 424.

more mutations in its genes. Such a modification of behaviour would by itself be extremely hazardous, but by a further mutation the egg laid is unusually small for so large a bird and is thus comparable in size with the eggs of much smaller species which act as foster parents. Another mutation must be presumed to reduce the incubation period, so that the egg hatches sooner than those of the foster-mother and the young cuckoo receives a supply of food sufficient to cope with its greater rate of growth. The mother cuckoo, also, must lay before the foster-parent begins to sit to ensure to her offspring the necessary start. To maintain its rate of growth the cuckoo chick must eject the young of its foster parent from the nest. For this it is provided with a body structure and a set of reflex responses nicely adapted to the task. Its back is wide and hollowed; its neck and forelegs are long; its wings so shaped that when held stiffly, they fence in and hold any small object on its back. Being the heaviest occupant of the nest the cuckoo chick rests on the bottom and in its fidgeting squeezes its foster sisters and brothers to the sides. Whenever, as inevitably occurs one rolls on to the cuckoo's back, it presses its beak on the nest bottom, splays out its legs, and pushes its hollowed back upward. It throws back its wings to retain the burden and slides its tail up the side of the nest until, when it reaches the rim, a backward heave of the shoulders ejects the luckless legitimate from its parental home.[1] The set of co-ordinated reflex actions alone could hardly have been assembled by a series of accidents, but to this must be added the behaviour and its timing of the mother cuckoo, the size of the egg she lays, the growth rate of the young and the complex mutually adapted features of its bodily structure. The calculation of the probability of the combination of these precisely interdependent factors, if each is the result of random mutation, would tax the capacity of the most efficient computer.

(iii) Finally we may observe the combination of adaptive structure, functioning and behaviour that involves the co-operation of several individuals, the total pattern of which would break down if any participant failed to play its role. Some of the most remarkable examples are provided by the nesting behaviour of birds and their care of the young. Nest sanitation (to limit exemplification to this) is for them of obvious importance, and is

[1] This description is a summary of the account given by C. E. Raven in *Experience and Interpretation* (Cambridge, 1953), pp. 137-8.

ensured by the most unexpected and ingenious arrangements. 'In some forms . . . the young defecate only after backing up to the nest-rim; in these, specially developed muscles ensure that the faeces are projected well clear of the nest.'[1] In others the intestines of the young secrete a gelatinous substance which forms a sac round the droppings which are then easily removed from the nest by the parents. In yet other species the nestlings restrain the function for long periods waiting with rear upturned until the parent releases them from their quaint vigil with a beak-tap on the posterior.

More astonishing still is the camouflage employed by *Hemipus picatus leggei*, the Ceylon black-backed pied shrike, which builds its nest on the bare branches of trees, disguising it with bark-flakes and lichen and constructing the sides flush with the branch to counterfeit a knot. The fledglings, in the absence of their parents sit facing each other with converging upturned beaks and half-closed eyes. To a late stage in their growth they are drab and mottled blackish grey in colour, almost indistinguishable from the tree-bark. The entire tableau from quite a short distance away is so good an imitation of a snag left by a broken branch as to deceive the most observant.[2]

Such coherence as these instances reveal of bodily form and colour, with physiological function and the co-ordinated behaviour of several individuals could not in the time which it has taken to evolve (for modern birds some 150 million years), be credibly attributed to the chance concatination of accidental mutations, even with the help of selection, unless aided by some further tendency towards auturgic self-maintenance. The complexity of the behaviour involved cannot be dissected into the piecemeal results of single, unguided, modifications affecting isolated characters (and we shall see that this is not in fact a correct description of the effects of mutation). In the last two examples consciousness and innate dispositions have already developed and these imply a degree of polyphasic unity which defies analysis into isolable, unintegrated parts and events.[3]

Biology offers vast numbers of instances of exceedingly complex and closely integrated systems like the few to which we have drawn attention. They are evidence, beyond reasonable doubt,

[1] Huxley, op. cit., p. 424.
[2] *Vide* W. W. A. Phillips, *Ibis* (14) 4:450, 1940.
[3] See Part III below.

that the process of evolution, like metabolism, growth and development, runs counter to probability against the current of increasing entropy, though no necessary contravention of the laws of thermodynamics need be presumed. In other words it may be described as a process giving rise, for the most part, to progressively more highly organized systems, more diversified yet more closely unified, more efficient and auturgically self-maintaining. These are the properties that have distinguished life from the outset and we may here remind ourselves of Blum's rule that in seeking to understand the source and origin of any process we must constantly bear in mind the type of functional properties that must be presupposed if the evolution of contemporary forms were to be possible. Random mutations and natural selection alone, though they undoubtedly occur, do not include the necessary functional property—which is *integration*. Random mutations are, by the meaning of term, disintegrated, unordered and irrelevant to already existing structure; selection can preserve and accumulate, but it cannot and does not co-ordinate or integrate. Where self-adjustment (auturgy) has already been at work to produce an adapted form, it will be preserved by natural selection; and mutations which cannot be integrated successfully and do not enhance the existing coherence of the system, are liable to be weeded out. But what the overwhelming evidence reveals is a continuous process of integration and some principle constantly enhancing the wholeness and unity of organizations which include ever greater and more complicated diversity, unifying not only the internal structure and functioning of the organism, but at the same time the organism as a whole with its environment. It is this principle which we must seek in the mechanics of evolution and partial though it may be, the evidence for it is undoubtedly forthcoming. It has been discovered and is emphasized often by those very scientists who rely so faithfully on random mutation and natural selection as the sole agencies of evolutionary advance.

4

There is evidence enough of the random occurrence of spontaneous mutations and the marked and spectacular effects of natural selection. The latter is after all logically inevitable and the process appropriately named, for nothing is more naturally to be expected than the survival in a competitive world of the best

adapted and the elimination of the least viable. But that single
genes control single characters and that mutations are correspondingly particulate has been amply disproved.[1] Accordingly
no simple summation of accumulated particulate modifications,
even as sifted by natural selection, may be presumed, and it is
plain that evolution is not a process of that kind. Genes are known
to be pleiotropic, that, is, to have multiple effects; and mutation
in one may modify several (not necessarily related) characters.
And characters are each the product of several genes. Not only
this, but single genes do not act singly. They affect one another:
'the internal or genetic environment of a gene may produce effects
upon its expression which are as striking as those induced by the
external environment'.[2] The position of a gene in the chromosome,
which may be changed by translocation or inversion, influences
its effects on the characters it controls. Within the genome there
is what is known as genetic balance and the gene-complex acts as
one organic whole.

As a result a mutant is immediately subject to control by the
genetic system within which it occurs. Mutations are 'buffered'
by ancillary changes in the effects of other genes and by gene
combinations which, as Huxley says, 'act as modifiers for the
major mutating gene and adjust it more or less completely to the
needs of the organism.'[3] The teleological tone of this phrase is
almost certainly inadvertent, but there is no suggestion of evidence
that the 'buffering' effect is the result of purely random shuffling
of genes within the gene-complex. If it were, the chances that it
would adjust the effects of the mutation to the systematic coherence of the organism (which is all that can here be meant by
the word 'needs') would be exceedingly remote.[4]

[1] *Vide* Huxley, *Evolution*, p. 62; Sinnott and Dunn, *Principles of
Genetics* (New York, 1932), p. 301; Waddington, op. cit., *Modern Genetics*
(London, 1939), and *The Nature of Life* (London, 1961).

[2] Huxley, op. cit., p. 64.

[3] Op. cit., p. 48.

[4] There is in fact some evidence to the contrary. The researches of
H. H. Plough recorded in *The Journal of Experimental Zoology* (XXIV,
1917) show that in *Drosophila*, the incidence of crossing-over is minimal
at the temperature optimum for the species, but increases markedly with
temperature changes either up or down. This fact shows that the effect
is not simply the mechanical acceleration of chemical or other processes
with rise of temperature. As the increase of crossing-over increases
genetic variation, it improves the chances that more viable forms will
turn up. This reaction seems therefore to be auturgically adaptive.

Yet this is indeed what the buffering effect does achieve. The great majority of random mutations are in the nature of the case deleterious, for they are intrusions into an inherently unstable and delicately organized system. But the system, being alive, achieves stability auturgically—that is, by self-adjustment to internal and external changes. Consequently the mutant gene, so long as its effects are not too drastic (so as to be lethal in heterozygotic as well as in homozygotic individuals), usually remains recessive and even if homozygotes fail to survive, the gene persists in heterozygotes the mutation being masked by the dominance of the normal form. Recombinations, chiasmata and changes in position-effect may then so modify the mutant as to render it harmless or even (in new environmental conditions) advantageous, whereupon the effect of selection is able to give it dominance in its turn over allelomorphic genes.[1]

The discovery of position-effect, Huxley tells us, has more or less revolutionized the conception of the chromosome which was at first assumed to be a random collection of genes strung together 'like coloured beads picked up haphazard by a blind man.' This idea has now gone by the board and even if it is assumed that the arrangement of genes was originally random, 'this randomness', he declares, 'must then be given a functional polish: neighbouring genes must be adjusted to each other by new mutation and by recombination'.[2] In fine, Huxley's own judgment sums up the position thus: 'If, as now seems established, it is the case with some or all genes that interaction with near neighbours in the same chromosome affects their expression in an important way, then it is clear that all the genes within a given chromosome must be delicately adjusted to each other so as to produce a harmoniously functioning whole.'[3]

More recent research has proved further that the chromosome is an even more complexly ordered series of overlapping units, than was formerly supposed. The gene itself is apparently divisible into what are called cistrons; the nucleotides of its DNA are matched in some intricate fashion with the amino-acid groups of its protein, and it is suspected that this regulates the kinds of protein manufactured in development. There are nevertheless

---

[1] Vide R. A. Fisher, 'The Evolution of Dominance', Biological Reviews, VI (1931), pp. 345–68.

[2] Op. cit., p. 86.

[3] Op. cit., p. 85.

larger regions liable to mutation, and some biologists have suggested that there are also still more extensive sections of the chromosome effective as higher functional fields. Chromosomes, therefore, so far from being fortuitous collections of genes which can be shuffled, exchanged and substituted at random, are themselves systems functioning organically within the larger organic system of the genome and the still more inclusive total organism. Mutations within them, whatever their source, are thus liable to be subjected to the systematic and corporate effects of their internal organization.

Even the mutation rate of any given gene may be affected by others in the complex,[1] and Huxley's detailed discussion makes it credible that the demands of mutual adjustment might exert a sort of pressure in the direction of required mutations. 'We must to-day consider chromosomes', he writes, 'not as being purely mechanical gene-vehicles, but to a certain degree as organic gene-arrangements.'[2] Thus it is wrong to look upon the effects of mutations simply as random events. When they occur, they become adjusted and integrated into the genetic structure by the auturgy of the organism and the evidence is by no means conclusive that their occurrence may not sometimes be the result of this same adaptive influence.

Dr. H. Graham Cannon, in a telling attack on neo-Darwinism, protests against the 'Mendelian error' of regarding the organism as a collection of characters instead of as a whole, and asks why we must assume that the effect of the genes on the body, in which there is such conspicuous interaction of parts and functions, should be only one-way. Clearly 'the needs of the organism' (to revert to Huxley's phrase) do exert some influence also on the behaviour of the genes.[3]

This position is in some measure supported by Waddington.[4] He argues that the genetic mechanism controls epigenesis so that certain paths of development are 'canalized' and the process exhibits what he calls 'homeorhesis'—a tendency to flow along restricted paths (or 'creodes') to specific end-characters. The

---

[1] Cf. A. N. Sturtevant, 'Essays on Evolution', I, *Quarterly Review of Biology*, 12 (1937); reference by Huxley, op. cit., p. 137.

[2] Op. cit., p. 87.

[3] *Vide* H. Graham Cannon, *The Evolution of Living Things* (Manchester University Press, 1958), esp. Ch. VI.

[4] *Vide The Strategy of the Genes*, Ch. V, and *The Nature of Life*, pp. 96–97.

course of development may, however, be modified if sufficient environmental or internal stress is exerted beyond a threshold. In this way the organism is adaptable and acquires new characters in response to external conditions. But after a number of generations have been subjected to such environmental pressure, the consequent acquired characters may be genetically assimilated. A mutation may occur which has the same effect on epigenesis as the environmental stress; or the whole genotype may be sufficiently modified by selection of certain relevant genes, which have all along been present in the population and which co-operate to alter the canalization of development. Thus Lamarkian evolution is simulated. When genetic assimilation is traceable to a mutation, the question whether the mutation was entirely accidental, or might itself be due to external and internal pressures already acting on the genotype is undecided. Waddington indicates some evidence, though not conclusive, of the possibility of the latter, including the discovery of so-called adaptive enzymes in bacteria and yeasts, which are capable of synthesizing the appropriate enzyme in the presence of a new and unusual substrate. If the action of the genes (as many believe) is enzymic, the possibility of mutative adjustment to new situations is not ruled out. Yet even if this possibility is not presumed and the effects are due to no more than selection of the relevant gene-grouping, the coherent character of genetic activity still remains evident.

A mass of evidence powerfully supports the organismic approach in genetics for which von Bertalanffy and others so eloquently plead.[1] The raw material on which selection works is not just a series of random and accidental, particulate and disconnected changes, but a persistently self-adjusting genetic mechanism displaying, in itself and in its effects within the total organism, the holistic and auturgic character of life. This self-adjustment within the system discloses the activity of a positive, integrating agency co-operating with natural selection to effect adaptation and generate 'an exceedingly high degree of improbability'. Selection inevitably preserves and intensifies the effects of this nisus to integration and sifts out those which tend to impede its action; for selection as we have seen depends on reproduction, itself a

---

[1] Cf. L. von Bertalanffy, *Problems of Life*, pp. 69–82. Waddington concurs: 'Organismic thinking has some contributions to make to evolutionary theory, as a complement to the atomistic outlook.' Op. cit., p. 98.

process of self-maintenance, in and through which this co-ordinating influence is already at work. Hence what cannot maintain itself or does so only less efficienctly reproduces less, and selection is *ipso facto* at work. At the same time modifications supplied by mutations, however occasioned, are integrated and moulded into the system, tracing in the course of successive generations a progressive evolution of continuously more adapted living forms.

5

Once we have detected the operation of some such agency, though we are still ignorant of its precise nature and can recognize it only by its effects, we are in a position to meet Blum's demand that we seek the type of functional property that must be pre-supposed to make possible the evolution of living things as we know them today. This functional property we can now recognize as auturgic wholeness. The question in fact is continuous with Blum's, who considers in what minimal conditions natural selection could act at all. We now ask what kind of entity must be pre-supposed for selection to work upon and what sort of process results. The question has already been faced in Chapter IX, above where it was shown that ordered totality is the prior condition of natural selection, and while modifications within this totality might occur by chance, the chance occurrence of coherent order itself, of a complexity anything like sufficient to account for as much as a protein molecule, is virtually ruled out by the vastness of its improbability, even on the time-scale currently contemplated for the history of the solar system. *A fortiori*, the progressive generation of systems continually increasing in ordered complexity to the superlatively high degree of which we have evidence, within the relatively brief period of a few thousand million years, is too improbable to merit serious consideration. Indeed, if it had occurred, further scientific investigation into the manner of its occurrence would be futile, because what happens by sheer chance is not amenable to the sort of rational explanation that science seeks.

Oparin had no doubt on this point: 'It is clear that no substance which forms a major component of protoplasm can be reproduced by a chance or easily attained relationship between the rates of reactions. It requires the absolutely constant, continually repeated chains and cycles of reactions which together comprise the network of the self-reproducing, living, open system.'[1] And Blum is of similar persuasion: 'The more we study living systems the more we marvel at their beautifully ordered complexity; and we estimate that the forming of these systems (or even much simpler ones) by a single chance act would have an improbability of the order of a miracle, that could have happened only once in our universe.'[2] But miracles are not normally admitted in science, and what is chiefly impressive in these descriptions and opinions of biologists, is the insistent emphasis on holism and order, antithetical to arbitrariness and chance, exceeding in degree of integration and complexity anything discoverable at the pre-biological level, and thus suggesting from the very beginnings of life the operation of some synthetic and organizing agency corresponding to 'radial energy'.

The distinguishing characteristic of life is metabolism, and metabolism is not merely a conjunction of various reactions more or less co-ordinated in time, but (in Oparin's words) 'a definite organization of processes directed towards the continuous self-preservation and self-reproduction of the living system as a whole'.[3] If this is so, the kind of organized whole presupposed by natural selection must always be auturgic. Mutation (in the technical sense) can only occur in a self-replicating system, and as self-reproduction is one form of auturgy, auturgic activity will not be explicable as the result of chance mutations. Chance may well play a part, even an important part, in the actual course of evolution, but if auturgic systems are the only sort on which natural selection can be exerted, there is no reason for supposing that mutations in such systems could not occur as the result of their own inner adjustments 'directed towards continuous self-preservation and self-reproduction'.

This position merits further reflection. A system, to be selected naturally must be better adapted to survive than alternative systems. But we have seen that less complex and less ordered dynamic processes are more probable physico-chemically than more complexly ordered systems.[4] They should therefore have

<hr/>

[1] *The Origin of Life*, p. 363. Cf. also pp. 371 and 373.
[2] *Time's Arrow and Evolution*, p. 178A.   [3] *Ibid.*, p. 288.
[4] Cf. Blum, *ibid*. 'One may take the view that the greater the time elapsed, the greater should be the approach to equilibrium, the most probable state. . . .'

the advantage for survival. But this tendency would be counter-acted if the more complex had the capacity through their complex-ity to adjust themselves to environmental change—i.e. if they were auturgic. In that case they would naturally be selected.

Indeed, what is it that must survive? Not merely a chain of chemical reactions, for clearly whatever happens some series of reactions will continue. The survival must be of the organic integrity of the system in question. No modification which does not maintain this has survival value, even if as its consequence some sort of chemical cycle persisted. The modification must have 'value' as an *improvement* of the system in the environmental conditions, as increasing its efficiency and operation. Otherwise survival will be jeopardized. But when we speak of 'improvement' and 'efficiency' we are using teleological language, and there must be some criterion of value by reference to which improvement and efficiency are measured. This clearly must be the maintenance of the system's integrity, or the enhancement of its coherence and of the interplay of function among its organic parts. But the maintenance (or enhancement) of the systematic integrity of the organism in changing conditions is precisely what we know as adaptiveness, and integrity must in some degree be presupposed before one can speak at all of its adaptation to environment or of the survival value of any mutation. It is obviously possible for mutation to be accidental, in fact it frequently is so, but its efficacy is seldom likely to be merely fortunate, that it is (or must be) always purely accidental is by no means established, and as soon as the priority of the integral, organic character of the system is admitted, auturgy takes precedence over chance, survival value can be interpreted only with reference to organic wholeness, and natural selection is seen only to operate upon coherent self-maintaining systems.[1]

---

[1] Cf. C. J. Herrick, *The Evolution of Human Nature* (University of Texas Press, 1956), p. 105: 'It seems to be obvious upon even casual inspection of our world as a whole, and especially of the living beings in it, that, however abrupt the transition from one level to another may appear to be, the process is continuous. The chain of "immanent causal-ity" is unbroken. At each successive level of change a new pattern of integration emerges, so that things preserve their individuality and at the same time are interrelated in such a way as to cohere in a unified whole. And yet these principles have been so generally ignored or given merely lip service that people condone their ignorance of causes by appeals to chance, randomness, accident, or chaotic disorder, as if these

For mere persistence in being is nothing remarkable. In fact physical conservation laws show it to be a universal property of energy and matter. Inorganic compounds are for the most part more stable and so 'survive' more easily than organic. Atoms persist more tenaciously than molecules; molecules are more cohesive than crystals. But strictly 'survival' is here an inapplicable term because these entities are not liable to death or extinction but only to decomposition into more elementary parts which can again be recombined. But the living system is a delicate and unstable equilibrium which, once it is destroyed, cannot be reconstituted, and anything that gives it greater stability assists it to survive. In general this is its own capacity of self-adjustment— its auturgic character. Survival value means, therefore, what maintains this special character, what maintains or more fully and stably integrates the system. Increased elaboration, growth, differentiation and reproduction are all direct manifestations of auturgy and all have survival value in the relevant sense. Changes which occur in the course of these processes have value for the organism only so far as they enhance its organic stability in the conditions under which it has to live. Their value thus consists in their contribution to its external adaptiveness and (*ipso facto*) to its internal wholeness.

The legitimate and precise meaning of adaptation, therefore, is harmonious co-ordination and integration of functions within the organism with reference to its environment. It is at once internal coherence and adjustment to external conditions. These two aspects are not separable because from its first origins and in its essential nature, the living system is an open one maintaining itself by constant commerce with its surroundings. The self-adjustment by which it keeps itself in existence at one and the same time effects an internal interplay of functional processes and a correlation of this internal activity with external changes. Adaptation, therefore, is always maintenance and enhancement of integrity. It is the paramount condition of survival, because what has to survive is fundamentally the integral individual and survival value has meaning only in reference to this.

Selection is then seen to be natural and automatic. It is in any case a metaphorical term, for no deliberate choosing out is intended by it. The frequent suggestion of Nature as a conscious

could explain anything.' Cf., also, Alex B. Novikoff, 'The concept of Intergrative Levels and Biology', *Science*, 101 (1945).

agent choosing from among alternatives what has survival value
is totally misleading and false. Selection is 'natural' because it is
inevitable; it is 'natural' because the best adapted naturally
survive. Strictly speaking there is no selection, but only the natural
and inevitable survival of what can best adapt itself to its surroundings at the expense of what is less well adjusted. The agency of
adaptation is not 'selection' (i.e. survival), which is strictly speaking
its effect and not its cause, but the auturgy of the living system
which exerts a constant nisus towards integration and order, that
protects the delicate structure of the organism both against
environmental change and against its own internal mutations,
making use of both to maintain it in being and to increase its
viability.

Of course the capacity of any organism to do this is limited,
but organisms have this capacity in a much higher degree than
anything else, and in them alone is the capacity able to increase
by its own exercise. Examples from biology of failure and degeneration, of aging and death are not therefore evidence against
the existence of this auturgic power. Without it there could be no
such examples. Moreover, even the known cases of degeneration
(as in some parasites), of extinction of types and the inevitable
mortality of the higher forms can be understood in terms of this
same persistent tendency to maintain life and order. If this is
done by specialization, it may become excessive and so involve
degeneration, or alternatively a fixity not further adaptable which
succumbs to external changes with which it can no longer cope;
if it is done by elaboration and complexity of structure, which
increases the versatility and adaptability of the system, this
inevitably differentiates the reproductive germ-plasm from the
non-reproductive soma and brings ageing and death. 'This', says
Huxley, 'is the price life had to pay for individuality and the
efficiency of its biological machinery.' Yet it is universally offset
in some classes by reproductive fecundity, and in others by the
lengthening and improvement of parental care and protection of
the young.

6

The interdependence of organism and environment in the self-
maintenance of living systems has been emphasized by J. S.
Haldane, and in their constantly increasing adaptiveness is further

forced upon our attention by what ecologists call a biocoenosis. The environment (both internal and external) is not only inorganic but also organic. Not only chemical exchanges are in constant process but also biological relations and interchange between living creatures of every kind. Adaptation is not only to climate and physico-chemical changes but also to bacteria, to vegetable sources of food supply, to symbiotic organisms, to prey and to natural enemies, as well as to an habitual way of life. Any selected region, pond, lake, forest, island or continent presents a biological unity in which the interrelation of species maintains a balance to which each living form in its own way contributes and is adapted. Interference with this balance by the intrusion of a new species (e.g. man) or the extermination of an old one creates an entirely new situation to which all the old inhabitants are forced to adjust. This biocoenotic community covers the entire earth, plants synthesizing organic compounds from inorganic, which are assimilated by animals devoid of photosynthetic powers, and supplying oxygen to the atmosphere, without which other forms of life would die; animals breathing out carbon dioxide needed by plants, manuring the earth in which they grow, and distributing their seeds to prevent congestion. Plants depend upon the breakdown by microbes in the soil of substances which their roots absorb as nourishment, and many higher animals are similarly dependent upon bacteria inhabiting their own intestines for the decomposition of matter which they ingest. The enmity of species maintains a balance which gives scope for life, for it permits no species to increase indefinitely. Man's interference often upsets this balance with detrimental effects that become rapidly evident. The destruction of forests, or the elimination of an essential species, or the inadvertent introduction of a new and destructive insect to an environment where it has no enemies, have widespread disturbing effects on the biocoenotic equilibrium. The unity of the biocoenosis is so complete and is governed by such exact laws of concomitant variation that it has been successfully analysed mathematically and provides the subject matter of one of the more advanced fields of mathematical biology.

The world of life as a whole is thus a single system of interlocking life-processes in an extravagant variety of living species. Pierre Teilhard calls this the 'biosphere' analogous to the concentric layers of the inorganic earth, the lithosphere, the hydrosphere and the atmosphere. The biosphere supervenes in time upon these rather than in space; it is generated within them rather than above them; and as they perpetually interact so does the biosphere with them, and they with it.

Thus organisms though unified and individualized to a high degree are not self-sufficient wholes but belong to larger and more comprehensive biological unities. In the sphere of life, just as in that of physics we find an over-arching polyphasic unity composed of members which are themselves polyphasic unities, and these are so united as to form a hierarchy, from viruses and bacteria to unicellular and multicellular organisms, from colonial forms to the communities of Hymenoptera, from symbioses to biocoenoses of ever wider scope. And finally the entire biosphere is itself inextricably enmeshed with the physical and inorganic totality.

The environment to which the organism is adapted therefore is itself a polyphasic system and evolution is not simply a progressive change in types and species of individuals but is a continuous process of self-adjusting balance within a biological system which includes organisms and their environment together. So Graham Cannon has maintained that evolution is a progressive adjustment of the balance between organism and environment which must be treated as a whole. It would then seem that the type of process envisaged is not only an on-going directional progress but at the same time a continuous self-organization of an entire world.

7

That there has been directional progressive development of specific forms within this wider self-organization (and as the expression of it), the facts give little room for doubt. Though within each phylum there has been persistence as well as change, so that modern protozoans are as much products of evolution from primitive forms as are molluscs or mammals, yet there can be no doubt that the more complex organisms developed from relatively simpler ones. At some stage, it seems safe to assume, the protozoic, to grow and differentiate, became metazoic. At later stages came bilateral symmetry, nervous systems and frontal heads, from which brains and more important sense organs direct activity. These became progressively more efficient in both invertebrates and vertebrates, but only in the latter is flexibility, locomotive efficiency and growth adequate for the regulation of blood temperature

and highly developed homoeostatic mechanisms. Among vertebrates it is only in mammals and birds that these characters were
perfected. The former specialized for flight and swiftness and the
latter, through monkeys and apes, evolved the powers of manipulation and the cerebral development which in man is the instrument
of conceptual thinking.

Many biologists of standing acknowledge the progressive
character of evolution and among those who seek to deny it there
are few who, in their accounts of the process or their descriptions
of particular species, do not unconsciously assume it. J. C. Herrick
sums up the situation as revealed by modern biological study as
follows:

'Those natural formative processes that show continuous directive
change are evolutionary. Organic evolution is a high-level manifestation of this formative process, which is repeated in similar
form in the personal development of every animal. The evolutionary processes show trends in various directions. Some are directed
toward increased independence and efficiency of the individual
animals, with a wider range of capacity for flexible adjustment
to diverse conditions. Some result in diverse specialization of
species, each of which is rigorously adapted to a restricted type of
environment and way of life. Others lead to specialization that is
so extreme as to be inflexible and incapable of readjustment to
changing conditions, with resulting extinction of the species.
Among the factors which influence the course of evolution, natural
selection is given special attention.

'Animals are commonly ranked from lower to higher, and this
implies that there is progressive evolution; but this expression
is meaningless without clear definition of what we mean by
higher and by progress. From the standpoint of the behaviourist,
progressive evolution may be defined as change in the direction
of increase in the range and variety of adjustment of the organism
to its environment resulting in more efficient control of behaviour
and of surrounding conditions.'[1]

There is no reason to demur at this statement whether one
claims to be a behaviourist or not. That intelligent animals
succeed better than the more purely instinctive in adjusting their
behaviour and so their total organisms to environmental conditions seems hardly possible to dispute. The very mark of

[1] Op. cit., p. 127.

intelligence is a high capacity for variation of behaviour relevantly adjusted to some felt need or conceived purpose. That man has this capacity in a far higher degree than other creatures is so obvious as to require no laboured argument. The suggestion that some insects (e.g. mosquitoes) have succeeded better than man in adapting themselves to the whole range of environmental conditions from tropical to arctic is both futile and unconvincing. It is futile because it tacitly accepts the idea it is intended to discredit, that evolution is progressive and that progress consists in successful adaptation; and it is implausible because it fails to acknowledge man's capacity by the use of his intelligence to overcome the limitations of biological adaptation. Man has augmented his natural adaptiveness so as to be able to survive in Antarctica in a way that no other organism could do. No mosquito can adapt itself to the conditions of space navigation or looks forward in hope to colonization of the moon.

It is sometimes argued that man by his interference with nature has sealed his own doom. He allows biological defects to survive and increase by artificially protecting their victims. He becomes increasingly dependent for survival upon his own artifacts and in a few centuries may be quite incapable of survival without them. The conclusion is, of course, speculative, for prediction of this sort is always risky, and the argument contains its own refutation. If man has been able—as no other species could—to interfere with nature to his own detriment, he has the same capacity to interfere again to remedy the situation, and constantly does so. On the other hand if he failed to do this, he would presumably revert to natural conditions which, by natural selection, would eliminate the unfit and strengthen the species which might then not only survive but progress. The presupposition is either that left to itself biological evolution is infallibly progressive and only man's interference with it has prevented its being effective in his case, or that man is so far superior to other animals that he is no longer wholly subject to the natural evolutionary forces, which completely govern the destiny of other species, and is able by deliberate planning to influence and largely to determine the conditions of his own survival. Either way, the case against progressive development is lost.

Even if the opinions of biologists are divided on this issue, the view that evolution is and has been progressive is supported by biological authorities no less modern and impressive than Huxley,

Simpson, Thoday, Oparin and Dobzhanski. Those who take the opposite view seem at times to be denying, not simply the progressive character of biological change and the supremacy of man, but that any process properly called evolution has occurred at all. For if the phylogenetic series is not progressive and apes are no advance on jellyfish, the history of life on the planet has indeed been one of constant change, but in what intelligible sense has anything evolved?

The conception of evolutionary progress is sometimes disparaged by thinkers who seek to be objective, on the ground that human valuation ought not to be introduced into science. But the objection is over-captious and ignores the patent facts. The valuation has been introduced as a scientific necessity for accurate description; it is demanded by the character of the organism and the very form of the evolutionary process. The value is survival value, the essence of which is now seen to be integral wholeness and self-maintaining auturgy. Another current word for it is viability. That evolution has generated forms progressively increasing in organization and adaptiveness tending to greater viability and capacity to survive, no ingenuous biologist today would wish to deny. The argument is palpably fallacious that we think in this way only because we picture the evolutionary process as ending with ourselves, and in our conceit we take ourselves to be superior to other species. Could we consult horses, dogs or monkeys—so the argument runs—or even less prepossessing creatures —we should probably find that they would hold themselves to be our betters and to occupy the summit of developmental perfection. But we cannot consult lower species because they can form no theories or opinions. And they can form no theories because they lack the intellect. If we were to ask their opinion, they could give us no answer and *a fortiori* not the answer alleged; because they have not the mental capacity to frame one.[1] And this confirms our position as their superiors. If we were not, we could have no theories about ourselves as a species or about them; we could not make the comparison, and we could not imagine ourselves supreme on earth. That we can is evidence that we are. We are liable to

---

[1] Cf. Nietzsche, *Vom Nutzen und Nachteil der Historie fur das Leben:* '*Der Mensch fragt wohl einmal das Tier: warum redest du mir nicht von deinem Glücke und sieht mir nur an? Das Tier will auch antworten und sagen: dass kommt daher, dass ich immer gleich vergesse, was ich sagen wollte—da vergass es aber diese Antwort und schweig.*'

singular error only when we make similar comparisons among the races of men, for then the judgment can be reciprocal.

The character which has most obviously become dominant through biological evolution, which gives the highest degree of adaptiveness and has the greatest versatility in self-adjustment is intelligence. That this has developed continuously since the emergence of vertebrate orders is evidenced by the continuous growth and elaboration of their brains. 'Mental activity is intensified and mental organization improved during evolution; like bodily organization, it is improved in different ways in relation to different needs' (this is Julian Huxley's testimony). 'Most trends in mental organization were specializations for a particular way of life, and eventually came to a dead end. However, one particular trend was progressive, and led to the final emergence of mind as the most important property of its possessors. . . .'[1]

In criticizing Teilhard for asserting that evolution is directional towards 'cerebralization', Medawar has pilloried this idea as a 'fatuous argument' and seems to regard the process of 'becoming brainier' with scorn, as if it were something contemptible.[2] That in itself is an evaluation and obviously a perverse one. But whether or not 'brainyness' is a desirable characteristic (and one somehow suspects that Professor Medawar would not be gratified by any suggestion that he lacked it), the available evidence of the course of evolution leaves no doubt that brain capacity has been on the increase since the emergence of animal life from the waters and throughout the evolution of mammalian species. 'Plants', says Medawar with sarcasm, 'do not count. . . .' But no such gibe is worthy of a biologist sufficiently instructed to know that evolution proceeds by ramifying specializations and that advance occurs by successive, overlapping deployments. Plant-life is one of the greatest and earliest of these. Each branching specialization has its own orientation and within any one there may be spectacular developments, yet in so restricted a direction that it precludes certain types of improvement which are achieved in other deployments. This does not, however, rule out the importance and contribution of the restricted line. And in another way, plants certainly do count, for we are concerned not only with individual morphology but with the evolution of a total biocoenosis to the economy of which plants are as essential as brains, and their evolution indispensable to that

---

[1] *Evolution in Action*, pp. 75–6.
[2] *Mind*, LXX (1961), pp. 102–3.

of cerebrate animals. What is 'fatuous' is rather the suggested denial of all this than Teilhard's exposition of it, who, with all the flamboyant enthusiasm of his description, never in any essential misrepresents the facts. Even his allegation of an 'inner' mental aspect of living forms is supported by Huxley[1] and may well be capable of an acceptable interpretation. At all events, the evolutionary process has produced bigger and better brains, it has thrown up as its latest fruit animals with developed intelligence, and (whether Professor Medawar likes it or not) its crowning product is the mind of man.

[1] 'I find myself driven to assume ... that all living substance has mental, or we had better say mindlike, properties; but that these are, for the most part, below the level of detection. They could only be utilized for biological ends when organs were evolved capable of intensifying them.' *Evolution in Action*, p. 77.

CHAPTER XIII

MECHANISM AND TELEOLOGY

I

The scientific evidence shows living activity, despite occasional exceptions which prove the rule, to be a process of co-ordination generating order and integrating an increasingly wide range of different factors into progressively more complex, intricate and flexible, yet more stable, wholes. This is true, in one way, of developmental processes, generating a complex adult organism from a fertilized egg-cell; it is true in another way of physiological activity as it maintains the organism in a range of varying external circumstances; and it is true in yet a third way of the process of evolution in which the already complex system of the organism is extended and its coherence enhanced by the continual integration of mutations in its genetic material, which give it adaptive advantages in special and changing environments. We should now be in a better position to consider questions that have been raised about the nature of this process and its relation to the end it produces. Is it simply an accidental outcome of a process of random shuffling? Is it something determined by inexorable laws such that from sufficient data the end could be calculated from a knowledge of its beginnings? Or is it a process in which the end is implicit from the start, and moulds its course throughout?

The discussion in the last chapter has disposed of the first of these three questions. The facts do not permit us to hold that the high degree of improbability generated by natural selection could have been the result of mere random shuffling and accidental changes. These may have played their part but cannot in their nature provide the integrating and organizing principles. Controversy persists however about the answers to the other two questions. Many thinkers assert that Laplacian deterministic laws—though not by any means all known as yet, would be sufficient to account for all the facts, and that there is, indeed, no alternative between determinism of this sort and completely indeterminate, uncaused, chance.[1] Others maintain staunchly that neither chance nor Laplacian determinism is capable of explaining the processes of life

[1] Cf. J. J. C. Smart in *Mind*, LXX, 1961, pp. 291–306.

but that some type of final cause must be presumed. This is the old dispute between materialism and mechanism on the one side and vitalism and teleology on the other.

The persistence of the dispute is atavistic and is due largely to misunderstanding and faulty or inadequate analysis of concepts. For clearly the idea of determinism in Laplacian terms is no longer tenable having been rendered obsolete by contemporary relativistic and quantum physics, and the vitalism which was little more than reaction against it is rendered equally obsolete by the obsolescence of its correlative opposite. The old-fashioned vitalism of *l'élan vital* and entelechies was never successful, however suggestive. The 'life force' was either just another mechanical force without the advantage of any explanatory function, and the entelechy was a mere mystery presiding over and directing a collection of old-style mechanical forces. 'Vitalism', says von Bertalanffy, 'is nothing less than the renunciation of a scientific explanation of biological data.'[1] No scientists nowadays openly and seriously support either of these two kinds of theory.

Nevertheless, there are still two schools of thought. There are still those who stoutly maintain their faiths in the possibility of reducing all biological laws to those of physics and chemistry, who point to the statistical laws of physics and assert that from the randomness of mutations order may be extracted by similar mathematical means and abjure all suggestions of teleology. This, it is held, is merely apparent in homeostatic processes, in ontogenesis and in phylogenesis, and is simulated by the effects of natural selection playing on random mutations and moulding negative feed-back mechanisms under the selective pressure of environmental conditions. The view has a certain plausibility so long as one forgets the odds against the actual production by any such process of the observed outcome of vital activity. If the statistical laws of thermodynamics were consistently applied this result would be virtually beyond expectation.

Not surprisingly, therefore, we find a large and influential body of biological opinion still supporting teleological or quasi-teleological views. They are not all alike, except in this particular. We have already noted how Oparin is quite ready to talk of 'purpose' and orientation as characteristic of evolution and living activity. Sherrington was to the end prepared to speak of final

[1] Cf. L. von Bertalanffy's criticism in *Mod. Theories of Development*, pp. 43 ff.

causes in biology. J. S. Haldane declared that biology had its own laws, distinct from those of the physical sciences, and that only failure of perception could miss them. Lillie and Agar unashamedly propound teleological doctrines and are even prepared to advocate a kind of panpsychism. E. S. Russell and E. W. Sinnott declare regulation and directiveness to be the distinguishing characteristics of organic activity; and others, like von Bertalanffy and Waddington, advocate the organismic approach.

There is, however, no real issue between these two groups, whose opposition is merely apparent. The organismic approach is really a combination and reconciliation of mechanism and teleology, and it is possible to understand that last term, as it properly should be understood, in a sense which exempts it from all legitimate objections.[1]

2

Teleological explanation is usually rejected because: (i) it presumes or implies some extraneous agency (e.g. God) directing and arranging living processes to fulfil its own deliberate purposes; (ii) it is anthropomorphic in crediting lower organisms with purposive activity similar to our own; (iii) it, tacitly or openly, attributes to living things the consciousness necessary to pursue purposes in the absence of any sufficient evidence of its existence, and (iv) it attempts explanation *obscuri per obscurius* by postulating as a cause of present activity an event which must occur in the future. This difficulty is avoided in the case of conscious purpose because the imagination of an end precedes and stimulates action. These objections are legitimate so far as they apply. It is alien to science to attribute phenomena to supernatural causes; it is not desirable to assimilate the activity of other organisms to human activity without good reason; it is not right unnecessarily to assume consciousness or any other property without adequate evidence, and it is subversive of systematic thinking to reverse the order of causal efficacy without clear explanation of the connection alleged.[2] But it is not necessary to make any of these inadmissible

[1] Cf. E. E. Harris, 'Teleology and Teleological Explanation', *Journal of Philosophy*, LVI, 1959.

[2] This remark is to be qualified, however, by the reminder that no scientist or philosopher has yet convincingly demonstrated the precise connection between efficient causes and their effects.

postulations or assumptions in order to recognize a character in living activity which may be aptly called teleological.

The most important and significant features of purposive action (as I have shown in another place, in more detail) are not that its *end*-state is its determining factor nor that it involves prevision of this end. Only some, perhaps the minority, of human actions are characterized in either way. What is far more typical of such activity is that it is part of a plan or system—a design of activity which need not and often cannot be consciously cognized as a whole by the agent. He need be only vaguely aware of the general outline of the plan and of the principles that govern its structure. These principles are what direct the activity and are not to be identified wholly with the final event in any series of effects. It would be more correct to say that the final event is never the goal of the action. When it fails of its purpose this is manifest; but even when it succeeds the final event is seldom what was aimed at. An author writing a book does not aim at the last page, or line (which may indeed have been written long before the work was completed), and his final activities of checking and proof-reading are still less the goal of his activities. That is a whole system of ideas and objects which is being progressively generated by the activity, and the principle of whose organization directs its course. The majority of human actions have this character and we shall return in due time to discuss it more fully; but we are already in a position to observe that living processes do for the most part generate integrated systems, and are themselves regulated and directed by the principles of order governing the systems they generate. It is in just this respect that living activity may be likened to and classified with purposive. If the word 'teleological' were confined to indicating this property of organized direction of an activity relative to a systematic structure, the legitimate objections would not arise, and its use would be scientifically admissible. Explanation would be 'teleological' if it made the parts of a whole intelligible in terms of the organizing principle that constituted them a totality, or processes understandable in terms of the dynamic system to which they belonged. In that case, the widespread modern distaste for teleological explanation would lose its justification, and the current attempts to explain away teleology in living processes would lose their appeal. For no very sound objections have been brought against this type of holistic explanation. On the contrary there is much to recommend it.

The idea itself is not unscientific and is fully amenable to scientific treatment. Everything we have so far discovered about physical nature bears this out. Explanation of particular events, comprehension of the character of particular entities, and understanding of the determining principles of particular processes, by reference to their membership and participation in an organized system, and in the light of the principle of organization regulating the system as a whole, and mutually adjusting its parts—this type of explanation is scientifically respectable, is enlightening, and is clearly necessary, if we may judge by the actual procedure and discoveries of contemporary science. This is what we ought to call teleological, not explanation simply in terms of some end-state, of a process taken to be causally determined by events which have not yet occurred.

Many of the polemics directed against the notion of teleology have been at pains to show that the presumedly teleological is really nothing but a determination of the details of a system by the principle of order that constitutes the whole. This is often explicitly admitted by the critic. Professor Ernest Nagel, for instance, in the course of a long and elaborate demonstration of the dispensability of the idea, admits that all we need is to 'focus attention on . . . the contribution of parts of a system to its maintenance', to 'view the operations of things from the perspective of certain related wholes to which the things belong', and to concern ourselves 'with properties of parts of such wholes only in so far as these properties are relevant to some complex features or activities assumed as characteristic of those wholes'.[1] So long as these qualifications are recognized, Professor Nagel considers 'teleological' explanation to be on a par with non-teleological, and if this is so we may surely regard self-maintaining systems, and explanation in terms of organizing relations, as teleological without ceasing to be scientific. For the rest the current philosophical critique of the idea of teleology largely exemplifies the reversion of contemporary philosophy to the mechanistic presuppositions of the classical physics which can admit no semblance of purposive action, except as imported into a mechanical world by an immaterial spirit, and which is unable to accommodate any genuine holism because it conceives all wholes as aggregates of separable parts.

[1] 'Teleological Explanation', in Feigl and Brodbeck, *Readings in the Philosophy of Science* (New York, 1949), p. 553.

3

On the other hand, explanation in terms of genuine wholes, whose members are never completely isolable or separable without critical modification of both whole and part, in no way excludes physics and chemistry, and is unlikely to be successful without careful examination and analysis of the mechanisms by which physico-chemical processes are correlated and integrated into a single system. Teleological explanation, in this sense, is obliged to be 'mechanistic', and, where the system to be explained is an integrated whole, any mechanistic explanation which is not teleological in this way must be inadequate. Vitalists were, after all, seeking no more than the recognition of the holism and auturgy of the organism in their repudiation of mechanism; and their search after entelechies and mysterious influences was no more than the search for that which integrates and perpetually regulates the living thing to harmony within itself and fitness with its environment.[1] So their demand is met by any theory that seeks explanation of the part in the light of the whole. Likewise their constant surrender to mechanism in detail is understandable, for without it there can be no complete explanation of the organizing relations which hold the living system together.

It is interesting to note in passing that there has always been a strong tendency among scientists to use human artifacts as analogous to and as models for explaining the working of the living organism. Its various functions are often referred to as mechanisms, as indeed they are. What is not always noticed is that human artifacts are devices for bringing about willed results. They are designed by conscious beings for specific purposes. They are deliberately planned to serve ends. They are all without exception teleological. Any machine theory in biology is therefore crypto-teleological and any talk of physiological or genetic mechanisms implies some form of teleology. It is indeed odd that some writers should have sought to illustrate the non-teleological character of biological evolution by comparing it with the development of some human artifact, like the Gothic Cathedral or the automobile.[2] It is true enough that the original

[1] Cf. Hans Driesch, *The Problem of Individuality*, where entelechy is designated 'the unifying cause'.

[2] Cf. H. F. Blum, *Time's Arrow and Evolution*, p. 209 (here the artifact is the Gothic Cathedral), and David Hawkins, 'Design for a Mind', *Daedalus*, 1962, p. 562 (who uses the automobile).

inventor (if we could identify one) of the motor car neither planned nor foresaw its later forms and that the designer of the modern car has merely modified earlier models, which he did not invent. The car has developed gradually by successive modifications ('mutations') of earlier patterns. But, quite apart from the fact that in its origins it was designed by human minds to serve specific human purposes, each new development has been the result of deliberately planned improvements to meet consciously desired conveniences. Each has been deliberately sought as a means of increasing efficiency and each has been adopted for its known advantages. If organic evolution were anything like this it must throughout be attributed to the deliberate effort and planning of conscious agents. The evolution of any such human artifacts is therefore a dangerous analogy for the anti-teleologist to use, though there may well be contexts in which it is by no means inept.

On the other hand, any purposive process, be its agent a human mind, an unknown entelechy or a mysterious life force, can be carried out in a material medium only by harnessing physico-chemical laws in the use of mechanisms. No vitalism therefore can give up the physico-chemical investigation of the material processes that go on in the organism or can abandon explanations in terms of physical processes. But equally no mechanistic approach can ignore teleological aspects implicit in the presence of devices performing specific functions however properly they are designated 'mechanisms'.

The proper science of such teleological mechanisms would be cybernetics—the science of regulation or governance. As yet it is a science in its infancy and what it has achieved still falls far short of explaining that self-regulating or auturgic property which distinguishes the living from the non-living. Whether the methods presently used in investigations going by the name of cybernetics will ultimately prove satisfactory remains to be seen, but, in as much as it seeks the method and principles of self-direction which organize various mechanisms into a single coherent system, it is a science of teleological order. It would, moreover, be foolish to imagine that the elucidation of feed-back mechanisms and interconnected servo-mechanisms eliminates teleology (meaning the dynamics of organized wholeness), for without that they would lose their distinguishing character and function. The idea of a servo-mechanism in isolation from a system of processes integrated to bring about a concerted result,

I*

in which the mechanism fulfils a specific function, would plainly be absurd, for so isolated it would be neither 'servo' nor 'mechanism'.

We must consider the nature of the relation between a servo-mechanism and the function it performs, as between a process of vital activity and the result which it produces. In both cases we are concerned with a dynamic system which is regulated for self-maintenance. This is obviously so for mechanisms subserving homeostasis. Neuro-muscular mechanisms co-ordinating sensory and motor organs and controlling movement perform subservice in the second degree: the mechanism subserves the organization of an activity which in its turn subserves the maintenance of the dynamic system. The mechanisms of heredity and development are instrumental to what Waddington prefers to call 'homeorhesis' regulating the course of change along a 'creode' (or determinate path). The effect is the same—that of constructing and maintaining a specific dynamic system, for reproduction is also a phase of self-maintenance. Evolution is the progressive modification of these processes, through the integration into the system and adjustment to it of accidental genetic changes. The process is channelled by selection as the external environment requires; and the habitual way of life of the organism (itself a manifestation of its active self-maintenance) contributes to determine its processes. Thus both mechanisms and vital processes are intrumental to the maintenance or construction of a totality and can justifiably be termed teleological, without any suggestion that they involve consciousness or the delibate purpose of some extraneous agent.

4

In every case we encounter regulation of part by the whole, of each phase in the process by the structural pattern being generated. So in every case we have what, in the stipulated sense of the word, is a teleological design or activity, or both; which is no more than to say a dynamic organized system. 'What', asks Waddington, 'is organization? It is rather a tricky concept to define, and it is probably sufficient to say here that it implies that if an organized entity is broken up into parts, the full properties of these parts can only be understood by reference to their relations with other parts of the whole system.'[1] The paramount

[1] *The Nature of Life*, p. 53. Strictly, however, an organized system cannot be 'broken up into parts' for that destroys both the system and the derivative nature of the parts. See Ch. XXII below.

condition is the priority of the whole and its constitutive influence upon the character and activity of the parts. A corollary of this, and the next most significant condition of organization is internal variety, without which there would be nothing to organize. A mere unit is not the same as a structured whole.

There is no room for doubt that the living organism is an entity of this sort: an organized whole of diverse parts dominated by the uniting principle of the totality. But yet more important is the fact that it is not just a spatial structure but an interplay of processes going on in time. Though at each stage there is a spatial pattern with its own coherence, it is not in itself *the* whole of which it is a phase. The entire sequence of intertwining processes and changing spatial patterns is an organized unity, in which the momentary pattern is continually modified in the direction of greater integrity and completeness. In such a process it is, as always, the organizing principle that dominates and directs and accordingly the whole is *generated* throughout the process. The course of the process is subject to and each successive phase subserves the increase of complexification and integration. Consequently, the dynamic totality, which at any stage the organism is, issues as a development in which the earlier generates the later and is related to it as means to end. Yet the final phase is no more '*the* whole' than is any other (it may be less so), for the entire process must be included in the totality. Nevertheless, the means-end relationship between successive phases gives the process its typically teleological appearance and is the reason why the end-state has been emphasized in such teleological movements. It is, however, not its coming last that makes any phase the fulfilment of the process, but its being the most complete and most fully integrated form of the system. Indeed there are processes, which answer to the required description, whose fulfilment is not at the end but in the middle (and even nearer the beginning than the termination of the series of changes). Most living creatures are of this pattern, for after they have fully developed they decline and die. But the principle of organization dominates throughout and is effective even in the period of decline which is off-set as a rule by some complementary process of regeneration, if not in the same organism, in its offspring.

5

This dominance of the whole in time makes living activity tele-ological in four different ways: (i) First there is what Waddington calls exogenous adaptation when the organism, with or without natural selection, adjusts itself to external pressures.

'Examples of such direct adaptations are legion. If muscles are continually and intensely used, they become thicker and stronger; if one kidney is removed from a mammal, the other hypertrophies; if the forelegs are absent at birth, or removed slightly afterwards, from rats or dogs, the hind-limbs become modified to suit the bi-pedal gait which the animals are forced to adopt; if skin is sub-jected to frequent rubbing and pressing, it thickens and becomes more horny; and one could multiply such instances almost in-definitely.'[1]

This kind of adaptability is prior to mutation and selection. Every living organism has the character of self-adjustment to external and internal change, a propensity which is neither ex-ceptional nor rare but typical and ubiquitous. Mutation may produce an organism capable of suitable self-adaptation to a particular environmental change, and selection will then ensure its continued generation; but its adaptiveness is inherent and not itself a process of mutation. *Arcella*, when deprived of oxygen, requires no special new mutation in order to secrete a bubble that will float it to regions of better supply, even if its ability to do this may depend on the activity of its genes, which may have been modified by some mutation in an ancestor enabling it to behave adjustively. Our own bodies adapt themselves constantly in most complicated ways to changing circumstances; to changes in temperature, to variations in oxygen supply, food supply, availa-bility of water and a hundred other circumstances. None of these adaptive reactions is produced, on the occasion of its occurrence, by a mutation—none could be. Their survival value is obvious, but their adaptive character is not consequent upon that; on the contrary, survival is consequent upon adaptiveness. The athlete improves his performance by training—that is, he takes advantage of the adaptive capacity of his muscles, his vascular and respiratory systems and his physiological functions generally to improve their

[1] Waddington, *The Strategy of the Genes*, p. 151.

efficiency in successive repetitions of exercise under conditions of effort and strain. No mutations occur during training, but the bodily functions change so as more efficiently to meet the environmental needs. The same is true of accommodation to altitude or cold. Again the *capacity* to change could be due to genetic arangements and these may be residual effects of past mutations, but the adaptive capacity is in itself teleological and in itself involves no genetic mutation. By means of such self-adjusting functioning the organism maintains itself in a wider range of environmental conditions as a viable, complete system of vital functions. Clearly an organism incapable of adaptive response, would not survive or reproduce and selection would eliminate it; but selection could not enable it to adapt when conditions altered.[1]

(ii) Next there is prolepsis in organic process: that is, there is anticipation in one phase of what will occur later. For instance, eggs are provided with yolk as nutriment for the embryo-to-be. In mammals, pregnant mothers supply deficiencies in the foetus at the expense of their own bodies as if a new homeostasis were created to maintain the needs of the growing off-spring before all else. But the young are to live in the future, so that here future needs are being supplied at the expense of the present needs of the mother's body.

In the human foetus a special muscle is provided to close the ductus joining the lung to the main artery of the body as soon as the lung becomes active at birth. This muscle is (so far as known) not used before birth, and after it has performed its single needful action, it degenerates and disappears, as does the channel it was needed to close.

Similarly the behaviour of some insects is proleptic. Scarabeid beetles collect sufficient dung for the complete supply of their larvae up to the stage of metamorphosis. Other insects lay eggs in suitable hosts or on a specially provided store of food for their offspring though the parents die before either the grubs or (in

[1] Cf. C. J. Herrick, op. cit., p. 135: 'The idea of "teleological causation" must be rigorously excluded from science. Yet the fact remains that all adaptations do have a future reference. There is an end to be achieved, and this implies some kind of natural teleology. Active search is now being made for the mechanisms of this forward reference of adaptive behaviour and human purposive action.'
The 'teleological causation' to be excluded is of the sort that we ourselves have rejected above and the compatibility of 'natural teleology' with 'mechanisms' is taken for granted.

many cases) the food ever develops. The Yucca moth, for instance, lays eggs among the ovaries of the yucca flower, which it then pollinates with a specially gathered pollen ball, but it does not live to see the fruit develop nor its own young which will feed on it. The free swimming larvae of polychaete worms, before they transform into the adult stage, sink to the sea bottom and explore it minutely until they find the right consistency of mud in which to burrow and the proper conditions for adult life. If for any reason they are unsuccessful, they delay metamorphosis until the right conditions can be found.

These proleptic processes are all obvious cases of subservience of the part to the temporal as well as the spatial totality. This totality down to the minutest detail may be contained in the arrangement of the genetic material and the proleptic activity may well be no more than the unfolding of the prearranged plan. If so, the arrangement of the genetic material is itself proleptic and embodies the whole which dominates the process of generation. It has no doubt survived because it has come to be what it is and so has been selectively preserved, but this does not account for the minute co-ordination of organs and functions which is the precise reason for its survival. That will become intelligible only with the discovery of the source and operative principle of the persistent nisus to wholeness and integrity of which the facts give evidence.

(iii) Thirdly, as Russell so copiously illustrates, living activity is directive towards a definite state of affairs—the completion of a specific whole. It is hardly possible to explain away all such movements in terms of mutation and selection. In particular, there is a wide variety of morphogenetic movements of cells and tissues to which no such explanation is at all appropriate. Among myxo-bacteria, *Chondromyces crocatus* emerges from its spore cysts as a throng of minute rods. These rods show a marked tendency to aggregate and will stream together from all directions to a single collection point. They seem to follow slime tracks left by other rods (like minute slugs), but will aggregate to a common centre even when no tracks are present. Bonner has shown that they will circumvent a groove made across any possible existing tracks. When a distant centre of aggregation is moved near a stream of rods they promptly change their direction of motion to join it.[1] The aggregation, once formed, grows both by division and

[1] *Morphogenesis*, pp. 170-3.

multiplication of rods and by further fusions, till when the colony reaches a certain stage an elaborate process of fruiting takes place. The mass forms a knob and is pressed up into the air by a continuous contraction of its base which elongates into a stalk. This is found to contain mostly gelatinous material, the rods being pressed up into the more bulky advancing blob. Finally this blob forms lobes each on its own stalk, like berries in a bunch, the rods becoming encased in a cluster of hardening cysts. The regulation of this whole series of movements as a definite pattern of development is evident, and its direction, despite disturbance and interruption, towards the completion of a definite whole is unmistakable.

The slime-mould, *Dictyostelium*, behaves in a comparable manner and if the attracting centre is placed on one side of a thin, glass shelf and the separate amoeboid cells on the other they will move towards it round the edge of the shelf. If two shelves are arranged with a space between them, the centre placed on the upper surface of one and the separate amoebae on the upper surface of the other, the latter will stream to the point nearest to the centre and congregate there, straining with their pseudopods to cross the gap, which if reduced to the length of one of them they will do, forming a hanging bridge between the edges.[1]

In other cases separate cells in a larger organism move about working together in concert to construct some essential part of its anatomy. So mesenchyme cells migrate to the proper places to secrete the substance of a skeleton, and the spicules of sponges are produced by the secretory action of migrating cells. Where the spicule is triradiate the cells move in threes with astonishing accuracy to form a double trefoil pattern. The spicule is laid down as a minute three-pointed star in the centre and is then built up with one trio of cells moving outward to form the diverging points, and the other remaining near the centre extending and thickening the conjugate base of the rays. Quadraradiate spicules are made by a fourth cell derived from a different source which attaches itself to the centre of the triradiate and secretes its own ray at right-angles in its proper position and orientation. This choreography of cell movements is in every case patently designed to construct a whole and when interrupted or obstructed is redirected towards its completion. As Russell points out, such co-operative constructive activities of cells are similar to the

[1] Cf. op. cit., pp. 179–80, and Fig. 66.

building activities of social insects and the nest-building of birds.

A last remarkable example of such morphogenetic movement is gastrular inversion in the asexual reproduction of the alga, *Volvox*. This is a green sphere made up of biflagellate cells each surrounded by jelly. The flagella protrude outward and by concerted movement give the colony a spinning motion first in one direction and then in the other. The upper cells are slightly larger and darker than the lower. In asexual reproduction the lower cells (gonidia) divide, forming a pocket which as it grows by continual division bulges inward. At this stage the flagellar ends of the daughter colony's cells all project internally, a position in which they could not exercise their locomotive function. The daughter colony then contracts towards the mouth of the pocket (the phialopore) and, forcing itself through this aperture, turns inside out, detaching itself in the process from the mother colony. So by their concerted movement the correct pattern of the organism is achieved, in which it can now function properly, and it swims about inside the parent until the older organism eventually dies, splits open and gives birth to the new. The mechanics of this process of inversion (which occurs also in other creatures) still defy explanation.[1]

All these morphogenetic movements are directed to the perfection of a definite structure, in itself a coherent whole and, in many instances, an integral part of a larger, more complete whole. That the movement results from some mechanical process can hardly be questioned, though as yet it is largely unknown. But whatever the mechanism, it is clearly guided by the pattern and structure of the whole to be produced, which then becomes the spatial instrument of a living process of self-maintenance with which the morphogenetic process is continuous. So the presiding and directing effect of the totality may never be overlooked, and only as subject to it have the contributory processes the form and character which they display to observation. This form is teleological in the way we have explained but it in no way excludes or evades mechanical and efficient causation.

(iv) The fourth form of teleology displayed by life is developmental and evolutionary progress. That evolution by natural selection is teleological from the outset is clearly Oparin's opinion: 'The living systems which were first formed', he writes, 'already had all the features needed for their selection to be of the nature

[1] Cf. Bonner, op. cit., pp. 188–201.

of the purposeful "natural selection" in the biological sense of the expression'.[1] He repeatedly speaks of 'a definite orientation of the process of the evolution of matter',[2] and of 'directed evolution'.[3] Discussing evolutionary progress, Huxley does not scruple to use the word 'improvement', which implies a standard of value. We have already argued that the survival value to which appeal is commonly made, is strictly coherence of integration within the system, and between it and the world of which it is a member, for the only survival which is relevant is of a viable living system (not of inorganic or of chaotic processes) and only through a sufficient degree of coherent integration do such systems survive. Taking this as the standard, improvement is a felicitous term and it is on the whole the mark of developmental and evolutionary progress, though the tendency to further integration often leads to excessive specialization, which distorts progress. Improvement in one respect alone may well disrupt by unbalance both the required integrity of the organism and its adaptation to environment. It may result in deterioration on the whole. Nevertheless it is clear that both individual development and evolutionary advance do produce increasingly complex systems increasingly unified. Ontogenesis from a single cell elaborates a multiplex integrated system of organs and processes. That evolution does likewise is partly disclosed by the fact that some evidences for its occurrence and course is derived from embryology. It has led from simpler organisms to more complex, from less efficient to more ingenious and more delicately adjusted mechanisms, from less to more versatile capacities—in short, to more adequately and completely integrated totalities.

6

Whitehead (like Leibniz) thought that in every actual entity there is 'appetition'—what he called 'a subjective aim at further integration'. Contemporary science, on which he based his philosophical theories, gives no little evidence of universal pressure towards increasing holism; and without committing ourselves to the implication of the terms 'appetition' and 'subjective aim', it seems safe enough to acknowledge the existence of a persistent drive in this direction. In the sphere of life it is abundantly evident and it is this alone which gave colour to doctrines of orthogenesis in their heyday, and such plausibility as it carries to

[1] Op. cit., p. 363.   [2] Ibid., p. 373.   [3] Ibid., p. 376.

Lamarkism. Evolution does not seem to be forced along creodes, like developmental processes, as the supporters of orthogenesis suggested, but its progress often gives that appearance because it is the result of a constant integrating nisus which incorporates each new and fortuitous change into an already existing system to preserve and intensify its coherence. At the same time the adopted way of life and the various habits acquired by a species are factors playing a part in the process and the restrictions imposed by selection accentuate it. Thus, when environmental pressures have led ungulates to a life on open grasslands, the presence of carnivores exerts a new pressure towards development of speed in locomotion. The total set of circumstances leads to the development of an integrated system of characters: grinding teeth and hard hooves, as well (in some cases) as stomachs elaborately adapted to deferred digestion (by cud-chewing), so that rapid grazing in exposed spaces may be supplemented by more leisurely mastication and digestion in comparative safety. The integration into a single pattern of all these characters, maintaining a viable system in a given set of external circumstances, emphasized and channelled by selection, gives an appearance of orthogenesis. So far as the actual course of evolution is directed, under the pressures of selection, persistently towards integration and co-ordination, it is orthogenetic. But in no other way; for flexibility and relevant variation are of the essence of auturgic self-maintenance, and for this very reason over-specialization, closing off alternative paths of advance, ceases to constitute improvement. In each new deployment in the evolutionary process it is the most generalized and least restricted species that forms the bridge-head for further progress.

Lamarkism stressing the effects of needs, and habits acquired to meet those needs, and alleging the inheritance of acquired characteristics, is prompted by the facts that environmental pressures do create needs which must be met if the organism is to survive. They can be met only if the organic system is suitably adjusted. When this occurs, it can be maintained in the long run only if the already present capacity to adapt is supported and confirmed by genetic emphasis on the requisite modifications. This may in part be accomplished through genetic characteristics already present in pre-adapted individuals, and further by the incorporation into and adjustment to the gene-complex of usable mutations.[1]

[1] Cf. the adaptation of *Drosophila* to excessive salt cited by Waddington, *The Nature of Life*, pp. 91–7.

The proliferation of the species is then pruned and shaped by selection to meet the environmental demands. So where the capacity to acquire a useful character is increased by genetic alteration we have the appearance and in some measure even the actuality of inheritance of acquired characteristics, and to this the acquired habits of the organism (genetic though they also are in origin) have contributed through their influence upon the direction taken by selection pressures. The totality which is constructed in the evolutionary process does include the factors stressed by Lamarkism, all of which have to be integrated in the complete system involving organism and environment; and the forces impinging upon that system, to effect co-ordination and mutual adjustment of parts and functions, may well include the organic influence of the complete organism upon its genome as well as the controlling effect of the genome upon the anatomical, physiological and behavioural system into which the organism develops.

7

In a process of organic concrescence such as we are calling teleological, the later phases are ovbiously not derived from the earlier by simple addition. The organismic character of the whole determines the form and manner of incorporation of every accretion. We saw how, in organic self-maintenance, the systematic character of the whole determined the form and pattern of growth, differentiating and organizing additional material as it was formed. We observed that development was always the elaboration of a diversified unity and never simple accumulation of substance. In such processes the guiding influence on the course of activity is the pattern of the whole that eventually emerges. In development this is easily admissible and relatively understandable because of the ubiquitous presence of the chromosomes presumed to contain the codified pattern of the completed system. But evolution is harder to conceive in this way. Nevertheless, if in evolution the primary influence is the trend towards integration and coherence, the pattern of the eventual outcome (not fixed or static, but variable relevantly to the organizing principle) must be the directing factor here as well. The adjustment of a given complex for more adequate interplay between its dynamic parts, and between them and its surround, is the imposition upon it of the principle of organization of the consequent whole. Despite the apparent sense of this statement, it does not imply production of earlier effects by later causes. The principle of organization is at work throughout and the consequent totality is its self-realization. It is implicit in the earlier stage and we rightly refer to it there as potential. This does not necessitate its evolution or fix its path inexorably, for as we already know, flexibility, relevant variation and versatility are the very means of its actualization.

But how, it may be asked, can the outcome of biological evolution be implicit in its beginnings? Its course is contingent upon the vagaries of physical, geological and climatic changes, not simply on organic potentialities—even though these do impose limitations upon it. In fact the limitation is mutual. Sometimes the more obvious aspect of the process sems to be the adaptation of the organism to changing circumstances; sometimes the limits placed upon viability by environmental conditions is more apparent. In actuality evolution is a balance between the two. In this mutual interplay of accidental factors, how can one talk of the immanence and directing influence of a totality the form of which must be unpredictable in essence?

Unpredictable by the scientist no doubt it is. Yet once it has occurred it can be recognized as in some sort necessary. Let us hear Julian Huxley on this point:

'Looking back into the past we see clearly enough that conceptual thought could only have arisen in an animal as against a plant; in a multicellular animal; in an actively feeding animal, with bilateral symmetry and a head; in one with a highly differentiated bodily organization, which was therefore doomed to die; in a vertebrate as against a mollusc or an arthropod; in a land vertebrate as against a fish; and among land vertebrates, only in a placental mammal with a constant temperature. And, finally, it could have arisen only in a mammal which had become gregarious, which had a long period of learning and experience, which produced only one young at a birth, and which had recently become terrestrial after a long spell of life in the trees. Clearly the path of progress is both devious and unique.'[1]

L. J. Henderson, long ago, in a book still respected by scientists,[2] worked out in detail how only in a physical and geographical

[1] *Evolution in Action*, p. 110.
[2] *The Fitness of the Environment* (Macmillan, New York, 1913).

environment, such as by the merest chance has come to be on this planet, could life have been generated and evolved. There is thus a sense in which the outcome of evolution was implicit from the beginning. We must not forget that organism and environment are inseparable, and in the last resort we are dealing with a single totality—the biosphere—the morphology of which is generating and incorporating focal organisms in a single process. The systematic principles of order within this totality determine the details, and these principles are what we call the laws of nature. Their discovery is the task that the scientist sets himself. Within the total morphology, the focal organism reflects and expresses these principles microcosmically within the macrosphere, producing a general structure similar to that in the physical cosmos, where a self-contained space-time world contains (or manifests itself in) coherent sub-systems determined by and expressing the universal principles of order.

If progressive integration is what characterizes this morphology it can only be by the progressive imposition upon the more uniform and uncoordinated of the organizing principle of the more complex and coherent. And if the nisus to integration is an inherent factor in reality, this principle will be immanent in things from the beginning and will, at every stage, be working itself out and realizing the potentialities of the available material in terms of its own demand for coherent harmony. Thus the process as a whole would be proleptic and the later stages would in some significant way be potential in the earlier, both in the sense that the material and propensities of the earlier must be capable of taking on the later forms, and in the sense that the principles of final order are implicit in the structure of the earlier complex. So in terrestrial conditions there is the potentiality of life, in primitive organisms the potentiality of elaboration, in auturgic self-maintenance of biotic activity the potentiality of consciousness and conceptual thinking. But this potentiality in no way entails rigid determination of the process of evolution. Rather the course is opportunistic, taking advantage of, and incorporating into the totality, whatever chance materials or conditions become available and can be made to fit. The polyphasic character of the whole progressively multiplies the possibilities of alternative expedients and increases the versatility of its agency for the realization of coherence. The details of the process have depended upon chance events and as the complexity of organisms and the plastic interplay of factors has developed, the variability of form and direction of activity, though always relevant to the central principle of organization, has increased incalculably.

The whole process is one and not a haphazard succession of unconnected changes. What emerges at the end must be conceived as what has all along been evolving, and what emerges is man. 'Hominisation' is a term applied by some biologists to the latest phase of biological evolution in which the mammalian deployment issues in monkeys, apes and hominids. By a legitimate extrapolation backwards the whole process can be viewed as one of hominisation, devious and ramifying though the route has been.

In all these ways biological development and evolution are teleological; but for the reasons stated, that word harbours so many unpalatable associations that it readily engenders antagonism in scientific minds. The proposal to drop these associations and redefine the concept as I have suggested above would deprive biologists of a cherished Aunt Sally, a deprivation that they might resent. It may well be unwise, therefore, to press too insistently for its general adoption. It matters less what terminology we use than that we understand clearly the conception to be conveyed and the nature of the process it is intended to describe. And that process is integrative and generative of systematic coherencies, the principles of organization of which determine, and therefore (if discoverable) explain, the details and components. It in no sense excludes or contradicts mechanics or violates physico-chemical laws for it is by their means alone that the adjustment of parts and variation of activities, relevant to the overriding principle of order, can be effected.

CHAPTER XIV

THE PHILOSOPHY OF
PROCESS AND ORGANISM

I

The world picture suggested by our review of the physical sciences is extended, and our notion of the fundamental principles of its general structure reinforced, by reflection upon the sciences of life. The physical world revealed itself as a single totality of distinguishable but inseparable elements, within which were generated microcosms each more fully and adequately embodying principles of order governing the whole. So also the biotic world is seen to be a single interconnected organic system containing a multitude of organisms each a complex whole auturgically maintaining its equilibrium by variations relevant to its own internal principles of order, which reflect and exemplify the general principles of organization governing the biocoenosis. The system of living species, more palpably than that of physical entities, arrays itself as a scale of forms increasingly complex and more closely integrated. Again, more emphatically than at the physical level, living reality reveals itself as essentially dynamic, as perpetual process, even where its structure appears to be most stable and permanent. Not only are the formed organs of the living body in constant process of decay and self-renewal, but the genes themselves, that seem to be the least changeable units of life, suffer constant dynamic breakdown and reconstruction. The living world is essentially a realm of dynamic wholeness, in which the realization of completeness is through a process of change; in which no whole is static, simple, uniform or undifferentiated; yet in which all movement subserves and tends towards order and coherence.

This dynamic interplay of factors in all living substance makes the separation of parts, however clearly distinguishable within the system, altogether impossible. For they flow into and constitute one another. This is true even on the anatomical level. There is strictly *no* living substance, only a complex of interacting chemical substances which live by the special form of their interaction. Organs have their specific characters (and often even their characteristic shapes) only in their functioning. Detached from the organism they are lumps of matter—proteinous or other— not organs of a living body. And when we remind ourselves that the parts of a living thing are strictly not material structures so much as functional processes, when we remember that the organism is an *open* system, we must at once acknowledge that the distinguishable factors which contribute to its organized make-up are utterly inseparable, are completely interfused and mutually constitutive in a thoroughly inextricable manner. They can of course be distinguished and given separate attention by the biologist, but whenever he forgets their indissoluble interdependence he is liable to gross misinterpretation of experimental findings.

Between the physical and the biotic there is no break, and the scale of organized forms advances by continuous complexification and successive self-enfoldments, as Tielhard asserts. The molecule by self-involution becomes organic. Processes of chemical inter- action by returning upon themselves in cyclical reconstitution of substances become metabolic. Energy-producing systems by feed- back of their own products become self-regulating (or cybernetic), and this self-regulation by constant incorporation, harmonization and use of accidental novelties evolves to more efficient, more versatile and more capable organisms. The process generates man, and man with all his shortcomings, acts by deliberate intention, exercising mind. This we shall find is again a 'folding back' or reflection upon itself of vital process, an activity super- venient upon the physiological which cannot be separated from the functioning of the body.

Further, the scale continues to be hierarchical. Nothing physical is cancelled by life, which incorporates in itself all the main physical forms—atoms (even when radioactive), molecules, crystals, with all their physical and chemical bonds. The inter- action of these forms is still subject to physico-chemical laws, if also to more special biological laws; and in some sense nothing is added on the purely material level. The difference is *prima facie* only one of complexity and the type of organization—a difference of degree—but it is one so marked and so critical that it also amounts to a difference of kind. What was before merely a complex and polyphasic system of chemical reactions, becomes an auturgic, self-adjusting and self-maintaining, living organism. Again, despite the continuity between them, the properties of the inorganic and the living are so divergent, as a result of this critical advance in organization, that they evince opposition, not only by contrast of general character, but also in mutual influence so that the organism maintains itself *against* the destructive tendencies of thermo-dynamics, *against* the strains and stresses imposed upon it by its environment.

Within the tree of life the same sort of relationship between phases of development and evolution pertains. They are all in various ways continuous with one another, all different degrees of organization and adaptation to special conditions; yet they provide marked contrasts—unicellular as opposed to multicellular, asexual as opposed to sexual, invertebrate as opposed to vertebrate, animals with exoskeletons of dead hard chitinous exudations as opposed to those with living bony endoskeletons, aquatic animals as opposed to terrestrial, instinctive as opposed to intelligent. In the biotic sphere we have, more obviously than at prior levels, a continuous process of development unrolling a scale of forms, both temporally successive and hierarchically coexistent. These are mutually related in three ways: (i) as differing degrees of realization of organic wholeness and adaptation, (ii) as differing kinds—phyla, classes, orders, families, genera, species—(it was mainly biological study that suggested the very notion of classifi-cation)—(iii) as contrasting and opposed forms (e.g. plants as opposed to animals) which diverge to opposite poles of a continu-ous gradation.

Again there is mounting heirarchy. The cell, independent in Protozoa, is still a self-contained unit in Metazoa. Asexual repro-duction by self-diremption still continues in the segmentation of eggs and the proliferation of cells in sexually reproducing species. The watery environment of early aquatic life with its characteristic salt concentration is still traceable in the bloodstream (the internal environment) of land animals. Automatic and instinctive activity (as will appear) is still the foundation of all intelligent behaviour.

2

The philosopher cannot afford to ignore all this in his effort to understand the general nature of things. The logician must take cognizance of it, if he seeks to discover the principles which make it intelligible. Clearly no foundation is provided by biological dis-coveries for any metaphysical atomism or purely extensional logic. The kind of metaphysic to which it points is Whiteheadian—a metaphysic of process and concrescence, particulate only so far as 'the real internal constitution' of 'actual entities' is made up by the 'ingredience' into them of other actual entities. It portends a metaphysic of internal relations and thoroughgoing interdependence of diverse elements within a single totality. The appropriate philosophy for contemporary science must be, like Whitehead's, a philosophy of organism. 'The whole point of the modern doctrine, he writes, 'is the evolution of the complex organisms from antecedent states of less complex organisms. The doctrine thus cries aloud for a conception of organism as fundamental for nature. It also requires an underlying activity—a substantial activity—expressing itself in achievements of organism.'[1]

There is no room here for the notion of facts as states of affairs any of which might be other than it is without affecting the rest. The merest alteration of hereditary material, giving an organism 0·1 per cent selective advantage, can change a whole population within a few hundred generations. As slight a modification may begin a series of steps leading eventually to the adoption by a species of an entirely new way of life (as the mammalian whales and dolphins have taken to the sea). A change of temperature or altitude, changes the workings of living bodies profoundly. Increase of salt in the environment of *Drosophila* increases the size of their anal papillae. There is no mutual independence of biological facts.

'Ah, but this interdependence is causal not logical' says the critic, begging the question at issue. What is causal dependence? We have already found that to be in part an epistemological question and therefore bound up with logical theory. If the notion of logical implication is derived from an atomistic metaphysic, it is no wonder that it fails to consort with factual interdependence. And when factual interdependence is metaphysically denied causality remains a persistent enigma and is ultimately rejected as an unviable concept.[2] So, in some forms, it may very well be; and if causality is repudiated then to say that facts are causally interdependent but not logically is simply to create confusion. Indeed, if we accept Bertrand Russell's analysis we must believe the whole and only basis of the conception of causal laws to be purely logical. But the discussion of this matter belongs elsewhere.

Modern biology sets the logician a definitive and alluring

---

[1] *Science and the Modern World*, p. 134.
[2] Cf. Bertrand Russell, 'On the Notion of Cause', in *Mysticism and Logic*.

problem. No other science has provided more material than biology for the elaboration of classificatory systems. A whole branch of the science, taxonomy, is devoted to nothing else. But the theory of evolution has revolutionized our conception of classes and converted a classificatory system from a static structure of serial subsumption, into a dynamic succession of morphological changes. The evolution of life is a continuous process and it has produced different forms and species in continuous series. Some of these have not survived so that the continuum, as we find it today is broken and the distinction of species appears sharper than it actually is. Biological classification going back to Linnaeus has largely reflected this discontinuity which, Dr. Charles Michener has said,[1] is for the most part due to gaps in our knowledge. There are cases in which forms have survived closely related to those from which newer species branched out, with the result that it is difficult for the modern taxonomist to decide where they belong in the existing scheme of classification. The same problem arises in the classification of fossil forms, which, had they all come down to us, would form a continuum of change difficult to split up into separate groups. Dr. Michener therefore recommends a revision of the traditional system of classification such as would recognize intergrades between taxa and permit of overlapping classes. Some forms would then be classifiable in either of two ways. Hyracotherium (for instance) could, he says, be regarded equally well as a primitive form of horse or a primitive form of rhinoceros.

The conception of overlapping classes, forced upon the taxonomist by the evolutionary continuum, obviously demands reflexion by the logician and calls for a new theory of the relation of genus to species. Not only must the logician re-examine and clarify the conception of class, but he must also elaborate a logic of change and of developmental transformation and must further demonstrate the relations between all these concepts.

The type of logic demanded is dialectical—a logic of process and interdependence of concepts. In the development of theory and explanation this emerges as a logic of question and answer, such as Collingwood advocated but never related to the one he actually worked out. It will display the class concept as something dialectically potent, generating a scale of concepts which is at once a

[1] *Vide* C. D. Michener, 'Some Future Developments in Taxonomy', *Systematic Zoology*, 12, pp. 151-72.

classificatory system and a developmental process. The notions of distinction, difference in degree and opposition must all be analyzed and related and the conceptions of logical determination and necessity reformulated.

The full investigation of these topics is not to be included in this part of our study. In the next section there will be occasion to allude to some of them again when the study of mental activity gives further pointers to the type of logic required. This will be adumbrated by questions arising out of the sciences of mind. When their findings have been reviewed we may proceed in a separate essay to investigate the logical and epistemelogical character of scientific discovery.

PART III
MENTALITY

CHAPTER XV

BODY AND MIND

I

Any study of mind is faced at the outset with the problem of defining and distinguishing its subject-matter. What is the mind? What processes are properly to be called mental processes in contradistinction with physiological and physical processes? Common experience tempts us to look to consciousness as the characteristic by which to distinguish the mental, but not all the activities generally held to be mental are conscious, and even if they were, there are then the further questions, how consciousness is related to those physiological processes on which it seems to be dependent and to that overt behaviour of which it seems often to be the condition. These are difficult and perhaps even insoluble problems, though some philosophers have considered them not to be genuine questions at all but only pseudo-problems arising from misleading linguistic associations, the factual basis of which either is not problematic at all or gives rise to questions of quite a different kind. Before committing ourselves on that issue it would be well to take some account of the facts and to consider whether or not they do give rise to genuine questions about psychophysical relationships.

Though consciousness may not invariably be the attribute of processes and activities regarded as mental, it certainly is a distinguishing mark of mind, at least in one respect. We unhesitatingly attribute mind to ourselves in so far as we are conscious and to any organisms the behaviour of which leads us to believe that they are aware of their surroundings. It cannot, therefore, be altogether wrong to contend that mind and mental activity, though not all or always conscious, have some essential relation to consciousness, and it is for this reason alone that we are inclined to identify any activity as mental. This does not mean that everything which is essentially related to consciousness is of necessity mental. Neural processes may well be so related, but we should still be more inclined to call them physiological. It seems hardly justifiable to classify as mental unconscious processes which never reach the level of awareness in any form. To say that mind consists of whatever is or may become conscious might therefore prove to be a useful provisional definition to adopt. It is, incidentally, one which seems naturally to be assumed by some neurophysiologists. Adrian, for instance (in distinguishing the functions of the cerebellum and the cerebrum writes:

'In spite of its resemblance to the cerebrum the cerebellum has nothing to do with our mental activity. Conscious experience seems to depend on what goes on above it in the cerebral cortex and its central masses.'[1]

The proposal to adopt any such provisional definition is likely to be met *in limine* by objections from those who maintain that the existence of activities and states of ourselves which may justifiably be called mental, does not involve the postulation of any special entity called 'mind', distinguishable from the body, or any identifiable condition called 'consciousness', distinguishable from physical and physiological activity. Behaviourists, in general, even though they may not (as, we shall maintain, they cannot consistently) deny the existence of conscious states, might well take this view. For them mental events would simply be vital activities of a definable class. Among contemporary writers on philosophical psychology there is a prominent group, who speak of mind and mentality, but nevertheless deny any revelation or experience to which the subject has privileged access, or any supposed illuminated field the inspection of which is confined to a single viewer or privately enjoyed in any indefeasible ownership. The details of these views need not be examined here. The primary difficulty is that of grasping what the authors understand by 'cognizing', 'being aware of', 'feeling', 'thinking', 'heeding', and similar terms, other than simply behaving in specifiable ways (which, however, they do not specify). If they mean only that, their position is indistinguishable from behaviourism; yet they persistently deny that they are behaviourists. We shall see, however, that they are by no means completely mistaken in their rejection of some of the ideas commonly entertained about the mind and consciousness.

To regard mind as comprising whatever is conscious or has a special sort of relation to consciousness does not necessarily

[1] E. D. Adrian, *The Physical Background of Perception* (Oxford, 1947), p. 31. This presumption of identity between consciousness and mentality is general throughout the book. Cf. pp. 5–7.

commit one to a belief in a peculiar *entity* called 'consciousness', externally related to physiological processes, nor in a separate spiritual substance mysteriously linked to the body. All that is meant by 'consciousness' at this stage is the kind of awareness that we all daily experience, and of which at least part of the function is to enable us to think about it. Precisely what it is, how it occurs, what sort of activity and process is involved in it, are matters to be investigated. We are emphatically not committed at the outset to any kind of psycho-physical dualism. Whether we find this an acceptable theory, will depend upon the evidence offered by the relevant sciences. If the evidence tends in the opposite direction, we shall use it as grounds for a different view. Contemporary writers who reject 'the ghost-in-the-machine' and the idea of privileged access seem to do so less on the basis of scientific evidence than on that of common linguistic usage; and while that is not a negligible guide to the nature of the matters spoken about, it seems hardly sufficient as the foundation for a clear and consistent conceptual scheme by which to understand mental activity in its relations to physical and physiological. This is so if only because common opinions of these matters are notoriously confused and ordinary language reflects them. The language of the scientists in the related fields might be a more fruitful source of enlightenment, but even this (as we shall find) is liable to become involved in paradox and contradiction which the philosopher is bound to make some effort to remove.

2

The problem of determining the relation between the mental and the non-mental is not very different in type from that of the distinction between life and the non-living, the most satisfactory approach to which, we found, was through the conception of a continuous scale of structural forms, and there is evidence to suggest that the relation between the body, as the structure and functioning of the material organism, and the mind, as a special kind of activity, might best be approached in the same way.

This is likely to be a more fruitful way of attacking the problem than by discussing directly the traditional theories of body-mind relationship, all of which assume in some manner a dualism for or against which the evidence has yet to be examined. Epipheno-menalism alleges the existence of consciousness as a sort of attendant

K

emanation from physiological process which has no effect or influence upon it or upon anything else. It is neither physiologically nor physically efficacious, yet it accompanies certain of the bodily processes as inevitably as a shadow accompanies the body itself. Parallelism presumes a spiritual counterpart to the body, neither having causal influence upon the other, though the first reflects in the stream of its own kaleidoscopic states all the changes which occur in the second. Interactionism differs from these only in postulating a two-way causal relation which they deny, between the physical entity and the spiritual. These three doctrines are variant legacies of the two-substance philosophy of Descartes, a conception rendered virtually inevitable in the seventeenth century by the mechanistic world-picture of Copernican and Newtonian science. The world-picture engendered by twentieth century science is so widely different that it provides little if any basis for such dualisms. The three traditional theories of psycho-physical relationship are therefore no more relevant to modern psychology and philosophy of mind (and presumably no less) than is Newtonian mechanics to contemporary physics.

Contemporary sciences of physics, biology and psychology all presume, with abundant empirical justification, continuity of gradation from the inorganic to the organic and from the physiological to the psychological. Yet the precise relationship between the main phases and levels is not clearly established, and the difficulty of understanding the transition from the first to the second is exceeded only by that of defining the relation between the second and the third. This latter relation we shall now try to elucidate, so far as we can, by tracing the developmental process in living activity from the biotic to the psychic.

There is an unbroken continuity between bio-chemical process, physiological activity and behaviour, and this might lead us, if continued in the direction of greater complexity and integration, to consciousness. The living system is a self-adjusting, self-maintaining, open chemical system, polyphasic in both the chemical sense of the term and the special meaning (which we have given to it) of systematically differentiated unity. Its interwoven cycles of chemical change, which at one and the same time constitute and, by their mutual adjustments, maintain the system, are its metabolism; and this issues in growth, reproduction, development and specialization of function and structure, in the ways already described. But growth, reproduction and the interaction of specific functions, while they are still the products of chemical activity require, over and above mere chemical reaction, organized movements of specialized structures directed to specific spatial arrangements of parts and organs and the performance of specific operations. The means by which these movements are effected are commonly (and appropriately) referred to as 'mechanisms', and their activation is continuous with (a development of) the chemical activity of metabolism. The working of such mechanisms and the processes they carry out in the body of the organism are suitably termed physiological processes, in contrast with, but not as separable from, biochemical processes. The latter minister to and sustain the former and there is no sort of sharp line that we can draw between them. The physiological processes are rather the grosser manifestations of the metabolic: the changes of electrical potential constituting a nerve impulse are relatively gross manifestations of the flow of ions within the nerve fibre; the stimulation of a muscle is the manifestation of the electro-chemical effects of acetyl-choline in the end-plate[1] and the contraction of the muscle is a gross manifestation of chemical changes in the fibre. In a similar way the process of digestion is a gross manifestation of chemical interchange, osmotic absorption and synthesis of compounds, in the tissues.

In comparable fashion, both metabolic and physiological processes merge with overt behaviour. They minister to it, provide the energy for exertion, and co-ordinate the mechanisms of the body. Yet what counts as overt behaviour grades off from what is typically physiological without any sharp dividing line. Homeostatic physiological processes maintaining the constancy of the water content and salt concentration in the blood include stimulation (by thirst) to the overt activity of seeking and drinking water, as well as the secretion of pituitrin with its anti-diuretic effect. The excretion of waste-products is at once a set of physiological processes and behavioural responses; and the same is true of sex which produces chemical and physiological changes in the body issuing in complex patterns of overt behaviour.

Not only is this true with respect to the single organism but a similar continuity can be traced in the evolutionary process. Activity at one level which seems largely metabolic (e.g. the absorption and expulsion of water by the amoeba) at a slightly higher

[1] Cf. J. C. Eccles, *The Neurophysiology of Mind* (Oxford, 1953), Chs. II and III.

level becomes both metabolic and physiological, and higher still, metabolic, physiological and behavioural. The wafting of cilia by many protozoans and lower organisms is paralleled by physiological movements in higher animals, like the activity of the ciliated cells of the membrane in the nasal cavity of man or the villi of the intestines. Yet somewhat more complex metazoans (ceolentrates) are provided with stinging capsules the barbed and whip-like filaments of which perform a more elaborate yet not dissimilar function from that of the cilia of Protozoa. These filaments are coiled when not in use and are automatically triggered by the brushing of prey against a sensitive hair. The activity is virtually physiological. But other coelentrates capture prey by more active sucking and grasping movements and, still higher up the scale, we find moluscs equipped with tentacles which they use in a skilled activity of stalking and hunting, all part of an elaborate process of acquiring and ingesting nourishment.

The study of behaviour of this kind is commonly held to be part of the proper province of psychology and to relate directly to mental phenomena. But just how behaviour is related to mental functioning is not clearly established. Aristotle considered motility in animals to be essentially dependent upon sentience and appetition, thinking of these as phases of consciousness; but many modern thinkers tend to define both sentience and appetition, in terms of overt activity, as response to stimulus, without reference to consciousness at all.

Indeed it is difficult in the extreme to find a sure criterion of the presence of consciousness in lower organisms. However suggestive of its presence their behaviour may be, it is always possible to argue that a purely mechanical device is conceivable, which nobody would wish to consider conscious, yet which could simulate that behaviour exactly. For example, the construction by the cuttlefish of a stony hiding-place from which to stalk and capture its prey is highly suggestive of an awareness of its surroundings and a conscious perception of and reaction to the situation in which it finds itself. But it is quite possible to imagine an unconscious mechanism, of the same kind as, but more complicated than, Gray Walter's *machina speculatrix*, which could behave similarly. It is of no avail to argue that any such machine implies the conscious, intelligent planning and programming of a human designer and constructor, and that what grows and develops of its own accord in nature cannot, therefore, be presumed similar to it. The present question is not whether in fact there is a similarity of internal organization which accounts for the similarity of observable behaviour, but whether the observable behaviour is a *sufficient* index of the presence of consciousness in the creature so behaving, and clearly it does not seem to be wholly sufficient. It might be a good reason for presuming the existence of a conscious designer, but that is another matter.

Nevertheless, as we ascend the scale of living species we find that their behaviour becomes more flexible and versatile in response to different situations, more intricately adjusted to organic needs and more readily adaptable to varying circumstances. At a certain stage of development we are inclined to describe such behaviour as more or less intelligent, in the same way as we describe human action, and there does not seem to be any clearly marked difference of character between human behaviour and that of the higher mammals such as to justify the postulation of any sharp break between the two. In our own case, however, we can have no doubts about the intimate association of much of our activity with consciousness. Even if we care to express doubts about the consciousness of other people (which normally we do not), we could still interpret their behaviour with good grounds on the analogy of our own, and the occurrence of one's own consciousness, while it lasts, is wholly indubitable and undeniable. Descartes was unquestionably right about that, for to doubt and to deny is *ipso facto* to be conscious. To doubt or deny is not to pronounce a form of words, to write them or in some other way to make them communicable (operations that might be performed by a machine). It is to judge, without necessarily communicating anything. It is, in short, to be in a state of mind or awareness with respect to some object. And if the subject of the judgment is one's own awareness, all doubt of its occurrence must be bogus and any denial false. Each one of us is invincibly apprised of his own consciousness. It is, therefore impossible truthfully to deny its occurrence, and consequently it is equally impossible to deny that consciousness ever occurs. In an extreme philosophical form, behaviourism is self-refuting.

Oddly enough, behaviourism in its attempt to admit as evidence only what can be publicly observed, and to exclude the report of any private experience, commits itself by implication to the very solipsism of which it strives to be the opposite. For all observations are the perceptions of observers and every perception is a conscious experience immediately open only to the subject experiencing. To be imparted it must be reported and the report is of a private experience. Reports can be compared of several different observers perceiving the same objects, but not only is each of them a report of private experience but the comparison must be made privately by the investigator and its result can become publicly available only as the report of a private operation. If then all reports of private experience are to be excluded from science, there will be no science whatsoever, save what will result from the enjoyment by the inquirer of his own private observations and the comparison he makes between them. These will include his observations of the behaviour of other persons observing the same or similar objects, but all of them will be private and, if the behaviouristic prohibition is to be strictly observed, none will be admissible as public scientific evidence. Each observer will then be confined to the unbreakable circle of his own experience within which the behaviour of others will figure only as his subjective perception.

Consciousness cannot be excluded from science—not even from physical science, although it is not its subject matter. There can therefore be no reason to exclude it from psychology for which it is, indeed, a legitimate object of investigation.

But even in ourselves we are aware of different levels of consciousness. We are not always conscious in the same way, with the same degree of clarity and articulation, or with the same sharpness of attention. There are times when, though we are conscious and can later attest to the fact, we could not assert 'Cogito ergo sum', because our consciousness is too clouded and confused to make coherent judgments. Nevertheless, we know that such low levels of awareness occur in ourselves—because we are aware of them and because they are states of awareness. We are also aware that our clearest and liveliest conscious states merge into and out of others that are less definite and more vague. We are aware further that these again merge into what escapes consciousness altogether, as when we fall from alert wakefulness to day-dreaming, from day-dream to dream proper and from that to dreamless sleep.

Or again, when our attention is fully captured by some object or activity, we may subsequently become aware that we had perceived a different object, to which at the time we paid no heed, and of which we say that we were for the moment 'unconscious'; yet we could not really have been so, because if we had, we could not later remember having perceived it. For instance, while reading I fail to notice the clock strike, yet when reminded of the time by a companion, I may realize that I did hear it, though, at the time, it escaped my attention. Then again, there are the innumerable examples of activities, learned with effort and close attention, which become automatic and which we later perform without the least attention—as I am now writing without attending to the movements of my hand and pen in forming the letters. Yet even such automatic actions cannot be performed without some degree of consciousness. I could not write under a general anaesthetic, or in my sleep (save in very special circumstances, when consciousness may not confidently be excluded).

Finally there are mental activities of the most highly specialized and developed kind, which occur unconsciously and yet influence and determine conscious activities, and even emerge at the conscious level in some phase of the process. Some mathematical prodigies, for instance, are able to produce immediately the answers to highly complicated calculations without being in the least conscious of how they accomplish the feat. Many mathematicians occasionally solve problems *between* the periods in which they give them close and conscious attention. Mozart declared that he was not fully aware of the way in which he composed a musical work, but became conscious of it first in disconnected snatches, and then suddenly and finally, without conscious transition, was aware of it complete and as a whole, so that he could write it down without further effort of construction or excogitation.

Further, Freud discovered that our conscious mental processes are constantly affected by repressed, unconscious, feelings and ideas, some of which can, under appropriate conditions, be brought to the level of awareness. And indeed, quite apart from the Freudian explanation of much of our forgetfulness, the daily phenomenon of remembering affords constant evidence of the interplay between conscious and unconscious activities of our minds, by intermittently reviving awareness of past experiences which in the interim, when we do not recall or attend to them, remain lost in oblivion.

Consciousness is therefore not *sui generis* but emerges from processes, which are of the same general kind and may with equal right be called mental, but which occur on a level of activity which is not conscious.

If we are thus aware of the indissoluble involvement of consciousness in our own behaviour and also of its emergence from lower less conscious levels of activity in ourselves, and if we can find no marked difference between the general character of our own conduct and that of others, nor between human behaviour and the behaviour of lower animals such as to justify our drawing a sharp distinction at any point in the scale of development, we have no obvious grounds for denying that consciousness in some degree and to some extent is involved in animal behaviour, at least at the higher levels. It is therefore legitimate to raise the question where, in the scale of evolution, consciousness first makes its appearance. Likewise, the question inevitably arises how consciousness is related to the unconscious processes in ourselves, both those which we feel justified in describing as mental (because their character and results are closely similar to those of conscious processes) and those which we describe as physiological. If this question arises with respect to ourselves, it arises equally wherever we presume the occurrence of consciousness in other animals. And the continuous process of evolution from them to us unifies the two questions and demands a theory of the evolution of mind within the process of the evolution of life, and an effort to discover its distinguishing character and to understand its relation to bodily changes.

3

In its most elementary form, conscious behaviour is that which depends upon sensitivity. It is response to a stimulus and the behaviouristic formula S-R, is despite the intentions of its authors, a tacit admission of the presence at least of sensation, for what is not felt cannot stimulate behaviour. In a mere chemical reaction there is neither stimulus nor response but only interchange of matter and energy.

Sensitivity, of some kind, seems to belong to organisms at every level. Plants are sensitive to light, temperature, and moisture and some of them respond to contact stimuli. Protozoan organisms, whether plant or animal react to stimuli in ways which suggest sensation, and colonial forms respond to touch and other stimuli, not only at localized points but in conglomerate masses, as in the behaviour of slime-moulds and myxobacteria already described. But the word 'sensitive' is highly ambiguous and is used as commonly in application to non-living things as to living organisms. The accuracy of scientific instruments, for instance, is usually described as 'sensitivity' and one speaks of a delicate fabric as

'sensitive' to light or heat. Moreover the word is loosely used, both
by scientists and laymen, so as to confuse the very different
phenomena of reaction by non-living things to physical or chemical
influences and those of human and animal experience. Our sensitivity to heat and cold is often, even by scientists, compared to
that of a thermometer, and though there is some justification for
the parallel, and certainly the one may be measured by the other,
the expansion of a column of mercury is something totally different
from the sensation we experience with changes of temperature. A
thermometer may register greater or smaller changes with accuracy
relative to the fineness of its bore but it gives no evidence of any
feeling whatsoever, and is not, therefore, sensitive at all the strict
sense of that word. When the temperature of the skin changes
sharply we *sense* the difference by a change in consciousness. Our
sensitivity is not a function of accurate registration merely. We
are sensitive to heat and cold but not to its minute changes. This
is not a failure of sensitivity but a difference *toto coelo* in the
manner of registration. In fact our temperature sensitivity is not an
instrument of measurement so much as a phase in a process of
adaptation. When this is complete the sensory registration of
temperature ceases until a change makes readaptation necessary.
We feel cold and heat only when the body is imperfectly adapted to
the temperature of its surroundings and our physiological and
behavioural responses are processes tending to adjust the body
temperature accordingly. But the fact, while it is important, is
incidental to the distinction between the delicacy of the reaction
of an instrument of measurement, which is termed its 'sensitivity',
and the experience, in the sensory mode, of environmental change
by an organism, to which it would be better and more correct to
refer as 'sensibility'. Failure to observe this distinction is liable to
lead to gross errors in attempts to elucidate living and mental
activity.

The relevance of sensation to adaptive activity in the organism
is especially significant. The reaction to stimulus is auturgic and
is a reaction of the organism as a whole, not simply a physico-
chemical change contiguous to an external change. The response
of the organism is an adjustive modification that subserves its
integrity and health. The immediate local reaction is therefore
conveyed to other parts by interaction and through interdependence of auturgic processes. Reactivity is thus not the only factor
involved in biological sensibility. Conduction of impulse and

K*

co-ordination of response are also involved. Further, conduction here is something more subtle and complex than the simple physical conduction of heat or electricity—though either or both of these may be involved in it—because it effects co-ordination of different, but mutually complementary responsive changes throughout the living system.

All living organisms, even Protozoa, display these features of reactivity to external influences and co-ordinated auturgic response involving communication within the living substance by some kind of impulse or internal stimulation. But in the course of differentiation of structure and function a special variety of cells is developed, the main and almost the sole functions of which are sensibility and conduction. These are the nerve cells, which in animals with nervous systems, are responsible almost entirely for the origination, regulation and integration of vital activities.

Whether or not the lower organisms without nerves can experience feelings is at best a matter of conjecture. The evidence we have of their sensitivity consists only in observable overt response. In ourselves we are directly aware of sensations and know immediately that our own mode of sensitivity belongs to a different category from that of a thermometer, a geiger-counter or a photoelectric cell; but the attraction of a plant to light or moisture, the lure of the moth to the candle flame, the withdrawal of *Paramoecium* from contact with a solid object, while they suggest some form of sensibility, give no evidence that it differs from the sensitivity of non-living mechanical devices.

The responses of higher organisms are sufficiently complex and discriminating to indicate at least sensitivity in a variety of modalities and a spectrum of qualitative differences within each. They exhibit behaviour from which we can safely infer that the creatures are differently sensitive to touch, to light, and to sound and that they can discriminate, within each of these, qualitative differences. How they do so may be in varying degrees obscure and the capacity is not itself sufficient evidence of consciousness, but known anatomical and physiological facts put beyond reasonable doubt the dependency of these reactions upon neural functioning. There is evidence also, as we go up the phylogenetic scale, that behaviour evincing this kind of sensitivity merges into behaviour which undoubtedly does involve sensation proper, the experience of which may well occur much lower in the scale than we can confidently detect.

4

Though the dependence of sensibility on neural activity is
established, it still remains to be elucidated how sentience can
result from or be associated with such activity. As sentience is or
may become a form of awareness, it pertains to mind as we have
provisionally defined it; and if the accompanying neural activity
is something less than mental—if it is to be regarded only as
physiological—the question of their relationship immediately
arises. But this is not a relationship between two different substances or separate entities. It is the relationship between different
phases of a continuous organic process. So the problem of the
relation of body and mind is still with us even if its character has
changed and a different kind of solution is demanded.

The question to be faced today is essentially the same as that
which faced John Locke three centuries ago, though the language
in which it would be presented is different. 'It is evident', Locke
wrote, 'that some motion must be thence continued by our
nerves, or animal spirits, by some parts of our bodies, to the brains
or the seat of sensation, there to produce in our minds the particular ideas we have of them' [external objects].[1] What the precise
relation is between the 'motion' conveyed by the nerves to the
brain and the 'ideas' produced by cerebral activity, how the brain
can produce ideas in our minds, were questions which Locke
refused to consider, and nothing we have since learned about
neural activity provides any obvious solution to the problem.

Positivists of the 1940's and the Wittgensteinians, who were
their philosophical kin, regarded the mind-body problem as a
metaphysical and therefore as a pseudo-problem and later thinkers
in direct line of philosophical descent have tried to dispose of it
by linguistic analysis; but more recently there has been a revival
of respect for metaphysics (of a kind) and some contemporary
philosophers have come to recognize that the mind-body relationship is no pseudo-problem, but one which at least in principle, is
capable of solution. This they profess to find in what has come to
be known as the neural-identity theory[2]—the view that the logical
subjects of statements about mental events are identical with those
of statements about the concomitant neural processes. Thus to say
that I have a toothache is to refer to precisely the same occurrences

[1] *Essay Concerning Human Understanding*, II, viii, 12.
[2] *Vide Dimensions of Mind* (Ed. Sidney Hook), New York, 1960.

as to describe the activities of the nerves of my affected tooth and their projection in the brain.

This theory is a pronounced advance upon the old theories of two substance interrelation, for it eliminates the need to explain how the alleged relationship can obtain and it fulfils the scientific demand for parsimony; but as an account of what is intended in ordinary speech it is obviously false and the theory is defensible only as maintaining that the sensations experienced are in fact identical with the neural events, so that to describe either would be (whether the speaker knew it or not) to refer to some one subject ontologically single and identical. In that case having the toothache would be nothing more nor less than the occurrence of certain neural processes. If this were a sufficient account of the matter it would be very convenient, because, on the one hand, introspection would then provide direct evidence of neural activity and, on the other, neurologists by observing the processes going on in the nervous system would be able to predict the experiences of the subject. No doubt if enough were known about neurophysiology and the corresponding phenomenal aspects of neural functioning this could be done to some considerable extent. Nevertheless, the contention that nerve processes and consciousness are identical would still leave much to be explained: how, for instance, the transmission of electrical impulses could be, without further qualification, the conscious experiences we all enjoy. The theory is after all not new. Thomas Hobbes maintained that sensation, like everything else, was 'nothing but motion', though 'its appearance to us is fancy'. The modern philosopher might say that it was nothing but electrical discharge with the same proviso. Yet the question remains how 'motion' or electrical discharge could 'appear to us as fancy', or for that matter could *appear* to us at all.

Moreover, it is far from plausible to allege that neural activity and awareness are identical events, for it implies that the characteristics and properties of the mental and neural events must be the same, and there is plenty of evidence to the contrary. If the subject of two different statements is the same event or set of events, then the attributes of that subject and the relations in which it stands to other events, as stated or implied by the two statements, must be identical. If to say that I have an acute toothache, which is a more intense feeling than the pressure of my tongue on a healthy tooth, is the same as to say that certain neural processes are taking

place in the nerves of one tooth which are in some way quantitatively greater or more evident than other events in the nerves of
another tooth, neurophysiological evidence should confirm this
fact. But such evidence as there is flatly contradicts it. 'In nerves
from the teeth, for instance,' so Adrian tells us,[1] 'the usual streams
of potential waves are set up by the slightest touch on the intact
tooth, but the exposure and laceration of the pulp, the mere
thought of which is painful, produces no more than a slight ir-
regularity of the electrical record—something which we should
take to be of no significance at all, if we had never been to a
dentist. . . .' The sensitivity of the nerves is thus not identical with
sensation and is more akin to the sensitivity of scientific instruments. The nerve reacts physically or chemically to stimulation
and transmits an impulse consisting in a wave of electrical negativity which passes along the fibre. The frequency and the velocity
of transmission vary within definite limits, so that the nerve may
be more or less 'sensitive', as a galvanometer or an oscilloscope
may be called sensitive, but the examples just given indicate that
the sensation which results from the neural reaction is something
other than the reaction itself.

Though the lacerated nerve of the tooth transmits hardly
noticeable impulses which are *felt* as the most agonizing pain,
the nerve cells of the brain, on the other hand, while extremely
active and undoubtedly instrumental to feeling, may be prodded
and electrically stimulated without occasioning any direct sensation at all—though quite remote sensations in other parts of the
body or in sense modalities other than touch or pain may be
experienced in consequence. The fact that the neural process is
in the brain and the sensation is felt in a different part of the body
is sufficient reason for denying their identity, just as it would be
highly unconvincing to maintain that the visual appearance of an
object a mile away is the same thing as a neural discharge in the
occipital lobe of brain of the percipient. Again, peripheral stimulation has been found to cause changes in electrical potential in
the sensory cortex equally in anaesthetized and in fully conscious
subjects, so that the nerve processes and the awareness can hardly
be the same.[2]

[1] Cf. Adrian, op. cit., p. 27.
[2] Cf. Forbes A. and Morison, B. R., 'Cortical Responses to Sensory
Stimulation under Deep Barbiturate Narcosis', *J. Neurophysiol.* II, 1939,
pp. 112–28.

Another, even more cogent, reason for refusing to identify neural impulse with feeling is the well attested fact that all neural discharges, both afferent and efferent, are alike. They are all changes of electrical potential which pass along the fibres to the cells and from cells to fibres. They do not differ in intensity with the intensity of the stimulus but only in frequency and in the number of fibres which they invade, and there is no qualitative difference between those which originate from the diverse sense organs, whether from the skin, or the retina of the eye, the cochlea or the labyrinth of the inner ear. Yet there is a vast range of qualitative differences among the sensations which result from the impulses transmitted by these different receptors, both between the sense modalities and within the range of each.

There is, however, a different form of neural-identity theory, which is espoused by psychologists of the Gestalt school. Having become convinced by impressive experimental findings that neither behaviour nor experienced phenomena can be adequately explained in terms of the conjunction and conglomeration of single units, whether simple reflexes or single sensations, they assert that both the physiological aspect and the phenomenal must be treated as *Gestalten*, wholes of parts which exist inseparably and only in the whole. Consequently, the analysis of behaviour into physiological units, into muscular or glandular responses to sensory stimuli, they consider to be misleading. Following Tolman, they refer to these physiological components as 'molecular' behaviour, in distinction from the total response of the organism to a total situation, which they call 'molar' behaviour. In the molar aspect of behaviour, it is alleged that the physiological configuration is isomorphic with the psychological and that there are not two separate processes but only one. Koffka explicitly declares that the physiological processes (the 'motion of the atoms and molecules of the brain') and the psychological ('thoughts and feelings') are identical,[1] but Köhler is more cautious and admits that ismorphism is compatible with the theory of parallelism, as indeed it also is with epiphenomenalism.

This identification of the psychological with the neural 'field' is not quite the same as the simple identification of conscious with neural activity. We have seen that the latter is impossible because

---

[1] *Principles of Gestalt Psychology* (London, 1955), p. 62. Cf. W. Köhler, 'The Mind-Body Problem', in *Dimensions of Mind* (Ed. Sidney Hook), New York, 1960.

neural impulses and feelings are often widely disparate in character. What is here being proposed is an identity of structural order—an isomorphism. Even so there are serious obstacles to be overcome. The actual spatial pattern of excitation in the cortex is by no means identical, though it has some correspondence, with the organization of the sense-field. For example:

'The area of cortical excitation which exists when we perceive a circle is divided into two halves, one in each cerebral hemisphere. Pathways connecting them exist, but these appear to play no part in our perception of the two halves of the circle as one whole, for this still occurs when the connecting pathway (the corpus callosum) is divided. Neither half is semicircular; it is roughly the shape of ⊃ , the closed end lying in front and the open end behind.'[1]

The shape of the excited area in the occipital lobe of the brain is always a distortion of the image projected upon the retina and is quite different from the figure of the object actually seen. Apart from the inversion of the retinal image, of which we are unaware in perception, the regions of the retina which give greater visual acuity are projected on the visual cortex so as to activate many more cells than the portions which give poorer vision. The extent of cortical surface corresponding to different regions of the retina is therefore disproportionate to the retinal areas. Consequently the pattern of cortical excitation corresponding to any retinal image is quite different from the shape either of the image or of the object seen (though there may be some topological correspondence between them).

Koffka might have objected to all this as referring only to 'molecular' correspondences, yet if these do not hold it is difficult to see how the neural and phenomenal characters can be identical in their molar aspect. Nevertheless to draw attention to the total configurational character of organic activity is highly suggestive and offers us a valuable clue to the solution of our problem.

5

What precisely is the molar aspect of physiological (including neural) activity? Surely it is nothing short of the complete

[1] W. Russell Brain, *Mind, Perception and Science*, p. 8.

behaviour of the organism. We know that neural, vascular, respiratory, muscular and visceral functions are all integrated into one process of activity. They are distinguishable, not separable, factors in the organic behaviour of the system. Might not the most fruitful hypothesis now be that consciousness, or the phenomenal field, is nothing more nor less than the form taken by this whole in the highest degree (so far considered) of its integration—the form of unity or organization of the entire multiplex, multitudinously articulated system?—and is it not to some such conclusion that Koffka's view should lead us?

By and large, this is the opinion of Francis Schiller, who asserts that consciousness is a convenient abstract term 'signifying the organization of complex processes in complex anatomical structures'.

'Among the examples of close interaction of objects in nature', he writes, 'that of living organisms and their environment is one of special complexity. We are baffled by the number of structures which our studies reveal. Observation hints that there is a device which the most complex of these organisms uses; this is loosely called mind, or thought, or consciousness, i.e. an efficient way of rapid analysis and synthesis. . . . We infer or postulate "mind" where the complexity of organization goes beyond the immediately observable and where we, nevertheless, have evidence of an agency which is effective, as well as capable of being affected.'[1]

We have already judged the unqualified identification of neural and mental activity to be implausible, and besides the objections already mentioned there is another, discussed by Stephen Pepper,[2] to which the view just proposed might be thought equally vulnerable. Pepper observes that some sense qualities are simple and unanalysable, whereas their neural (and *a fortiori* their total physiological) counterparts are multiplex. He seeks to overcome the difficulty by maintaining that the sensed experience is a fusion of

---

[1] *Vide* 'Consciousness Reconsidered', *A.M.A. Archives of Neurology and Psychiatry*, 67 (1952), p. 209. By 'immediately observable', presumably 'physiologically specifiable' is meant. Cf. S. D. Ingham, 'Some Neurological Aspects of Psychiatry', *J.A.M.A.* III (1938), where consciousness is described as a 'state of activity of the entire nervous system'.

[2] Cf. 'The Neural-Identity Theory of Mind', in *Dimensions of Mind*, pp. 45–61.

subliminal elements, indistinguishable phenomenally but dis-
criminable in the physiological analysis of neural processes. This
expedient, however, does not help so long as the identity alleged
is between neural events on the one side, in apparent isolation
from the other physiological processes, and mental events on the
other; for the neural processes are subject to thresholds as are the
sensory, neurones being activated only by impulses of minimal
intensity. But if neural processes are not taken in isolation the
case may well be different. These thresholds may themselves be
the accomplishment of a fusion—a summation of subliminal pulses.
Just how such subliminal impulses are summed so as to discharge
the cell is not yet known, but it is not improbable that the
process of summation is rooted in the metabolism of the cell
body.

More than this, the functioning of neurones and their metabolism is intimately dependent upon the other processes going
on in the organism—general metabolism and the supply of substances circulated in the bloodstream. They are responsive in
various ways to the over-all state of the body as a whole, and
neural activity is not by any means a collection of molecular
processes isolable one from another. Not only does the nervous
system behave as an organic whole, but it is also subordinate to
the wider whole of the complete organism and in an easily conceivable sense sums up that total organic activity within its own,
both responding to it and regulating it.

The physiologist, though impressed with the organicism of all
this, cannot describe it precisely except in molecular terms, even
if he qualifies his descriptions constantly by drawing attention to
the mutual dependence of the contributory processes. As Schiller
implies, a degree of complex integration is reached that goes
beyond the range of physiological observation and description.
But the whole is manifestly governed by an auturgic principle
which unifies it in all its multiform variety; and at a definite level
of integration this unity can only be expressed as, and become
effective in, behaviour which is 'informed', in both the senses
'given form' and 'guided by knowledge'. This is *conscious* behaviour, a class of activity at a specifically high level of complexity and
integration.[1] It is one single performance, not a double activity of

[1] Cf. Eliot Slater in *The Physical Basis of Mind* (ed. Laslett) (Blackwell,
Oxford, 1950); pp. 44–5: 'When behaviour reaches a certain degree of
complexity it will begin to have a conscious or mental aspect'.

two processes running parallel, part physiological and part mental, nor even two processes, in interaction.

Adrian reminds us that the intelligence of man is fully active even when the cortex is cut off from all peripheral stimuli with the exception of those from the head and neck and a few from the arms.[1] Dr. Percival Bailey, similarly, writes: 'It has often been said that we think with our entire body, but it can be readily demonstrated that mental processes go on with negligible disturbance in the absence of all parts of the body below the fifth cervical segment and after most of it is lost above that level except for the brain stem and cortex.'[2] It is indeed clearly established that the functioning of the cortex is most intimately concerned in human conscious experience; but the cortex cannot function alone. Dr. Bailey is surely suggesting that mental functioning is indifferent not to the literal absence of all parts of the body below the fifth cervical segment, but only the absence of afferent *neural connection* between the brain and these other parts of the body. The blood supply to the cortex must not be interfered with[3] and that presupposes numerous other bodily functions, all the autonomic functions, in fact, and the continued activity of the body, so far as that is possible without exteroceptive and somatic sensation. This bodily activity can, of course, go on without the cortex and without consciousness—but then the vital functioning is integrated at a lower and less comprehensive level. No scientific evidence has yet been found of mental activity or cortical functioning proceeding without the metabolic processes implemented by visceral, respiratory, endocrine and vascular action which minister to the health and efficiency of the whole nervous system (cortex included), though themselves regulated and controlled by means of neural links. The brain appears to be the most highly developed organ of discrimination, integration and organization, the highest ranges of which are impossible without the cortex. Consequently, there is a close correlation between its activity and conscious experience, which precisely is the form taken by activity in those higher ranges of discrimination, unification and organization.

It has been adumbrated, very dimly and barely in passing, by

[1] *The Physical Background of Perception*, p. 6.

[2] 'Cortex and Mind', in *Theories of the Mind*, Ed. Jordan Scher (New York, 1962), p. 8.

[3] Cf. Adrian, loc. cit.

Sir Charles Sherrington, and more definitely and explicitly by Edmund Sinnott, that consciousness may be no more than the phenomenal manifestation at a high level of activity of what at lower levels is the unconscious teleology of the organism.[1] This is the hypothesis that is being adopted here, but with the additional proviso that the organic auturgy operating at all levels expresses itself as conscious behaviour only when it reaches a level of complex integrity which could be realized in no other way, so that the animal could not do what it in fact does if it were not conscious. To those who allege that many conscious activities can be simulated by machines we need reply at this stage only that simulation is a matter of degree and the performance of the machine may be like that of the conscious organism in many but possibly not in all respects. The differences may be subtle and even inconspicuous, but their effects may be far-reaching and such as consciousness alone could bring about.

As long ago as 1923, Lashley made an attempt to formulate the conception of consciousness as 'a complex integration and succession of bodily activities'.[2] But his object then was largely to discredit certain vitalistic theories and to advocate more confident reliance on the physiological and experimental approach to psychological questions. The early essay in which he stated his case is remarkable as a radical defence of a Behaviourism which makes no attempt to deny the occurrence of consciousness but seeks only to redefine it in terms which would make possible physiological description and analysis of all mental phenomena. But Lashley seeks to reduce consciousness to a complex of physiological mechanisms (albeit extremely elaborate). We are seeking to regard it as the activity itself of organizing and integrating bodily mechanisms and processes, an activity which operates at lower levels as the auturgic process of metabolic, homeostatic and automatic physiological adjustment, but which attains the form of awareness only at a high grade of intensity, in processes continuous with these but co-ordinating a much wider variety of ingredients.

[1] Charles Sherrington, *Man on His Nature*, Ch. X, pp. 239–40; Edmund W. Sinnott, *The Biology of the Spirit* (New York, 1955), pp. 68–73.

[2] 'The Behaviouristic Interpretation of Consciousness', *The Psychological Review*, Vol. 30, 1923, p. 344.

More recently a similar idea has been expressed by C. J. Herrick,[1] who writes:

'Awareness cannot be "reduced" to physicochemical categories or adequately described scientifically by ever so complete an explanation of the mechanism employed. This is as impracticable as it would be to try to describe the properties of an electric current in terms of the dynamo that generates it. . . . The awareness itself, although not definable in terms of conventional physiological criteria, is an experienced event which has observable integrating efficiency and which is demonstrably in organic relationship with preceding and following organic processes.'[2]

And again:

'Consciousness as we experience it seems to be a high-level integration of some kind of nervous processes, the exact nature of which is still to be discovered.'[3]

To this should be added the qualification that the nervous processes themselves are integrants of a wider and more intricately ramifying organic system, the still more intimate and articulate unification of which is their special function.

Consciousness thus transpires as a very high grade of that same spontaneous activity of analysis and synthesis[4] which one seems forced to postulate at all levels of the processes of nature in order to account for the hierarchy of polyphasic unities which the sciences reveal to us. There is no obvious break in the gamut of increasingly coherent forms. Mind supervenes; it is not imposed upon matter from without, but is a sublation or sublimation of a process which has been operative from the primordial origins of things.

If the relation of conscious activity to unconscious organic functioning is what is here suggested none of the three traditional theories of body–mind relationship describe it accurately. Consciousness is not epiphenomenal because it makes a radical difference to the whole character of the behaviour it informs. There is no parallelism between mental and physiological activity, for all physiological activity below a certain level of complex integration

---

[1] *The Evolution of Human Nature* (Austin, Texas, 1956).
[2] Op. cit., pp. 292–3.
[3] Op. cit., p. 322.
[4] Cf. Herrick, op. cit., Ch. 8.

is unconscious, and at the requisite level for consciousness it does not generate a second parallel activity but is a single integral activity in which lower physiological process ministers to a more comprehensively integral functioning: the functioning of mind. Consciousness is not a new sort of stuff, it is an activity in a specially high degree and form of organization. Interactionism gives a more plausible account of the matter, but is still not correct. There are not two agencies influencing each other, but two or more levels of activity, the lower ancillary to, sublated in, and integrated with, the higher, which at a certain stage of development is conscious (or mental) activity. Each level, of course, has effects upon every other for they all (in the higher phase) belong to a single, though complex, dynamic totality. Changes at lower levels (e.g. visceral) modify the general character of the whole, but so likewise does the conscious apprehension, in which the whole system issues, modify the character of lower level processes (as, for instance, when the cognition of certain objects excites emotional reactions associated with visceral and vascular changes). This, however, is not strictly interaction between separate processes, so much as the integration of mutually determining phases of a single complex governed by a holistic principle.

What is being advocated is not a theory of emergence, and consciousness is not to be regarded as a new quality supervening upon a special constellation of neural activity, as it was for Samuel Alexander. His view has something to recommend it, but it fails to make the new emergent intelligible and breaks the continuity of evolutionary process by postulating it. For us consciousness just is the form of integration which the whole complex assumes at the appropriate level of organization. Without consciousness the form of organization is different, less comprehensive, and less articulate. Consciousness is not something extra which is added, not a mysterious new aura which supervenes; it is a higher phase of unification, a more articulately whole form of being and behaving.

Our object henceforth will be to try to illustrate this view and, so far as possible, to give support to the hypothesis by considering the character of mental functioning in its various aspects, to see whether it may not be more enlightening to regard them as specially highly integrated forms of organized activity, than to think of them as some peculiar kind of quality or glow attaching itself to special patterns of neural process.

CHAPTER XVI

FEELING

I

In psychology the word 'feeling' has a technical use, but here I propose to give it the wider meaning familiar in philosophy which covers sentience of every kind prior to discrimination of modalities or the distinctions between sensation, emotion and pleasure–pain tonality. The word is used here, as it was by Bradley, Collingwood[1] and others before them, to refer to the most elementary form of experience, and this I take to be the use given to it by Susanne Langer in the following quotation:

'When the activity of some part of the nervous system reaches a critical pitch the process is felt';[2]

And it reaches a critical pitch when all the interwoven processes of the organism are summed up and integrated in it. The activity of the mid-brain, the hypothalamus, the thalamus, the amygdala, the hippocampus and the reticular formation, seem to play a specially important part in this integrative process, and it is these organs that neurophysiologists find intimately concerned with feeling.[3]

This is what Wilder Penfield calls the 'centrencephalon' which he believes to be the seat of ultimate co-ordination indispensable to consciousness. But its functioning cannot be separate from that of the rest of the nervous system and of the total organism. Levels of brain activity are seen by Schiller as 'a matter of organization and quality, rather than one of quantity and degree', in which specialization decreases progressively as we ascend from the periphery to the cortex.[4] The integration of all the chemical changes going on in the body, the electro-chemical discharges that they occasion

---

[1] Cf. F. H. Bradley, *Essays in Truth and Reality*, Ch. VI, and *Appearance and Reality*, *passim*; R. G. Collingwood, *The New Leviathan*.

[2] *Philosophical Sketches* (Johns Hopkins Press, Baltimore, 1962), p. 9.

[3] Cf. *Reticular Formation of the Brain*, Henry Ford Hospital International Symposium, 1958, Ed. H. H. Jasper, L. D. Proctor, et al.; and H. E. Himwich, 'Emotional Aspects of Mind: Clinical and Neurological Analyses' in *Theories of the Mind* (Sher).

[4] Op. cit., p. 224, quoted above.

in the nerves, their mutual linkage as afferent and efferent impulses, and their common organization in maintaining adjustment to environmental conditions—what *unified* form could all this take other than the blurred, vague, confused registration of manifold reactivity which we call sentience?

Strictly speaking feeling is not an isolable state of consciousness. It is in itself barely (and may not always be) a state of consciousness at all, for in consciousness it is already an element in something more articulate, it is already becoming percipient. Paul Janet relates it to the release and regulation of energy for action and Piaget regards it as the energetic (or 'affective') aspect always correlative to the aspect of structure in every action.[1] But the mustering and release of energy is something physical. Only when its concentration, distribution, regulation and organization have reached what Susanne Langer calls 'a critical pitch' is it felt.

Feeling is the form that this organization takes. It is the integrated summation of the total physiological system and as such constitutes the psychical field, the articulation of which in consciousness, in ways we shall presently try to describe, converts it to perception. This is in harmony with Piaget's distinction of feeling, as energetic, from cognition, as structural, which he declares to be inseparable correlatives of all action. But the difference may turn out to be one as much of degree as of kind. Attention, the instrument of articulation, has intimate kinship with feeling, and the structuring which results from its activity is but the further complexification—the reflexive analysis—of the field concomitant with higher syntheses. What is to be noted here is that feeling, as the energetic aspect of mental activity—according to Piaget, its source of supply and direction—is no mere passivity but itself an active process.

This view of feeling must and can only be taken as an hypothesis at this stage. It is virtually impossible in the present state of our knowledge to produce evidence that feeling simply is the integration of physiological processes at a certain pitch of intensity, because feeling as such and unelaborated is so difficult, if at all possible, to separate and display in its purity. Phenomenally we catch it only in more elaborate forms of awareness (as we shall presently explain). Physiologically it is in the nature of the case undetectable because physiological description is limited to molecular reactions and processes.

[1] *Vide* J. Piaget, *The Psychology of Intelligence*, Ch. I.

Nevertheless, evidence is forthcoming in plenty that changes in pressure or in the chemical constituents of the blood, in the oxygen or carbon-dioxide pressure in the lungs, in the disposition and tonus of the muscles, or in the electrical potential of peripheral (or other) nerve endings, do produce changes of feeling. Neurologists find that the activity of the mid-brain structures are strongly affected by certain hormones and by special drugs which react with these hormones, and that these effects are reflected phenomenally and behaviourally as emotional change. Consequently, it is not unreasonable to assume that such changes alter the pattern of organization of vital processes centrally achieved by the activity of the brain and that this alteration, as also the activity involved in adjusting the pattern to recover equilibrium, is what is felt.

If this is so, and if the total synthesis of physiological functioning is concentrated in primitive sentience, it contains more than the mere integration of the organized processes in the body. For these are responsive in one way or another, to all the impinging influences of the outside world. We have already stressed the interdependence, acknowledged by biologists, of organism and environment, so it now becomes evident that the sensibility of the organism, subjectively constituting a psychical field, is a focus of effects converging from the entire enveloping world. Feeling is the confused inner registration of all physical changes in the surrounding *milieu*, as they are reflected in the mechanical and electro-chemical changes in the body. They are interlaced in the auturgic processes of life and fused together at the pitch of organization which takes the form of feeling. It is in this manner that sensibility, for Hegel, sublates or 'inwardizes' (*erinnert*) the natural qualities of the world and the physical alterations of the body.[1] It reflects the world at large and its impingement upon the organism in what William Wallace lists as 'the influences on the mental mood and faculty, produced by climate and season, by local environment and national type, by individual peculiarities, by the differences of age and sex, and by the alternation of night and day, of sleep and waking'.[2] Witness the expression in human temperament and mental cast of geographical conditions like altitude and humidity, of scenery and weather, as well as of type of

[1] *Vide* G. F. W. Hegel, *Ecyklopädie der Philosophischen Wissenschaften*, §§ 391–404.

[2] *Hegel's Philosophy of Mind* (Oxford, 1894), p. 120.

physique and state of physical health. In feeling the world is held implicitly, as if in suspension, for later conscious elaboration as knowledge.

Feeling in its most primitive form does seem to be the 'stuff' of consciousness—its Aristotelian prime matter—the logical origin *a quo* of the development of awareness, and terminus *ad quod* of its dissipation; yet at the same time, and always, its attendant basis. Consciousness never takes flight from feeling and becomes devoid of it, though feeling may, and probably always does to some extent occur at levels below the recognizable threshold of consciousness. On this point we shall presently be more explicit.

2

Feeling is a term that is variously applied, not only to sensation, whether produced by somatic, peripheral or so-called 'distance' receptors, but also to tones of pleasure and pain and to emotions. There is some reason to include emotions among somatic sensations, for the feelings of bodily changes, visceral and other, do seem to be a main component of emotional states. Nevertheless there are somatic sensations of the same general sort which are not especially emotional and to lose sight of the distinction would be to jeopardize clarity. Yet these distinctions are largely products of abstraction, for as it occurs in primitive form, whether in animals or human beings, feeling is almost certainly undiscriminated and no phenomenal distinction is made between emotional, hedonic, or sensory, elements of all three being merged into a single (though far from simple) aesthesis.

The primitive phase of feeling is virtually impossible to describe phenomenologically, for to describe it is *ipso facto* to discriminate within it elements which are not phenomenally discriminated. Accordingly one finds little account of it in scientific literature, if only because it approaches the unobservable. Many psychologists, however, postulate some such undifferentiated phase before the structural characters of mind emerge. Some psychoanalysts maintain that there is an undifferentiated phase of psychic activity before the development of what Freud called the 'id' and the 'ego', that the former is not a prior matrix of psychical experience but is formed *pari passu* with the ego in a process of mutually complementary interrelations.[1]

[1] Cf. H. Hartmann, E. Kris and R. M. Loewenstein, 'Formation of Psychic Structure', *The Psycho-Analytic Study of the Child*, II, 1946.

It is something near to this primary phase of feeling that Koffka discusses when he attempts to find an example of a totally homogeneous psychical field. But what seems to approximate to pure feeling immediately differentiates itself into less vague components. Koffka's example is Eugen Guido Lammer's autobiographical description of his recovery from unconsciousness after a climbing accident.[1] The state of consciousness described is one of fogginess in which vague inhomogeneities gradually emerge, as the field of awareness becomes progressively organized. The first distinguishable elements are sensory, vaguely unpleasant (in this case) and emotionally coloured. Then the field becomes bipolar with a self distinguished from a not-self. Complete homogeneity, Koffka presumes, would be 'nothing but fog', and that we might well consider, like Kant's 'manifold of sensation', to be as good as nothing. But what is of importance here is that no such bare fog is described by Lammer. From the first there is some inhomogeneity and vague differences in sensory modalities are felt before the self is distinguished as the subject of the experience. The awakening consciousness is from the start an activity of organizing and distinguishing. What precisely is it that is being organized?

The 'dark fog' that Lammer recalls is visual and is diversified by a central brightness (later identified as the hole in the snow through which he had fallen into a crevasse). But all this is apprehended undiscriminatingly as simply felt. He includes, in turn, auditory elements (whirring and humming), feelings of effort (to 'think'—i.e. presumably to identify and organize further), discomfort, clammy coldness, and then with the emergence of the ego, as opposed to 'that light point there outside', a dream experience. This later development is relatively well advanced from the first phase of raw primitive feeling. There is little doubt that what was happening in this experience was that a number of different responses to environmental influences—adjustments to temperature, to light, to sound—were being at once distinguished and integrated as features of a total situation in which overt activity of the organism was requisite for further adaptive adjustment for self-maintenance. There was a feeling of discomfort with its emotional tone of aversion, a source of motivation or conation. The action required of the victim to extricate himself from his predicament demanded an organized apprehension of the situation in which he was placed—a coherent

[1] *Principles of Gestalt Psychology*, pp. 323–5.

grasp of the elements that constituted it. And the process of achieving this is precisely what his description of his own felt efforts to organize the sensory field—even before they were felt *as his own*—amount to. Each sensory datum is an organic, physiological reaction to an environmental stimulus, but the awareness of it is its integration into and organization with others in a greater measure and higher degree than occur at the physiological level where homeostasis is achieved. It is an integration and ordering in a degree at which the elements in their mutual relation acquire meaning for a subject as the elements of an environing situation. The nucleus of an awareness of a self emerges concomitantly with that of the objects of its behavioural world. In Koffka's account of the matter this is made very clear, even though he quite rightly admits that in infants the organization of a stable ego is very improbable until a much later stage of development. And, we may add, is possibly only inchoate at any stage in animals.

Awareness is thus not the *counterpart* of organization but is the form and degree of organization in which feelings acquire significance as objects with respect to which an active subject must behave in certain ways in order to maintain itself. This involves an 'internalization' of the influences which contribute to the feeling—a subjectivization of them. And that is no more nor less than the amalgamation and union into a single focus of the whole organic system that is striving to maintain itself, as well as its relations to environmental factors to which adjustment is to be made. The first phase of this drawing to a focus is feeling. It is, as it were, the turning in upon itself of the physiological system, its concentration as a new pitch of centreity, at which the subsequent process of articulation of the psychical field becomes the life of the mind.

The auturgical drive to self-maintenance governing the whole process manifests itself as the emotional tone of the felt complex, unpleasant when adaptation is deficient and pleasant when it has been or is being achieved. These feeling tones are not means to ends, they are the forms in which auturgic needs and their fulfilment acquire significance. And the process of organization is not simply cognitive or contemplative but is active—a doing, auturgically motivated. It is at once conative and emotive, and so far as its organization reaches a level at which objects become significant and apprehensible as relevant to its conative trend, both the drive and its tendency are cognized as feelings (pleasantly or painfully emotive) and the organism becomes aware. But cognition must not be thought of as a kind of light suddenly switched on to illuminate the objects. To become significant is no more nor less than to be set in an ordered context, to be grasped as a factor in a multiplicity of interrelated distincta, and so to be grasped *is* to be cognized. This, however, implies an activity of distinguishing and relating, of diversifying a field and ordering, through relations, the manifold of resulting components. The process is both analytic and synthetic, two-edged but not two-fold, and it is an active process, not a passive acceptance or a static *anschauung*. It is this activity which is consciousness, unifying a multiplicity into a complex oneness, and reflecting upon its own content so that (in Hegelian terminology) it is such *for itself*, and not merely *in itself*.

But the differentiation of primitive feeling into emotion, conation, exteroceptive and proprioceptive sensation, and their different modalities, is a subsequent development, which proceeds together and interdependently with the polarization of the psychical field into self, or ego, and not-self. In fact, many of these distinctions are made only at a highly sophisticated level of awareness by the psychologist in the analysis of his subject matter, and only with difficulty (if at all) are they detected introspectively. Even when and in so far as they are distinguished no single mode is ever completely devoid of elements of the others. Every sensation has emotive tone and every emotional stirring exerts some conative pressure. Exteroceptive sensations are commonly fused with feelings of strain which are essentially proprioceptive and kinaesthetic. In Metzger's experiments on homogeneous visual sensation, subjects experienced the first gradual illumination of the field as a kind of reduction of pressure. Elements of the self and the not-self, likewise, overlap. Clothes, possessions, sometimes even other persons are included in the ego, and, as Koffka asserts, felt emotions are as often as not ascribed as qualities to external objects rather than to ourselves.[1]

Originally feeling is a vague virtually centreless conglomeration of diverse tonalities within which, by processes which psychologists have gone some way to analyse, a centre crystallizes, as the ego, a body image is formed, sensations are singled out and localized (more or less successfully) in parts of the body, modalities are discriminated, and objects are structured. These processes are not

---

[1] Cf. Koffka, op. cit., p. 326.

separable and not even properly distinct. Each depends on the others and they progress hand in hand.

It is not our task to give detailed accounts of this multiple development of the psyche. All that is needed is to draw attention to certain features of it that have specially significant bearing upon metaphysical and epistemological problems. Something further, however, first needs to be said here about the different forms of feeling, as they become distinguished in later development, the warning having duly been issued that in treating them separately one is always abstracting to lesser or greater extent.

3

The deliverances of touch, sight, hearing, taste and smell are grouped by psychologists together as the forms of exteroceptive sensation, of which, perhaps, the most mysterious aspect is the fact that the sharp contrast between the qualities of different modalities has no counterpart in neural activity. There is no trace of a similar contrast in the neural impulses that accompany these diverse sensations. The neural processes seem to differ from one another only in that they activate different parts of the nervous mechanism and trace different patterns of neural pathways, while the sensations that accompany them are almost incomparably distinct in quality. Yet they have, apparently, mutually transferable characters, and we are apt to describe colours and shapes in terms of touch and sound, sounds in terms of colour, and smells in terms of all the rest.[1]

Seventeenth-century writers like Hobbes and Locke thought of sensations as atomic and isolable elements of awareness produced in the mind by a relatively simple process of mechanical transmission of physical impacts upon the body. Locke presumed that a simple and isolated stimulus was conveyed by a linear progression of causes to the brain where it produced 'an idea'. For him this was a 'simple idea of sensation' and it was natural for him to treat such simple ideas as separable occurrences independent of one another—'as distinct ideas in the mind . . . as the taste of sugar, and the smell of a rose', however closely 'united and blended' they might be 'in things themselves'.[2] The conse-

[1] Cf., 'Screaming red', 'rough outline', 'rhapsody in blue', 'a warm smell' and 'a nauseous hum'.
[2] Cf. *Essay Concerning Human Understanding* II, ii, 1.

quences of this doctrine, as it was developed by Hume, are notorious, and it has been enormously influential both in philosophy and psychology, as the origin and background of the sense-datum theory in the former and of the stimulus-response formula in the latter. For Locke and those influenced by him atomicity was fundamental to the mind, its growth and development being little more than the accumulation and conjunction, in various groupings, of simple elements.

The evidence of contemporary neurophysiology has demolished this position completely. There is an unmistakable trend today in physiology and also in psychology (as in biology generally) to relinquish the more atomic hypotheses and the purely analytic methods of explanation and adopt a more synthetic approach. We have seen how the organismic view has advanced in biology generally; in neurophysiology, similarly, the older tendency to analyse neural structures down to simple reflex arcs and to build up the more complex from these has given place to an insistence upon more widespread patterning to account for even the most elementary reactions, and to many writers the application of the field concept to physiological phenomena has a strong appeal.

Contemporary neurophysiologists agree in large measure that a sensation is not the simple end result of a linear conduction of nervous impulses from the periphery to one or a small group of brain cells, but that the simplest sensory experience involves an elaborate ramification and patterning of neural activity in the cerebral cortex and possibly also elsewhere.

Though there does seem to be localization of function in the cortex in some respects and to some extent, the most recent evidence does not support the view that precisely localized areas have sole responsibility for specific sensations. It is known that lesions in certain areas prevent their occurrence and that unless the neural impulse reaches a definite region the corresponding sensation is not experienced. But there are some who believe that other areas than those to which specific sensory modes are attributed may be involved in the actual production of awareness. Penfield maintains that these localized points of the cortical functioning are but way-stations in a more elaborate system of connections and that the diencephelon is primarily essential to consciousness. Others suspect that the so-called association, or silent, areas may also be involved, particularly those immediately

adjacent to the sensory area concerned. These areas are often
assumed to be specially important also for memory and learning.
If this is the case, sensation may be something physiologically
far more complicated than has hitherto been assumed. Much of
this, however, is speculation; what is generally accepted is the
importance of patterned activity. 'It has become abundantly clear
in recent years', writes Le Gros Clark, 'that sensory discrimination
depends largely on the pattern of stimulation of receptor mechanisms.'[1] Russell Brain repeatedly draws attention to the importance of patterns.[2] It is with these, he maintains that sensations are
correlated and E. L. Hutton asserts that the weaving of patterns
out of elements essentially the same is all that the neurologist ever
finds.[3]

The notion of strict localization of sensation in limited parts of
the cortex has recently been further and more drastically modified
in the light of other discoveries. Afferent activity seems to be
effected and controlled in complicated ways by the activity of the
reticular formation of the brain stem. Dr. Robert B. Livingstone
writes:

'The cerebral cortex has lost some of its supremacy except in the
sense of altitude. Clearly the cortex does not seem to be the first
step in sensation, nor does it appear to be the last either. Something fairly continuous and dynamic seems to be taking place all
along the descending pathways—during wakefulness . . . not only
does the brain stem reticular formation affect consciousness . . .
but it also appears to alter the content of consciousness. And its
effect proceeds from the sense receptors to wherever you wish to
pick the end-point.'[4]

As long ago as 1933, Bartley's and Perkins' experiments on the
brain activity of dogs[5] under specific sensory stimulation led to
the conclusion not only that the entire cortex is involved in each

[1] 'The Anatomical Perspective', in *Perspectives in Neuropsychiatry*
(D. Richter, Ed., London, 1950), p. 23.
[2] *Mind, Perception and Science*, Chs. II (p. 30), VI and *passim*.
[3] *Perspectives in Neuropsychiatry*, p. 161.
[4] 'Central Control of Afferent Activity', in *Reticular Formation of the
Brain*, pp. 181–2.
[5] S. H. Bartley, 'Gross Differential Activity of the Dog's Cortex as
Revealed by Action Currents' and 'A Study of Cerebral Action Currents
in the Dog under Sound Stimulation', *University of Kansas Stud. in
Psychol. I*, Psycho. Mon. 44, 1 (1933).

special reaction but that when it is 'passive' there is an over-all pattern of activity of the same general type as when it is 'active' (i.e. reacting to stimulation), and that specific stimuli do no more than modify a basic pattern of activity. Bartley concludes that 'a field theory of the nervous system is demanded if its activities are to become intelligible'.[1]

It is clear that there is no simple neurophysiological counterpart to a 'simple idea of sensation' or simple datum. If any such thing as pure sensation occurs in consciousness (which, as will later appear, is not the case) its neural accompaniment is an intricately patterned and organized complex of events. In like manner the reflex arc is no longer regarded as a simple elementary unit of neural organization. The most primitive reflex activity has been found to involve a far more complex structure of interconnections between nerve paths than was originally imagined. The nervous system as a whole, in the light of contemporary knowledge cannot be conceived as a bundle of relatively independent circuits externally linked. In 1938 Golla wrote '. . . even on the neurophysiological level we have to regard the nervous system as an organic whole and not as integration of reflex arcs'.[2]

These conclusions have been corroborated by a mass of experimental and clinical evidence provided by the work of K. Lashley, K. L. Chow and P. J. Hutt, W. Penfield and L. Roberts, Le Gros Clark and many others. Brain functions are not simple mechanical structures located precisely here or there in the principal neural organs, but are patterned organic activities to which different neural structures may contribute equipotentially. It seems as if within the neural mechanism, there is the same kind of auturgic variation relative to a single function as is evident in other forms of living activity, and something akin to a field concept for the understanding of neural processes has proved attractive to many thinkers. The position is summarized by Francis Schiller as follows:

'In any given central nervous system, specialization, so far from increasing, does, in fact, diminish as we ascend from the periphery to the brain stem, and from the projection areas to those of association and elaboration. It must be assumed that the greater

[1] *University of Kansas Stud. in Psychol. I*, Psycho. Mon. 44, I (1933), p. 54.
[2] *Journal of Mental Science*, Vol. 84, 9, 1938.

part of the human cortex is relatively equipotential in function, or at least multi-potential as compared with the projection systems. There is a branching and tree-like spreading out, a giving up of the principle of centralization, as we ascend from the brain stem to the cortex.'[1]

On the other hand, attempts like those of Köhler to elaborate a theory of electrical fields in the cortex to account for the phenomena of perception have broken down. Experimentally not only has confirmation been lacking but actual disconfirmation has been afforded. The experiments of Lashley and his associates on chimpanzees into whose brains gold conductors were inserted after they had learned to make specific perceptual discriminatory responses, showed that no disturbance of visual habit resulted such as would be expected if the visual percept depended upon a special electrical field pattern to the brain.[2] The field, however, is in this connection more a concept than a physical entity. It is a biological, or organic 'field' rather than electrical or chemical (though these are not necessarily excluded), and is expressive of the dynamic wholeness of the living system whose analysis into parts is always subject to the integration of those parts into a single structure.

Whether or not a field-theory in neurophysiology is found satisfactory there can be no doubt about the facts of neural reticulation in the brain and the rich interweaving of connections between the areas in which localizations have been determined. New mechanisms are continually being discovered, but they are almost invariably mechanisms of co-ordination and interaction between functions. They are all subordinate structures in a single co-ordinated system.

The work of a large number of physiologists justified the shift of outlook from the linear and localized conception of neural activity to the patterned and reticular conception. Though precise, point-to-point, transmission paths have definitely been discovered between peripheral receptors and the cortex, it is no longer possible, from the neurophysiological viewpoint, to think of sensation

[1] Cf. Francis Schiller, 'Consciousness Reconsidered', *A.M.A. Archives of Neurology and Psychiatry*, 67 (1952), p. 224.
[2] *Vide* Lashley, K. S., Chow, K. L. and Semmes, J., 'An examination of the electrical field theory of cerebral integration', *Psychol. Review*, 58, 1951, pp. 123–36.

L

as the simple end-result of a simple neural process and it is clear that Locke's statement of the position was highly over-simplified. In the words of Russell Brain: 'There is evidence . . . that even from the periphery relationship between several fibres conducting impulses is involved in the simplest sensation';[1] and the brain activity involved is patterned activity even in the simplest sensory experience. It would seem that a sensation is always a structure, not an internally simple datum, as has so often been assumed by epistemologists. No neurophysiological evidence can be found for the occurrence of simple sense-data like those upon which whole schools of philosophers have based their theories of knowledge, and today powerful trends of development in physiology move in the opposite direction.

4

Phenomenological considerations have, in like manner, compelled psychologists to abandon the notion of simple sensory data.

The explicit adoption of the field concept in psychology is due to Wertheimer and it has been consistently applied by Köhler, Koffka and the whole school of Gestalt Psychology. It is not incompatible with the ideas and methods applied by other schools (e.g. the Psycho-analytic) and many writers have adopted the concept.[2] As applied to the nature of sensation it gives results which should have had revolutionary effects upon epistemology had they not largely been overlooked by philosophers.

The sense-datum, as a simple entity (like a red patch, or a tone) presented to our awareness against a blank background, was taken to be the simplest element of awareness so long as both the physiological and the psychological approach was made in terms of local stimulation. But it should have been obvious at once that even if local stimulation did inscribe a 'simple idea of sensation' on a *tabula rasa* (which experimental evidence has long disproved), this would not result in a simple datum. For the alleged datum, be it colour-patch, sound or tweak of pain would not be the whole of what was presented but would necessarily occur against a contrasting background and in succession to contrasting predecessors. In awareness there are no mere blanks, the absence of

[1] Op. cit., p. 66.
[2] Cf. Kurt Lewin's Topological Field Theory and the Sensory-Tonic Field Theory of Werner and Wapner.

stimulation is itself a stimulus. Consequently, the so-called sense-datum cannot be taken as separable from its spatio-temporal context together with which it makes up an organized field.

This structural articulation cannot be eliminated by enlarging the simple datum to fill the entire sense-field. The experimental work of Metzger.[1] established the fact that the simplest possible case of sensory awareness is always an organized field and that nothing less ever occurs in consciousness. Homogeneous stimulation of the retina by dim white light of uniform brightness produces first the appearance of a grey fog which increases in density with depth. This variation in apparent density is evidently subjective, for in Metzger's experiment the source of the light was a uniform whitewashed surface so arranged around the subject as to reflect light of equal intensity from all points. Increasing intensification of the light at first produced the effect of an expansion of space (with a feeling of release of pressure) but as soon as it was sufficient to reveal inhomogeneities in the reflecting wall (its 'grain'), the foggy appearance changed to that of a white surface (at first filmy but subsequently plane) at a definite distance from the observer. The intervening space then appeared transparent and empty. At every stage the apparent datum is organized and at none is it homogeneous, whatever the actual source of stimulation might be. It is *ab initio* tri-dimensionally structured and its articulation increases in complexity and definiteness more so than does that of the distal stimulus—the brighter light, simply revealing a grain on the two-dimensional surface, produces a three-dimensional articulation of the appearance into transparent foreground bounded at a certain depth by a plane white surface.

This experiment establishes the fact that experience of a uniform, undifferentiated sense-field does not occur. Every sense-field is always, in phenomenal experience, organized as a whole.[2] It is evident that in some cases (like the instance discussed) the more

[1] W. Metzger, *Optische Untersuchungen am Ganzfeld*. II. *Zur Phänomenologie des homogenen Ganzfelds*, Psych. Forsch. 15, 1930.

[2] Confirmation of this conclusion in general though not in all details has been provided by more recent experiments on perception by Walter Cohen. *Vide* 'Spatial and Textural Characteristics of the *Ganzfeld*' and 'Color Perception in the Chromatic *Ganzfeld*', Amer. Jour. of Psych., LXX and LXXI, 1957, 1958. It was found that fog distance was not significantly related to intensity of illumination (due probably to the elimination of surface texture in the apparatus), but that separation of the field into fog in front of a ground does occur.

important aspect of the organization will be spatial, and in others it will be primarily temporal; but in actuality it is always both.

Recognition of these facts by the epistemologist should wean him away from the habit of trying to build up our knowledge of the external world from atomic data picked out by local stimulation. This, after all, one might be inclined to protest, is a habit which went out of fashion at the end of the eighteenth century. Unfortunately, it did not. Twentieth-century writers of the eminence of Bertrand Russell, G. E. Moore, C. D. Broad and H. H. Price have all given way to it. Carnap and Ayer have not been innocent of it, and the majority of logical empiricists and linguistic analysts, their protestations to the contrary notwithstanding, still harbour it in the not too distant background of their argumentation.

5

We shall see anon that the discrimination and contradistinction of the modes and qualities of sensation are consequent upon the activity of attention and we must return to them when we consider what it achieves. But attention has significant relation to other forms of feeling; in particular to emotion and conation, upon which some reflections may be made at this point.

Emotions are highly complex psychological phenomena, seldom appearing simple even to introspection. They are never devoid of sensory elements, though these, as James and Lange forced upon our attention, are for the most part interoceptive, somatic sensations. Even so, they are often so closely associated with exteroceptive sensations as well that it is difficult to disentangle the two. It is not by chance nor purely in metaphor that we constantly describe feelings of depression as gloomy and of exhilaration as bright.

It is also well established that emotional states are conditions of tension within the organism, consequent upon the disturbance of equilibrium, that they are felt as such, and that they impel to action—that is, they have conative efficacy. But this is not invariable, and the release of tension also has emotional value (relief, gratification and kindred feelings); and some forms of emotion may well accompany the cessation of drive: rest and composure, or lassitude.

But to speak of emotion as a state of tension is apt to mislead. The disturbance of physical equilibrium also gives rise to tension;

and no doubt the equilibria involved in the living organism are in part (or perhaps wholly) dependent upon physico-chemical equilibria. When these are disturbed physical tensions no doubt occur. But a physical balance, when upset, may be restored in either of two opposite ways, both of which are equally effective. If a weight is hung from a spring attached to a hook, a state of tension results, which may be released, either by removing the weight and allowing the spring to hang free, or by detaching the spring from the hook and allowing both weight and spring to fall to the ground. So in an organism, disturbance of physical equilibrium may be redressed either by restoring relations between parts and activities typical of the normal organization, or by dissipating the organization and producing a different physical equilibrium. The tensions which are operative in living systems, however, are always resolved in such a way as to preserve the essential organization. The strain is always in the direction of self-maintenance; even when it fails to produce this result, it drives towards it and never away from it. The stronger the opposing tendencies the more marked is the auturgic drive against them. In fact tension in a living system has relevance only when it 'pulls' in the direction of self-maintenance. And it is only that sort of tension that is felt as emotion. It can be relieved only by fulfilment, never by frustration. If this is remembered much misleading talk confusing organic and psychological tensions with mechanical pushes and pulls may be avoided and many misconceptions entertained in machine-theorizing may be corrected.

6

The close relation of sensibility to movement has been recognized at least since Aristotle. Both W. H. Sheldon and C. J. Herrick declare that the origin of mind is cradled in the motility of the body.[1] Life, from the outset is a high degree of organization of processes and movements rather than a mere spatio-temporal structure of static parts. The primary characteristic of the living system is commerce with its surroundings: not only continuous exchange of matter and energy, but also constant adjustment and re-adjustment to external change. The total integration of physico-chemical and physiological processes which at the critical pitch

[1] Cf. Herrick, *The Evolution of Human Nature*, p. 312, and W. H. Sheldon, 'On the Nature of Mind', *Jour. of Philos.*, 1941.

is sublated in feeling, includes this adaptation of the organism. Changes to which adjustment must be made function as stimuli, and the nisus to adapt will be felt. Any such stimulus at any moment becomes a focus of adaptive activity, and so (if we may appropriate a phrase of Whitehead's) becomes a 'lure for feeling'.[1] The need for adjustment to the external change as the means of self-preservation of the system constitutes an 'interest' for the organism and the auturgic tendency, which is now felt, exerts itself by directing activity towards the stimulus and conentrating upon it the requisite realignment of parts and processes. This direction and concentration, as felt, is the direction of *attention* to the relevant element in the psychical field and concentration upon it. Accordingly, as is to be expected, attention becomes the primary source of organization of the field, and, in the phase of feeling, it is the form assumed by the auturgic nisus that directs the organization of the living system as a whole.

Recent discoveries by neurophysiologists of the neural mechanisms concerned with sleep and waking, emotional reactions and sensation bear out the hypothesis that the mechanism of attention is an integral part of that of feeling in general and serves to control and to discriminate elements within it. The reticular activating system of the brain stem seems to play a most important role in all these functions. 'The reticular system, the hypothalamus, and the limbic system all seem to be intimately related to the regulation of sleep and consciousness and to emotion', states Dr. Geoffrey W. Harris.[2] It has also been shown that emotion serves as a means of arousal and a determinant of attention. 'On several occasions', writes Dr. Charles Shagass, 'it was noted that the "sleep" threshold rose rather markedly when the patient was angry.'[3]

The reticular formation together with the mid-brain structures have thus been found instrumental in controlling sensory and

---

[1] Whitehead, of course, applied the phrase differently.

[2] 'The Reticular Formation, Stress and Endocrine Activity', in *Reticular Formation of the Brain*, p. 209. According to Harris the reticular formation 'would appear to be constituted by multiple short neuron relays from the tegmentum of the medulla and mid-brain up to the cerebral cortex via the hypothalamus and thalamus. A pathway [he adds] from the cerebral cortex to spinal regions, passing in the opposite direction through the same structures, is also established' (*ibid.*, p. 207).

[3] *Vide* Charles Shagass, 'Explorations in the Psychophysiology of Affect', in *Theories of the Mind*, p. 136; and of Susanne Langer, op. cit., Ch. IV.

emotional states and to be involved in the regulation of endocrine secretions closely bound up with the latter. The reticular formation especially seems to perform a function that can enhance or inhibit impulses from the receptor organs, and facilitate efferent motor impulses. This function is interrelated with cortical activity and may well be part of the mechanism for directing attention.[1] It is also thought that the neural basis of conditioning and learning is the mutual influence of ascending and descending reticular pathways.[2] That attention is intimately bound up with learning is well known. So there seems to be supporting evidence from neuro-physiology for the ideas that feeling, for which these brain structures appear so largely to be responsible, is the foundation of consciousness, and that attention is a part or aspect of the same neural activity: a self-direction of the functions involved in feeling, through the operation of part of its own mechanism, to selected elements of its afferent input.

All this, in the light of our earlier discussion, is of special significance; for we are about to find that attention is the pre-eminent agency in the process of discrimination and organization of factors within the psychical field. Here we have a fresh indication that further development and more elaborate structuring come about as a result of some sort of *enroulement sur soi-même*, in this case the turning in upon itself of feeling in the form of attention.

Adjustment to environmental alterations is not limited to chemical change. Even the secretion by *Arcella* of its bubble-float moves the organism towards the supply of oxygen which can re-dress the disturbed balance of its metabolism. And the pursuit of food, which is no less a drive to redress a failing balance, involves movement, if only (in some organisms) the wafting of cilia. The felt integration of biological processes must include such dis-equilibria when they occur, the tendency to redress them, and likewise the urge to make the necessary movement. The felt want is appetite. The element in the psychical field which registers the environmental change demanding adjustment is the stimulus to action, and the resulting movement is the response. Movement without feeling is quite conceivable at levels of integration where

[1] Cf. H. H. Jasper, 'Ascending Activities of the Reticular System', in *Reticular Formation of the Brain*, Ch. 15.

[2] Cf. Livingstone, op. cit.; Henry Gastaut, 'The Role of the Reticular Formation in Establishing Conditioned Reactions', *ibid.*, Ch. 28.

the whole process is effected by chemical reactions of a relatively simple kind. Whether or not this is the case in protozoans is a matter of speculation. But if and whenever the process is highly complex and intensely integral the assumption that it is felt is not extravagant and we enter the realm of wants and appetites and approach that of desires and their fulfilments.

Attention, felt want or appetite, leading to desire, are the expressions of auturgy raised to the psychical phase. One may say that they are the operation of that pervasive trend which Teilhard calls 'radial energy'—the nisus to higher integrations—on the mental level. They are, as Spinoza averred, the *conatus in suo esse perseverare*, expressing itself on the level of life and mind. From this point on, the development of mind is generated by the operation of attention (as an expression of biological and psychological drive—a form of conation) upon the contents of feeling which constitute the psychical field. It is an operation at once practical and cognitive, manifesting itself as behaviour—as informed and directed activity.

CHAPTER XVII

CONSCIOUSNESS

I

To be fully aware of any object is to have it in the focus of attention. Consciousness is proportional to attention and the level of one corresponds to the level of the other, so that the primordial phases of consciousness are those at which attention is most diffuse. Attention introduces into the psychical field a series of gradations of definition and acuteness, of which, if attention is highly concentrated, there may be only two easily distinguishable levels; but more usually there are three or four. For example, a man looking at a scene through a window on a wintry morning will be sharply aware of some object which has caught his attention, say, a car skidding on the ice of a sloping road. The scream of the tyres will be prominent in the field of his awareness and the visual details of the car, its spinning rear wheels, its colour and shape and its abortive movements. He will be aware also, though somewhat less intensely, of the general background, of houses and trees, of pedestrians passing to and fro, of snow-covered landscape, the voices of children calling, other cars hooting and possibly the twittering of sparrows. But these sights and sounds will be less vivid and not so sharply discriminated. At a still lower level will come the appearance of the window frame and the objects in the room around him, odours of the household (a meal cooking, or the like), the ticking sound of expanding or contracting metal in the domestic heating system, and so forth. Still more vague will be his awareness of the pressure on his body of the chair he is sitting upon, the tactual sensations at separate points from his clothes, faint somatic sensations and the general feeling of tonus in his limbs. Any of the contents of any of these levels may be brought into the focus, the whole organization of the field being thereby radically changed; and intensity of sensation, though for the most part it does, by no means always corresponds to focus of attention.

While this description is not in all minutiae complete, it sufficiently illustrates the function of attention as an organizing agency. It may not be the only organizing agency at work upon the contents of the psychical field, a fact to which Gestalt psychologists

L*

have brought much interesting testimony. But it is the major source of systematization, without which the others would probably be less, if at all, effective.

Attention singles out from the range of feeling some item or area, some group of elements restricted by its selective activity and makes it central to a structure which shades off through lower levels of articulation and preciseness in the manner illustrated. It thus produces a pattern, the simplest form of which is the visual pattern of figure and ground. But we must be careful not to think of the field of awareness only in visual examples. A sound, sharp and intense, or faint and intriguing, or an itch, or pain, or some other somatic sensation, may as easily occupy the focus of attention as a visual object. The field of awareness may be altogether devoid of visual sensation, as in the case of the congenitally blind, but is still an awareness with a definite pattern of central definition and peripheral vagueness in varying degrees. By shifting from one element (or restricted group of elements) to another attention generates the awareness of relations between them, and so, through learning, on the foundation of memory and habit, builds up the framework of an elaborate system of objects.

With these other factors in the process we shall concern ourselves anon. The major contention to be made at this stage is that consciousness is nothing more nor less than this activity of selecting, relating, structuring and systematizing of the psychical field of feeling. To be aware of something is to be apprised of it in a surrounding milieu, to apprehend it against a background, to grasp it in contrast to something else, to define it (more or less) in relation to a context. Degree of consciousness is precisely degree of distinctness and articulation of such contrast. It is not something other than the related elements which is poured over them to reveal their outlines, as developing fluid is poured over an exposed photographic film to reveal the details of the photograph. Consciousness is the activity itself of organization. Nor is it an agency other than and different from that which integrates the organic activities on the physiological level and raises them to the level of feeling. On that level it becomes the activity of attention, which, as we have seen, is a form of feeling, turning back upon itself and so developing the differentiated unity to a yet higher stage of organization, at which it becomes more specifically and effectively comprehensive, articulating still more intricately the

contents of the totality. This higher stage is consciousness—
the self-articulation, through the operation of attention, of the
psychical field.

Consciousness is thus a matter of degree, with continuous
gradation from what we may call full consciousness (in the sharp
focus of attention—not consciousness of the entire psychical
field) to unconsciousness.[1] The lowest stage in which awareness
is just emerging, as in the first moments of awakening from deep
sleep or recovery from swoon, are those in which attention is
all but absent and awareness is diffuse. This is the nearest approach
to homogeneity in the psychical field that is ever experienced.
Complete homogeneity never is, for however diffuse, feeling is
always diversified, even at the point of subsidence of organic
activity into the unconscious phase. The lowest level of awareness
is already in some degree, though only slightly, articulated, and
degree of consciousness corresponds to level of attention, and so
to degree of organization.

It follows that feeling as such is not *per se* conscious, but
is the potential object of attention and becomes conscious only
in the form of an organized psychic field. It is that which the
articulation of the field by attention brings to the level of awareness; or that which, being out of the focus of attention in varying
degrees, remains to that extent less conscious. The psycho-
analytic distinction between unconscious and conscious mentality
must be understood in these terms. It is, in the main, a distinction
of levels of attention, the unconscious being that which, for one
reason or another (sometimes neurotic or psychotic), constantly
inhabits the lowest levels of attention and is excluded from the
focus. The aim of psycho-analytic treatment is to stimulate
those facilitative influences which may bring it into the focus
and so make the subject aware of what is being repressed. In part,
the distinction may refer to processes which never can be raised to
the conscious level because they are effected by neural processes that
are integrated in one or more subordinate systems at the level
below that of feeling and which come to consciousness, when they
do, only in a more developed guise. So the mechanism (whatever
it be) and actual process of recall goes on below the level of
consciousness and emerges only as a fully fledged recollection, the
process by which it was revived never being revealed in more than
the slightest and most fragmentary way. But, for the most part,

[1] Cf. Eliot Slater, op. cit.

unconscious processes of this kind are not the direct concern of psycho-analysts.

We are now able to clarify somewhat and to elaborate the provisional definition of mind adopted in Chapter XV. We said there that we should count as mental whatever is or might become conscious. Now we see that this includes feeling, throughout its range, which may enter into consciousness in varying degrees; it may be fully organized or may remain in the dimmest margins of attention, barely conscious at all, or may even lapse altogether into unconsciousness. Below this level we are in the sphere of pure physiology which is by no means irrelevant to psychology but is not its proper subject-matter.[1]

2

The operation of attention has the effect both of analysis and synthesis. By selecting an element within the field and giving it definition, it at once brings out its relations to other elements, at first more or less vaguely and with a degree of generality proportional to the lack of definition of the background. The shift of attention and its consequent delineation of the boundaries of other elements makes comparison and further interrelation possible. The field is thus analysed into its components, but at the same time and by the same process, these components are linked together in systematic order. The form of this order is not simple and it becomes progressively more complex as experience grows. In fact different systems of relational order emerge, all of which have to be related to one another. Obvious examples are temporal and spatial orders; but they are not the only ones. The segregation of the ego from the non-ego is another, and its internal organization differs in kind from that of the surrounding world. Besides this, within each system, the elements singled out from the sentient

---

[1] R. G. Collingwood restricted the subject-matter of psychology to feeling and denied that it could concern itself properly with thought. (Cf. *Essay on Metaphysics*, Ch. X–XIII). In that feeling is a proper object of study for the psychologist he was right; but whether or not thinking takes us beyond that concern is a question to be decided only after we have defined thought and its relation to feeling. It may well be that thought has two aspects, a formal one which is not part of the psychologist's study but of the logician's, and an informal aspect which falls within the boundaries both of psychology and of philosophy. Cf. Piaget, *The Psychology of Intelligence*, Ch. II, and *passim*.

matrix are sorted according as they fit more or less closely into the specific form of structure that is emerging.

This is not the place to describe the process in detail, but two important points must not be neglected. The first is that the movement of attention from one focal point to another is not in itself sufficient to establish relationships between the contents revealed. This movement of focus is being wrongly conceived if we think of it as if it were a spot-light traversing a surface and picking out objects in turn. Of course, this serves, for some purposes, as a useful simile. But the illumination of a shifting beam passes and leaves the objects first revealed once again in the dark while it high-lights others, and the activity of relating requires the terms of the relation both to be held together by the agency that at once distinguishes and compares them. There must be some characteristic of the mind which makes this possible, and it is difficult to identify. Some authors have referred to it as the 'transcendent' character of consciousness, and on the level of psychological investigation, it proves to be a highly elusive property. Memory will not help to solve the problem for memory itself (as we shall later have occasion to insist) presupposes the same characteristic.[1] Perhaps the clue is to be found in the two-edged character of all mental activity, at once uniting and distinguishing. Attention, strictly speaking, does not single out separable items one by one. It organizes the field as a whole, and the components which become more definite in the focus are never simple but are themselves always complex structures. The 'transcendence' of consciousness may well be its inherent holism; for it is not a lambent illumination passively revealing separate items, but an analytic-synthetic discursus, clarifying a totality by articulate integration; and the character of the whole, its principle of coherence, always informs and is immanent in the part.

The second important point is made by Collingwood in *The New Leviathan* (4.5–4.54). Attention, by selection of some element in the range of present feeling, creates an object of the sort that some philosophers have called 'a datum'. But it is not something

---

[1] Lashley attempted to evade the difficulty by appealing to memory traces (Cf. 'The Behaviouristic Interpretation of Consciousness', *Psychol. Rev.*, 30, 1923, to which reference is made above), and also Bertrand Russell in *The Analysis of Mind*. But neither author observes that 'transcendence' is as much presupposed by memory as by any other form of consciousness.

'given' in the sense that, *qua* object, it is already formed before it is 'taken'. It is, of course, already there as something felt, but the feeling is vague and *unformed*. It is the activity of attention that gives it outline and definition. It is made in being discovered. Perhaps a less misleading term to apply to the product of selective attention is 'sensum', so long as that is interpreted widely enough to include any of the various forms of sensation. But the sensum is an object created by the selective activity of attention and it is never simple. Not only is it constituted by interrelation with the contiguous field (both spatial and temporal, though these terms are strictly applicable only at a fairly high phase of development), but it may well exhibit internal 'forces' of organization which operate automatically, and the functioning of which is never raised to the level of explicit awareness, but is observable only in its results. This has been plentifully illustrated by Koffka and the Gestaltists, by the manner in which simple visual objects automatically shape and group themselves into organized forms.[1] There is no need to assume that such internal 'forces' of organization are anything other than the activity of attention as it impinges upon the focal region of its operation. For (we insist) it is an activity and not simply a revelation, it is a constructing, a distinguishing, a sorting-out and a holding together of discriminate elements. What the experiments of Koffka, Hartmann, Fuchs, G. M. Heider and a number of others force upon us the fact that the cognitive activity of the mind is an integrative activity and that it generates objects in accordance with definite principles of organization and cohesion. Moreover, these findings are by no means inconsistent with the view that this activity either co-operates or is identical with attention. Hebb points to experiments by Carmichael, Hogen and Walter and by Zangwill as showing that the internal sensory dynamic postulated by Köhler and the Gestaltists is relative to attention even in comparatively simple cases of figure-ground organization.[2] He distinguishes attention as a 'nonsensory' factor in contrast to mere elements of stimulation and advocates a theory of perception in which both play an equally important and mutually complementary part.

That objects are generated by attention and are not given ready-made is further borne out by clinical and experimental

[1] *Vide Principles of Gestalt Psychology*, Ch. IV.
[2] D. O. Hebb, *The Organization of Behavior* (London, New York, 1949), pp. 21–6, and *passim*.

findings. M. von Senden's[1] reports of the post-operative experience of the congenitally blind whose sight has been restored by corneal graft have been much criticized because of the comparative crudity of his methods of testing, but they have revealed some facts that later investigation has supported. According to Senden patients with restored sight can at first only distinguish colours, but are altogether unable to discriminate visually between shapes or recognize objects, even though they are quite familiar with them through touch. A figured object is seen at first only as an amorphous 'unitary' area of brightness against a contrasting background. The patient is initially unable to distinguish a square from a circle or either from a triangle, although tactually he is fully familiar with these figures and can identify them at once if allowed to handle them. By efforts of attention he gradually learns to see the corners of rectilinear shapes and to distinguish figures by counting their angles. The ability to see the difference between two contrasting figures presented together is developed before the capacity to identify and name the shapes, despite complete familiarity and ability to do this by tactual discrimination. Only after long training can simple objects be seen immediately and promptly named. Even then if the context or the colour of the light is changed, the object will not be recognized.

A. H. Riesen[2] obtained similar results with chimpanzees reared in total darkness, and though they have been rendered less impressive by later work, they have not been altogether superseded. Later research has shown that in the absence of visual stimulation some neurones fail to develop and others become deficient in chemical constituents. But these effects have not proved sufficient to explain the complete initial perceptual incapacity of subjects with restored sight or the subsequent development of the capacity.[3] Experiments on visual discrimination with rats by Lashley and by Hebb show that creatures with less complex brains are unable to generalize simple shapes without training. Rats that learned to distinguish a white triangle on a black ground failed

[1] *Raum und Gestaltauffassung bei operierten Blindgeborenen vor und nach der Operation* (Leipzig, 1932). *Space and Sight* (London, 1960). Cf. also I. London, 'A Russian Report on post-operative newly seeing', *Amer. J. Psychol.*, 1960, 73, pp. 478–82.

[2] 'The development of visual perception in man and chimpanzee', *Science*, 106, 1947.

[3] *Vide* D. O. Hebb, 'Semiautonomous Process', *American Psychologist*, 18, 1 (January, 1963), p. 23.

to recognize it if the brightnesses were reversed. Those reared in darkness took six times as long as others that had seen from birth to learn to distinguish horizontal lines from vertical.[1]

Hebb has proposed a theory of neural integration to explain this process of perceptual development which would also account for the configural character of percepts stressed by the Gestaltists. His theory has not been confirmed by direct neurophysiological evidence but neither is it in conflict with known facts and though more recent research has shown the need for modification of the theory, it still has considerable plausibility.[2]

There is no reason to assume, without definite evidence, that what is true for vision is not also true for the other senses. The perceptual discrimination of objects is not an immediate revelation but a skill which we learn in early infancy by a gradual process. It is an activity of organization, of selection, of distinction, correlation and synthesis in which objects are constructed out of the deliverances of feeling.

3

Though we have allowed the cognitive aspect of consciousness to dominate our discussion so far, this must not be taken to mean that the effects of attention are confined to cognition. On the contrary, the cognitive elaboration runs *pari passu* with behavioural development. The close relation between feeling and movement has already been emphasized, and the connection between attention and behaviour is obvious, for behaviour is the reaction and adjustment of the organism to environmental stimuli and stresses, and these are precisely what excite feelings and arouse attention. Organic activity is what is felt, and the differentiation and ordering of feeling goes hand in hand with the organization of behaviour.

This is illustrated in studies which have been made of infant development by psychologists with a variety of theoretical approaches. Instinctive and reflex movements of the new-born child are associated with primary needs, and these again are (on our hypothesis) registered in feeling. Hunger is felt as an indescriminable amalgam of sensation and emotion which is expressed by

[1] K. S. Lashley, 'The Mechanism of Vision', *Journal of General Psychol.*, 18, 1838, and D. O. Hebb, 'The Innate Organization of Visual Activity', *Jour. of Comp. Psychol.*, 24, 1937.

[2] Cf. Hebb, op. cit.

wailing. With these psychical and behavioural functions, and the mother's response that they bring, the reflex activities of sucking and swallowing are closely associated and the feelings of pleasure and satisfaction that they occasion. So attention is drawn to oral sensations and to the tactual awareness of breast and nipple. Investigators have found that the sucking of hands and fingers by infants is no less innate and instinctive than seeking for sustenance, and that it relieves oral tensions and arouses autoerotic pleasure.[1] So attention is drawn to parts of the body as tactually felt and emotionally relaxing. Early in life (at 16 weeks) infants bring their hands together over the chest in mutual finger play, effecting further self-discovery by double touch. Hoffer records that infants, at an early age, bring hand to mouth with a resolute gesture and follow it with the eyes.[2] So visual and tactual sensations come to be correlated and parts of the body to be noticed, as well as external objects which minister to needs and relieve tensions. This process is accelerated when the child, as he soon does, begins to manipulate other parts of his body and to use his hands as instruments to convey objects to his mouth, while at the same time he learns to recognize persons (primarily his mother) who respond to his cries, supply his needs, fondle him and evoke responses by their endearments.

The behavioural aspect of mental development is underlined by Piaget, who describes it constantly in terms of adaptation, tracing it back to these infantile instinctive and reflex activities and the gradual modification and elaboration of the behaviour to which they give rise.[3] He refuses to regard the exercise of innate reflexes as purely mechanical, and emphasizes the systematic character of this functioning. Behavioural development is then a further elaboration of the system.[4]

[1] Cf. A. Gessell and F. L. Ilg. *The Feeding Behaviour of Infants* (New York, 1937), and *Infant and Child in the Culture of Today* (New York, 1942); Willie Hoffer, 'Mouth, Hand and Ego-Integration', in *The Psycho-Analytic Study of the Child*, Vol. III, 1949, pp. 49–55.

[2] Op. cit., p. 57.

[3] *Vide La Naissance de l'Intelligence chez l'enfant* (Paris, 1948).

[4] Op. cit., p. 27: '*Ce qui frappe à cet égard, c'est que, dès leur fonctionnement le plus primitif, de telle activités donnent lieu, chacune en elle-même et les unes par rapport aux autres, à une systematisation qui dépasse leur automatisme. Presque des la naissance il y a donc "conduite", au sens de la reaction totale de l'individu, et non pas seulement mise en jeu d'automatismes particuliers au locaux reliés eux du dedans seulement.*'

4

In this process of elaboration, schemata of some kind are laid down for the recognition of objects. Precisely what they are is as yet scarcely known, though they are assumed to exist in both neuro-logical and psychological forms by a number of thinkers. Not all writers use the term in the same sense, but a consensus of opinion among neurophysiologists and psychologists appears to be forming in favour of the idea of mental schemata underlying both percep-tion and patterns of behaviour. Russell Brain has drawn attention to its use by Wernicke, Head and Holmes, by Wolters and Bartlett, and there are numerous others who do not use the term but cer-tainly adopt an analogous concept.[1] The significance of the concept is its implication once again of organized structure. The process we are here considering is throughout one of ordering, arranging, inter-relating, articulating and co-ordinating.

In its course, one of the most important schemata that comes to be formed is that of the body—the 'body-image', as some writers call it. This becomes integral to the ego, as the field is gradually distinguished or 'polarized' into self and not-self. Psychoanalysts complicate this antithesis by the introduction of the further distinction between 'ego' and 'id'; but all seem agreed that these are elements, which separate out from a more general and vaguer psychical matrix, and that they do so by a gradual process of mental development. The self is distinguished not only from other things but also from other persons by processes which are not separable. Nor is ego wholly identifiable with body image, though the latter is an important factor in the formation of the former. Sometimes the body, or part of it, is excluded from the self; at others the self may come to include what, in different circumstances, would be regarded as parts of the not-self. To give a detailed description of the process is the task of the psychologist and not our present purpose.

So the world of objects in relation to a central subject-self comes to be constructed, not just by arbitrary arrangement of subjective

[1] Cf. Russell Brain, 'The Concept of the Schema in Neurology and Psychiatry', in *Perspectives in Neuropsychiatry*, pp. 127–39; F. C. Bartlett, *Remembering* (Cambridge University Press, 1932); H. Head and G. Holmes, *Studies in Neurology*, 2 (1920); A. W. Wolters, *B.J. Psych.* 24 (1933). Also Adrian, op. cit.; Lashley, *Biol. Sympos.*, 7 (1942). For criticism see R. C. Oldfield and O. L. Zangwill, *B.J. Psych.* 32 and 33 (1942).

phenomena, nor even by the imposition (Kantian fashion) of inherent principles of order upon a subjectively presented manifold, but by an activity which is at once practical and cognitive, at once physical and psychical. To perceive a material object in the actual world is to have acquired a disposition (or a system of dispositions) to behave in certain ways, some of them physically overt, some of them mental: dispositions of association, recognition, and imagination. To perceive such an object, as a thing in the world, involves at least a habit of imagining its hidden surfaces and other unsensed sensory characters and of associating them with what is immediately sensed in a definite schema, of setting these in a spatio-temporal frame, and of relating them to other objects. It involves also a readiness to behave in certain ways towards what is perceived: e.g. to move round it to avoid collision, or to adjust the tension of appropriate muscles in preparation to lift it up. The sum total of all these dispositions in their integrated and orderly operation is what being conscious of the object amounts to.

The position is well summed up by Taylor and Wolpe, two scientists, pursuing the line of thought set by Pavlov and Hull:

'Consciousness, then, follows the emergence of a higher level of organization. In order to give a full and adequate description of this organization, it is necessary to specify not only the acquired reactions of the organisms, but also the objects to which these reactions are directed, and, in particular, those properties of the objects and their spatial and temporal relations to the organism that have served to reinforce the organism's reactions and confer on them the status of conditioned responses. The environment compels us to abandon this kind of behaviour and to adopt that; for this kind involves us in encounters with substances that are damaging to the life process, while that kind involves encounters that promote the life processes. The organism is moulded by the environment to constancies of neural response that yield consciousness—not as a self-sufficient "entity" but as a relating of the organism to the environment. The organism is conscious when it has developed mechanisms that enable it to respond in an appropriate way to objects from every angle of approach.'[1]

[1] J. G. Taylor and J. Wolpe, 'Mind as Function of Neural Organization', in *Theories of the Mind*, p. 221.

Clearly 'mechanisms' that enable an organism to do this must be intricately and delicately adjusted to one another as well as to the environment. They must be labile and adaptable to fortuitous demands. They must have the effect of bringing to bear a whole system of relations of objects in space and time upon the object in the focus of attention. They can, then, as the authors realize, be nothing short of the mechanism of consciousness itself, which not only initiates a response appropriate to a situation but appreciates its appropriateness.

The passage has further interest for us, because it recognizes the auturgic tendency to self-maintenance in the organism which adapts its behaviour to objects so as to avoid what is noxious and encounter what is beneficial to its life processes. And it recognizes that this behaviour results in a high level of organization of response which could be achieved only by a conscious organism.

The objects to which response is made are grasped by the conscious mind in their setting. Attention, generating awareness, elaborates into knowledge the world already contained in primitive sentience, and explicates the relations between its parts and elements in such a way that response to any one feature is informed (or 'conditioned') by its relation to numerous others. The effect is thus unification, as well as articulation. The response is to a situation, not just to a stimulus, and the boundaries of the situation are not sharp. They shade off into a vaguely apprehended penumbra of decreasing relevancies. The organism in its response to objects appropriates them and makes them its own, sometimes by physical absorption, sometimes by external utilization, and sometimes negatively by rejection (for to know what to reject and to have the power of rejection is to have control over what is repulsed, and is so far to be in possession of it). And as experience grows and knowledge develops, the area of precision widens and the relevance of remoter influences is allowed for in the responsive activity. So in its higher forms consciousness becomes all embracing, and scientific knowledge seeks to encompass the entire universe.

The characteristic of conscious behaviour, that it is a response to total situations and not just to a congeries of separate stimuli, may enable biologists and psychologists to recognize it when it occurs in lower animals incapable of reporting their experience. To this we shall return for indeed much of what we have been saying here is anticipatory and should, by rights, come after we have discussed a number of important mental functions which are contributory to the constructive process we have been outlining. However such discussion, so far as it can be undertaken in this study, will be facilitated by this preliminary sketch of the wider and more inclusive vista.

Though we have said that the process of construction of a world is not accomplished simply by the imposition upon a subjectively presented manifold of *a priori* principles of organization, clearly it does involve the imposition of principles of organization upon a relatively confused qualitative multiplicity—what we have called feeling. To insist that the process is as much practical as theoretical does not alter the fact that the practical activity is centrally directed. The ultimate source of the organizing principles remains obscure, and the relation to the actual world of the resulting system, as a system of knowledge—for so it becomes— remains to be investigated.

The first of these matters is a metaphysical question the answer to which could probably not be reached short of a review of the whole course of the argument of this study. For we have found mental organization to be continuous with biological and biological with physical. Each in turn revealed itself as a manifestation of some active nisus to wholeness and integration recognizable even in the spatio-temporal matrix of the physical world. The principles sought are those of polyphasic unity, no less immanent in the operation of physical laws than in the exercise of conscious mind. To this question we must address ourselves at the end of our study, for it is integral to the understanding of the nature of knowledge and so of science itself, as well as fundamental to the metaphysical interpretation of the world, as a whole.

The second matter is the epistemological question *par excellence*. It is the question of the criterion of truth and the validity of the entire content of mind as knowledge of the world. Consequently it has direct bearing upon the nature of science, its status in human life and its acceptability. Before it can be attacked, however, there are still many preliminary investigations to be undertaken.

The activity of mind being both practical and cognitive two methods have been used in the study of psychology: one concentrating mainly on behaviour, and the other concerned primarily with cognitive processes and phenomena as subjectively experienced. There is no reason to regard either of these methods as superior to the other in scientific rigour. Both may be, and have been, pursued with due attention to accuracy and objectivity. Both, in various ways, are subject to difficulties of observation, measurement and precise determination of detail; but similar difficulties beset other fields of scientific investigation also (biological especially). Such difficulties are no reason for abandoning the methods, which are not only fruitful of results but indispensable to the proper understanding of the special subject-matter. They are only reasons for seeking to improve them. Finally, neither the behavioural nor the phenomenological approach is sufficient by itself. Each demands and illuminates the other, as is to be expected if the object of study is at once both a pattern of movements and a form of experience.

We shall accordingly proceed to examine first the behavioural and then the cognitive aspects of mental activity, not forgetting their inseparability and mutual involvement. Our object, however, is not to make a psychological study, but to examine the pronouncements of ethologists and psychologists on these topics as matters for philosophical reflection.

CHAPTER XVIII

BEHAVIOUR

I

Under the powerful influences of Watson and Pavlov, the distinguishing characteristic of contemporary psychology has come to be emphasis upon behaviour. Behaviourism has modified the methods and approach even of other schools whose interest has been primarily phenomenological. The 'objective' approach has come to be acknowledged as essential to scientific method in the subject; the practice of writers to generalize from their own introspective experience is no longer in evidence, and introspective methods, when they are used, are carefully controlled and correlated with observed behaviour. On the other hand, with the passage of time, and the impact of widespread criticism,[1] features of behaviouristic theory which originally made it distinctive have been largely abandoned. Its mechanistic and atomistic excesses have been mitigated, allowance has been made for the patterning of stimuli, for motivation and for the occurrence of awareness (always tacitly assumed in one way or another), if only as intervening variables between stimulus and response; and the behaviour, of which psychology is now regarded as the special science, is recognized as something more than ordinarily complicated.

The term itself, however, is not very precise for one may speak of any activity at any level, whether of elementary particles, of atoms, of molecules, or of living tissues, as behaviour, and it becomes necessary, therefore, to make clear just what sort of behaviour is the proper subject-matter of psychology, and the behaviour of what sort of entities. It is usual, and safe enough, to assume that a certain range and kind of living behaviour is intended. It is the behaviour of organisms; though not every form of organic activity is always directly relevant to subjects of primary interest to the psychologist.

Differences in approach between different schools of psychology correspond in large measure to the various ways in which they

---

[1] An interesting review of this is to be found in George Humphrey, *Thinking* (London, 1951), Ch. I.

understand this term. For William McDougall the psychologist's concern was with purposive behaviour and purposiveness was its distinguishing characteristic. But the nature of purpose itself requires elucidation (which does not immediately prove easy) and the concept has been frowned on by many who consider its application to animal behaviour unduly anthropomorphic. The distinction most useful for the elucidation of the matter is perhaps that introduced by Tolman between 'molar' and 'molecular' behaviour.[1] The proper subject-matter of psychology, he holds, is molar behaviour, the total response of the organism as a whole to a complete situation, in contrast to the local response of a particular muscle or gland to a local sensory stimulus. The S-R formula applies properly only to molecular behaviour, the stimulus being defined as a simple excitation of a sensory receptor nerve and the response as the reaction occasioned by the resulting efferent discharge. Tolman draws attention to the fact that what McDougall understood by behaviour was its molar form, whereas Behaviourists like J. B. Watson and his followers think of it only as molecular.

All molar behaviour, however, implies molecular and can presumably, in principle and in some sense, always be analysed into it. But here again the question arises whether, even if it were complete, which in the present state of our knowledge it seldom if ever is, such analysis into elementary parts gives a true account of the events to be explained and supplies all the needs of explanation—whether it exhausts the significance of the whole, or may possibly dissipate and obscure it. Is the appreciation of a symphony built up exhaustively out of visceral, glandular and similar responses (many of them conditioned, no doubt, in complicated ways), to auditory stimuli? Tolman, certainly, and many other psychologists would answer in the negative. They hold the view that molar behaviour has properties of its own which are not accounted for by molecular analysis, and though this view is still subject to controversy, tacit admissions of its truth are present even in the work of its strongest opponents (Tolman detects them in the writings of Watson himself)[2] and it may justifiably be taken as the prevailing view today.

Thus Tinbergen defines behaviour as 'the total of movements

[1] *Vide* E. C. Tolman, *Purposive Behaviour in Animals and Men* (University of California Press, 1949), Ch. I.

[2] *Ibid.*, pp. 5–6.

made by the intact animal'[1] and, although this might be taken in either of Tolman's two senses, the behaviour which Tinbergen describes and seeks causally to explain is undoubtedly molar. He asserts that it is one-sided to regard behaviour merely as reflex reaction to stimulus (whether simple or conditioned), or to attempt to reduce it to tropisms, and he objects to what he calls the 'generalization of reflexology'.[2] The old notion of behaviour as an additive conjunction of simple and conditioned reflexes has, in any case, become obsolete, since physiologists, from Sherrington onward, have demonstrated that the most elementary neural circuit has elaborate ramifications and effects much more than a direct automatic reaction to stimulus. As Thorpe (reporting Sherrington) argues, 'the organism's response is always multiple, involving a large number of receptors and . . ., far from being independent of one another, the responses show a great deal of mutual excitation and inhibition'.[3] To this has been added some damaging attacks by experimental psychologists including Lashley (1929, 1942),[4] Lewin (1926),[5] Leeper (1935)[6] and Koffka (1928, 1936)[7]. Koffka has convincingly demonstrated the failure of the reflex hypothesis to explain the facts, even of such admittedly automatic and unconscious actions as the accommodation, convergence and fixation of the eyes, and the scientific conception of behaviour today is of structured systematic activity on the part of the complete animal, analysable, no doubt, but not into separable and independent segments, and so directed as to make its dependence upon cognitive awareness virtually indubitable. It is, as we have said, and shall forthwith attempt to show *informed* activity.

Molar behaviour is relative not simply to stimuli but to an environmental situation. 'The term "stimulus"', Tinbergen tells us, 'is, in a sense, misleading, in spite of its apparent clarity. . . . A close study of . . . the complete stimuli to which an animal's

---

[1] N. Tinbergen, *A Study of Instinct* (Oxford, 1952), p. 2. Cf. W. McDougall, *An Outline of Psychology* (London, 1926), p. 56: '. . . purposive action is a total reaction of the organism'.
[2] Op. cit., p. 15.
[3] *Learning and Instinct in Animals* (London, 1963), p. 81.
[4] K. S. Lashley, *Brain Mechanisms and Intelligence* (Chicago, 1929), and *J. Gen. Psychol.* 26 (1942), 241–65.
[5] K. Lewin, *Psychol. Forsch.*, 7, 294–329.
[6] R. Leeper, *J. Genet Psychol.*, 46, pp. 3–40.
[7] Cf. *Principles of Gestalt Psychology* (London, 1936), pp. 310 ff., and cf. *The Growth of the Mind* (London, 1928), Ch. III.

instinctive movements respond . . . shows that they are in reality, very complex and not readily measurable.'[1] Even the very simple begging behaviour of young nestlings is a response to what Tinbergen describes as 'a clear example of a "configurational stimulus" '—the size of the parent's head in relation to its body. More complex behaviour, though of animals even lower in the phylogenetic scale, is clearly response to a much wider 'configuration'. The homing behaviour by which the wasp *Philanthus triangulum*, learns and returns to the locality of its nest, is a reaction to the complete configuration of land-marks in its vicinity.[2] The mating activities of some fish and of birds, a very elaborate train of typical behaviour patterns, is often initiated by response to the breeding site which may be a territory of some considerable extent and is presumably recognized by a constellation of features and characteristics. What we have here is not a 'stimulus' but a 'stimulus pattern' and in the more developed instances a complete situation or *milieu*. Response to such a pattern as a whole implies mutual influence between numerous stimuli impinging upon the exteroceptors, such that, in mutual conjunction, none of them remains unchanged. It implies a process of organization internal to the organism which combines these stimuli into a unified system to which a single (if complex) response is made. There is no evidence of one-to-one correspondence between simple stimuli and simple responses which are then summed on both sides to produce the complex reaction to the situation as a whole. Even when optimal situations produce only partial responses ('intention movements') in weakly motivated animals, there is nothing to suggest fragmentation of the stimulus situation correlative to that of the response. This capacity of the organism to apprehend and unify the stimulus pattern strongly suggests some form of consciousness, but we are not limited to suggestion. What may be claimed as adequate evidence of consciousness is easily accessible.

2

The environmental situation to which response is made in behaviour is seldom or never identical with the actual physical environment in which the subject acts, but it related to it in a special way. The receptive potentialities of the sense organs of

[1] Op. cit., p. 76.
[2] *Vide* Tinbergen, op. cit., pp. 147–8, and W. H. Thorpe, op. cit., pp. 258–9.

different species are so different that each is liable to react to quite different stimuli. Each has what von Uexkull called its own *Merkwelt*. Tinbergen translates this term without more ado as 'perceptual world', assuming without question that behaviour is dependent upon the animal's awareness of its surroundings. Against those who are more sceptical or who consider the assumption unwarranted there is more conclusive evidence. Quite apart from the limitations and specializations of the animal's exteroceptive organs, the actual environment in which it acts may contain features to which its behaviour is totally inappropriate, as when a horse shies at an old coat lying in its path. The situation, containing an old coat is not the one to which the animal reacts, but one containing (apparently) a lurking beast of prey. Koffka calls this the 'behavioural environment', which bears to the actual physical (what he calls the 'geographical') environment the same relation as does the apparent to the real. Behaviour adjusted to an object which is merely apparent, and not real, is mistaken behaviour, capacity for which is a sure mark of awareness.

The distinction of appearance from reality is an epistemological distinction possible only in relation to a conscious subject. Nothing can appear to an unconscious animal, or to a machine. A machine cannot make mistakes—though it may malfunction, and through its malfunctioning it may perform otherwise than was intended by its designer. But it cannot, while in complete working order, mistake one input for another. Possibly an ambivalent 'stimulus' may cause a machine to jam or perform in a relatively random fashion. If, for instance, it is designed, or programmed, to select the smaller of any two presented objects, it may oscillate between or select either at random of two that are of equal size. But it could not systematically 'choose' one of them as smaller, like Revesz's chickens which, when trained to peck from the smaller of two containers and then presented with two equal Jastrow shapes, systematically went to the one which *to us* appears smaller by illusion. That the behaviour of the Revesz chickens is no isolated case has been proved by Warden and Baar, who found that the Ring-Dove is similarly subject to the Müller-Lyer illusion.[1]

[1] *Vide* G. Revesz, 'experiments on animal space perception', *Proceedings of the VII Int. Congress of Psychology* (Cambridge, 1924), pp. 29–56, cited by Koffka, *Principles of Gestalt Psychology*, p. 32. C. J. Warden and J. Baar, 'The Müller-Lyer illusion in the Ring-Dove *Turtur risorius*, *J. Comp. Psychol.* 9 (1929), pp. 275–92, cited by Thorpe, *Learning and Instinct in Animals*, pp. 395–6.

In this case of the chickens their behaviour gives direct evidence of consciousness, because it can be interpreted only as mistaken behaviour which takes one of two equal figures to be smaller than the other. It is not evidence of malfunctioning because the chickens, regarded as machines, had been 'programmed' to select the smaller object. They did not oscillate or choose at random, now one now the other; nor did they fail to choose. They behaved as trained (or 'programmed') to behave, and selected systematically

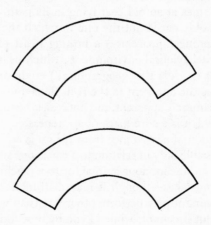

as they had done in cases involving no illusion. The only possible conclusion, therefore, is that one object of the pair *appeared* smaller to them. And this it could not do unless they were conscious of and responded to the situation as a whole in which it could so appear, unless that situation as it appears were different from the actual situation containing two objects of equal size.

It is a well attested fact that the illusion used in this experiment is due to psychological factors and cannot be adequately explained in purely physiological terms. The behaviour of the birds could not be represented simply as neural response to the retinal images, for in training the shapes were presented in varying relative positions and distances from the birds. Their reactions to the objective size of the presented objects could not, therefore, have been correlative to differences in the sizes of the retinal images. An S-R type explanation of their behaviour in training would have to presume a definite and constant relation between the afferent stimuli which clearly does not obtain between the two segments in the Jastrow figures. Nor may it be alleged that the chickens merely behave *as if* one of the objects were smaller and that nothing follows from that as to their being conscious. For they did not behave randomly and would not have selected as they did (without malfunction) unless that object *seemed to them as if* it were smaller. Seeming, without awareness, is a meaningless word. In oblivion there is no seeming.

Consequently, there is a recognizable type of behaviour which is direct evidence of consciousness: that is, mistaken behaviour, or behaviour of a healthy, normal organism adjusted to a situation other than that with which the organism is presented. Further, such behaviour cannot be regarded simply as the sum of molecular responses to single sensory stimuli. The effective stimulus is the awareness of the total situation and nothing less. In the case of the Revesz experiment, the least effective stimulus was two objects in relation—a spatial pattern involving comparative sizes. The visual stimuli from each object separately, if summed, would presumably have evoked a different response, or none. For the Jastrow shapes taken separately do not appear to differ in size.

The disjunction of seeming from being, appearance from reality, may well prove fundamental for the understanding of consciousness and mind. Without restricting mind to conscious states, we have found reason to hold that only where consciousness supervenes can mind in any definite sense be present; and if this be correct, there is no mind without appearance of some degree or kind. But we must be careful not to conclude too hastily what sort of appearance is involved. Just how the world can and does appear is the fundamental question of epistemology, and it may prove to be equally fundamental in psychology. The question whether consciousness exists or not really resolves itself into whether there is any appearance. For this reason the phenomena of illusion are crucial for both psychology and epistemology. As we have seen, they establish in psychology the notion of behavioural environment, and so, once and for all, the inclusion in the subject-matter of psychology of conscious states. In epistemology the distinction of seeming from being has important connections with the relation of falsity to truth; and what precisely constitutes seeming, how this distinction can arise at all and what exactly is involved in it, are central epistemological questions.

Of course, not all behaviour which is performed in a 'behavioural' environment is mistaken. The distinction of appearance from reality is forced upon us by the occurrence of mistakes, but their absence does not eliminate it. The reality may appear as it actually is. How we discover whether it does or not will be considered later, but whether it appears (or is cognized) at all, can be inferred, in all cases other than our own, only from the nature of the behaviour that it occasions. If this can be properly understood only as molar behaviour, in response to a total situation apprehended as such, if it is behaviour which would not be possible without perception, consciousness cannot but be presumed.

Even without appeal to mistaken behaviour, there are examples in plenty where doubt of perceptual awareness would be merely captious. The ability of Tits, Jays and Green Finches, as reported by Thorpe[1] to draw to themselves food, attached to a string but otherwise inaccessible, by pulling and holding a loop of string with beak and claw, is clear evidence of their ability to appreciate a situation perceptually—to say nothing of Trevor Miller's Blue Tit, which learned to reach food adhering to the under side of an inverted bell, by landing upside down on a perch suspended from the centre of the bell, and rolling up the string to which the perch was attached. The result of O. Koehler's experiments, demonstrating the ability of Jackdaws, Ravens and Parrots to select groups of objects according to their number, can hardly be explained without the assumption of a most discriminating form of perception. The birds were trained to select from among several boxes, the one marked with the same number of spots (of different and irregular pattern, size and shape) as appeared on an adjacent card, the key number being changed in successive trials, as well as the position and arrangement of the boxes.[2] 'This astonishing work of O. Koehler and his pupils,' Thorpe asserts, 'seems finally to have proved beyond question the existence of ideation in animals, for, in contrast to much previous work, it is marked by control so rigorous as to place it in the highest class of animal behaviour studies.' In fine, behaviour is overt movement in response to a perceived situation, and contemporary ethologists either take as obvious or emphasize as essential its dependence

---

[1] Vide op. cit., pp. 374-83.
[2] Vide O. Koehler, ' "Zahl"-Versuche an einem Kohlkraben und Vergleichversüche an Menschen', Z. Tierpsychol. 5 (1943), and 'Ability of Birds to "Count" ', Bull. Anim. Behav. No. 9 (1950), summarized by Thorpe, op. cit., pp. 388-94.

upon perception, a fact to which McDougall drew attention long ago. Tinbergen's constant reference to signs and signals ('sign-stimuli') as the releasers of instinctive acts, obviously assumes this dependence, while Thorpe asserts with insistence that 'perception is a basic characteristic of the drive of the living animal'.[1]

Perception, however, like all aspects of consciousness, is a matter of degree, verging upon primitive feeling at one end of the scale, and developing into explicit judgment, at the other. Consequently, in the lowlier phyla of animals it becomes difficult at times to distinguish clearly between behaviour and physiological process; and even when this is possible, it seems more easily plausible to account for the animals' movements in terms of simple stimulus and response. Even so, there is some evidence very low in the scale of sensibility, and it would be rash to try to decide precisely where sensation first occurs or where behaviour first becomes definitely perceptual. Even in the activity of individual members of the higher species (including man) there is a similar gradation of levels between which the boundaries are anything but sharp.

The nature of the evidence for sentience and percipience is, moreover, nothing more nor less than the adaptable coherence of the pattern of behaviour which it informs. Discriminatory behaviour showing capacity to distinguish differences in the environment and react relevantly to them is evidence of sentience. Behaviour relating appropriately to a situation grasped as a coherent whole is percipient. It is the organization and integration of behaviour, its dynamic unity and relevant variability within a recognizably coherent system that is the mark of consciousness; not the supervention or imposition upon it of some extraneous influence independent of the physiological working of the organism, or the inspiration into that organism of some mysterious essence deriving its existence from an alien source. That behaviour as observed and studied by ethologists has these characteristics of structure, organization and relevant variation in reference to a total situation, the evidence leaves no room for doubt. This will (I hope) convincingly appear in what follows.

3

Not only is behaviour 'informed' activity in the sense that it depends upon some degree of perceptual apprehension of the

[1] Op. cit., p. 13.

environmental situation, it is also 'informed' in the sense that it has dynamic form or structure, the character of which has been strikingly demonstrated by recent ethological studies.

In the 1920's McDougall made the concept of instinct fundamental to his account of behaviour. An instinct, he maintained is 'a fact of mental structure', which he distinguished from mental functioning and regarded as an 'enduring framework of the mind' to be inferred from its observable activity. This 'mental structure' he likened to the structure of a work of art rather than to that of a machine, but even the form of a poem or a symphony he held to be no more than analogous to that of mind.[1] An instinct he defined as 'an innate disposition which determines the organism to perceive (to pay attention to) any object of a certain class, and to experience in its presence a certain emotional excitement and an impulse to action which find expression in a specific mode of behaviour in relation to that object'.[2] In succeeding decades McDougall's theories suffered an eclipse. The notion of specific instincts was scouted by psychologists and that of mental structure was felt (perhaps) to suggest too strongly a spiritual substance, which there was no scientific warrant to presume. However that may be, the recent work of biologists and ethologists, especially Konrad Lorenz and N. Tinbergen, has in large measure reestablished a position similar to that which McDougall maintained. The idea of specific instincts has been revived (if with modifications), and the existence of structured behavioural dispositions copiously illustrated. Tinbergen seeks to give this structure a physiological basis (albeit in part hypothetical) which makes the idea more acceptable to the modern scientific outlook and is entirely compatible with the view here being maintained that mental activity is a specially high degree of organization and unification of organic functioning.

Tinbergen defines an instinct as 'a hierarchically organized nervous mechanism which is susceptible to certain priming, releasing and directing impulses of internal as well as of external origin, and which responds to these impulses by co-ordinated movements that contribute to the maintenance of the individual and the species'.[3] Though he indentifies it as a 'nervous mechanism', it is clear that this is only one factor (though no doubt

---

[1] *An Outline of Psychology*, pp. 41–2.
[2] Op. cit., p. 110.
[3] *A Study of Instinct*, p. 112.

the most important) in a larger organization including (as Tinbergen himself shows) elaborate muscular mechanisms, endocrine
glandular arrangements, and sensory and perceptual acts. Its
operation involves 'a total reaction of the organism'.

The internal motivating factors include the secretion of hormones (such as impel to sexual behaviour), internal sensory
stimuli (like the contractions of the stomach in hunger), and
(possibly) automatic nervous impulses generated spontaneously in
the central nervous system.

The activation of these motivating factors initiates a phase of
appetitive behaviour which may be relatively simple but is often
highly complicated and prolonged (like the migration of birds, or
their exploration to find suitable nesting places). Tinbergen
maintains that appetitive behaviour is truly purposive, in view of
the fact that it definitely pursues a characteristic goal. It is, he
says, bafflingly complex, involving simple reflex and conditioned
reactions as well as highly plastic and variable activity sometimes
involving insight.

The purpose of appetitive behaviour is to bring about a situation
in which the animal is confronted with one or more highly
specific 'sign-stimuli' which automatically release activity of a
more stereotyped kind typical of the operative instinct. These
sign-stimuli have a gestalt character, are in varying degrees complex and they activate what is called an innate releasing mechanism
(I.R.M.). Usually a series of them, in a determinate order of
sequence, is necessary to evoke the complete pattern of instinctive
behaviour, and they may co-operate in releasing the appropriate
activity according to a rule of heterogeneous summation. The
train of instinctive behaviour culminates in a series of stereotyped
movements, known as 'the consummatory act' such as eating,
coition, fighting, or the like. Relatively simple and stereotyped
though these consummatory actions are, even the simplest 'fixed
pattern' involves a more or less elaborate system of co-ordinated
muscular contractions which is itself innately and elegantly organized.

The reproductive behaviour of the male stickleback illustrates
the hierarchical structure of this scheme. Seasonal increase in the
length of the day and rise in temperature stimulates internal
motivating agencies which excite appetitive behaviour and produce the change in colour typical of the courting male. He swims
to shallow fresh water and seeks a suitable territory for nest-
building. When he has found this, he builds a nest and defends

M

it against other males, stimulated to threat and combative behaviour by the appearance of 'red male intruding into the territory'. The appearance of the female releases the behaviour of
courtship, a zigzag dance followed by his leading the female to
the nest and directing her into its entrance. He then stimulates
her to lay the eggs by nudging her with his snout ('quivering'),
and when she leaves the nest having deposited the eggs, he enters
it himself and fertilizes them. This situation releases the activity
of caring for the eggs ventilating them by 'fanning', an activity
which continues with daily increased vigour until the eggs hatch
and then stops abruptly.

Tinbergen represents the hierarchical arrangement diagram-
matically thus:

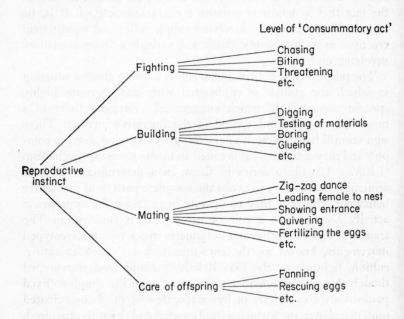

Lorenz put forward the hypothesis that each fixed dispositional
pattern builds up a kind of specific nervous tension, and is always
more or less ready for release, but is inhibited by the I.R.M. until
the appropriate sign stimulus is found. The build-up of tension
may increase under the influence of internal motivating stimuli
which correspondingly reduce the threshold for release. If the
tension becomes excessive the action pattern may be performed in

the absence of the external stimulus, as a so-called 'vacuum' or 'overflow' activity. The neural basis of an instinctive hierarchy has thus been represented by Tinbergen as a series of centres of neural organization, ordered consecutively as superior and inferior, each level being controlled by a special innate releasing mechanism, which when activated produces either (or, in succession, both) appetitive exploration and one or more consummatory activities.

What is particularly notable is that within the framework of this organization there are regions of plasticity and adaptability. In the first place, appetitive behaviour is, for the most part exploratory and variable, and is characterized by purposive, striving towards the appropriate releasing situation for the consummatory act. Behaviour in this appetitive phase is not stereotyped and is suitably adapted, within the limits of the animal's capacity, to different situations. Thorpe gives convincing examples from the nesting of birds of the complexity and plasticity of their behaviour in seeking and using materials. He cites also Hingston's experiments with Eumenid wasps, which he induced to break off the routine work of building and provisioning the nest and to vary their methods of construction in order to mend holes which he had artificially made in the nest. And finally he describes the elaborate and versatile methods of tube building of the caddis larva (*Molanna*) as revealed by the work of Dembrowski and used by Russell as one of the outstanding examples of variably directed activity.[1]

Secondly, the occurrence of a sign-stimulus does not necessarily determine which of a number of alternative mechanisms will be brought into play in the discharge of the consummatory act. For instance, the appearance of an intruding male in the chosen territory of the stickleback excites combat, but more specific stimuli will determine whether the fish threatens, pursues, bites or displays some other typical fighting behaviour. The action is suited to the cognized situation. Again, the hunting peregrine on seeing its potential prey will adapt its form of attack to the type and situation of the quarry. It may make sham attacks in order to isolate a single individual from a flock. If attacking a sick gull it may make a sham attack to induce it to fly or, if this fails, deftly pick it up from the surface of the water. If attacking a small mammal it may pursue and capture without preliminary feints.

[1] *Vide* Thorpe, op. cit., pp. 42–6.

Instinctive behaviour, therefore, displays the characteristic of relevant variation. It is systematic organized behaviour, but not wholly set in unchanging rigidity. The aim and principle of its organization is preserved in spite and by means of variations adapting it to changing eventualities. It is, within limits, labile, but directed and (in F. H. Bradley's phrase) 'controlled by' an objective or general purpose. This relevant variation was a characteristic noticed earlier in our discussion of biological development and morphogenetic movement, and is the mark of polyphasic unity.

Such instinctive hierarchically organized, dispositional structures cover the whole range of an animal's behaviour and are species-specific. The activities they determine are contributory to the maintenance of the life of the individual and are likewise variously adapted to favour the continuation of the species; for instance, by providing sexual isolating mechanisms which prevent interbreeding between different sub-species and by ensuring the protection of the young through maternal care. This adaptive value of instinctive activity is, of course, genetically determined and the product of natural selection in the evolutionary process. The innate organization of behaviour, therefore, reveals itself as a continuation—an elaboration—of the auturgic activity of the living organism. In Tinbergen's words: 'The more fully behaviour (or any other life process) is studied, the more evident it becomes that we have to do with highly "improbable", intricately adapted means of maintenance.'[1] Instinctive behaviour is a further development, a further phase of the same tendency towards self-maintaining, organized unity as has been discerned in other biological processes.

An instinctive hierarchy of dispositions is itself an organized system of activity variable relevantly to the overruling principle of unity—the function served in the maintenance of the animal's life. Within the system there is a series of levels 'of integration' to which Tinbergen and others draw special attention. The neuro-muscular mechanisms that subserve the consummatory acts are internally integrated, for the most part reflexly, and the consummatory act itself is an integral combination of these mechanisms. A group of consummatory acts are organized under a higher integrative centre which regulates their release either as alternatives or in succession. A number of such groups are subject to

[1] Op. cit., p. 153.

further co-ordination and combination under a (presumed) still higher integrative centre, which brings them into operation in the appropriate sequence and mutual relation. Each stage except the last is characterized in the opening phase of its activity by appetitive behaviour, revelantly variable and often prodigiously adaptable to changing circumstances. So that once again, in the structure of innate behaviour, we find an organization of activity ranged in levels of integration, a polyphasic unity deployed as a hierarchical scale.

This hierarchy however is not just the pattern of neural arrangement to which the behaviour-patterns correspond. Each stage of instinctive behaviour is also a stage of development. The stereotyped movements of the consummatory act are the most primitive and are not only typical of the simpler organisms but are in some cases the first to develop in the maturation of instinct in higher species. The next higher centre gives scope for behaviour more variable but still limited in its range, and such as is characteristic of more complex organisms. The wide-ranging appetitive activity under the control of the highest centre is the most complex and variable, and has greatest capacity for improvement. This is characteristic of the most fully developed animals, gives the fullest opportunity for learning, and is generally the last to develop in the course of maturation.[1]

Instinctive behaviour accordingly is clearly a continuous extension of the process of organization of activity that we have all along been recording. It is not only continuous with physiological activity but is itself structurally ordered. Each instinct is a polyphasic unity displaying relevant variability and each is hierarchically ordered as a scale of activities varying in complexity.

4

McDougall insisted that instinctive behaviour was essentially purposive, but Lorenz maintains that this is the case with appetitive behaviour only, which is a striving towards an end. The end itself, he contends, is not a situation or special object but the performance of the consummatory act, which itself is not purposive but mechanical and stereotyped. The justification of this view, is presumably, that once the animal is presented with the appropriate sign-stimulus, so long as the relevant motivation is operative, the typical consummatory act will be released whether or not it

[1] Cf. Tinbergen, op. cit., Ch. VI.

achieves the biologically functional object; as a dog will go through all the motions of digging a hole on the living-room carpet and of covering a bone with soil (pushing towards it with his snout), though there is no earth to move and the bone remains exposed to view throughout and at the end of the performance. Moreover, the performance of the consummatory act exhausts the motivation, in Tinbergen's words, it 'consumes the specific impulse responsible for its activation'.

True as this may be, Lorenz's interpretation seems somewhat perverse. The consummatory act is in every case nicely adapted to the achievement of a biological purpose and in many cases will not, or cannot, be performed if its object is absent, except in cases of vacuum or overflow activity which are admittedly not purposive. The hunting, capture and eating of prey does not normally occur in the absence of a suitable object, and the automatic performance of a consummatory act in the presence of a dummy or fake stimulus often gives the impression of frustration rather than satisfaction of the motivating impulse. Repetition of such performances certainly does exhaust the available motivating energy, but often the appetitive urge will outlast such frustrations and the animal will vary its behaviour to circumvent them. For instance, when members of a certain species of wasps bring prey to the nest they invariably lay it down at the entrance and enter the nest without it for preliminary exploration before introducing the paralysed caterpillar. In an experiment performed by the Peckhams (following Fabre) the prey was removed to some distance while the wasp was exploring the nest. The wasp on emerging looked for and found the prey and repeated the performance. This frustrating sequence was recapitulated a number of times, until the wasp finally omitted the ritual exploration and dragged the prey straight into the nest. Again, the fanning movements of the male stickleback will be continued for precisely the time that is normally taken for the eggs to hatch, even when half-matured eggs are experimentally removed from the nest and fresh ones substituted. At the time when the first set are due to mature, the fanning movement falls off, but does not (as is usual) cease altogether. It then again increases, stimulated by the lowering of the oxygen content of the water due to its consumption by the new eggs. The increase in activity continues to a new culmination and ceases on the day when the second clutch is hatched.

There seems thus to be some evidence that even the consummatory act is not altogether an end in itself but is directed to an ulterior object. If striving towards a goal is taken as the mark of purposive behaviour it would seem that consummatory action as well as appetitive should come under that head. But clearly no good progress can be made towards settling the vexed question whether or no behaviour is purposive until some better definition can be given to the meaning of that word. Activity directed towards an end or goal is certainly not a satisfactory definition, for it is too wide. Most biological and even some physico-chemical processes will satisfy it. Strictly speaking purposive action is action deliberately planned to achieve a preconceived objective and so may well be restricted to human conduct. To what extent animals act purposively, in this sense, can only be conjectured, and their ability to do so must at best be very limited, though their behaviour, like that of Wolfgang Köhler's chimpanzees, sometimes strongly suggests purposiveness to the observer.

In the case of instinctive activity it must be carefully noted that the end, whether consummatory act or what that achieves, is not just an isolated event, but as the term implies, the culmination or completion of an ordered whole of activity. The cycle of reproductive activity is a system, every phase of which is essential to its success, and each phase is initiated only when the prior phases have been completed and have brought about the appropriate and essential situation for the next act. The stickleback's fanning would be unavailing and pointless, unless eggs had first been laid and fertilized, and it is not performed except in their presence. In the rearing of young birds there is no definite act in the behaviour of the parents that can be described as the end. Feeding the fledgeling, whenever it occurs, involves stereotyped consummatory movements (the reaching out, gaping and fluttering of the young and the insertion of the food into its beak by the parent), but the point at which the fledgeling becomes self-supporting is not sharply defined and the parents' interest falls off gradually until they begin to prepare for the next brood. Every part of the instinctive pattern of behaviour is essential to it and ethologists have seen reason to assert that even the exploratory activity of appetitive behaviour gives some degree of satisfaction for its own sake.[1] 'In this situation' writes Thorpe, 'the "goal" is not the con-

---

[1] Cf. Thorpe, op. cit., p. 47, 'Hinde concludes that appetitive behaviour and consummatory act differ only in degree and no absolute distinction can be made between them.'

summatory act itself but the experience of having constructed a perfect, or virtually perfect releaser for the next phase of the appetitive behaviour'. In short, the 'goal' is no merely final act or condition, but the fulfilment of a complete cycle or system, without which no single act or phase of the behavioural train has significance. An instinct is thus an organized totality of which the parts are fully explicable only in the light of the completed system. It is a dynamic system, and instinctive behaviour is teleological behaviour, as that term was defined in Chapter XII, but it differs from the teleological processes of morphogenesis in that it is prompted and directed by, and attains satisfaction through, sentience and perception.

5

While animals are thus provided with innate dispositions, enabling them to behave adaptively, and beneficial to the processes of life and reproduction, they possess also the capacity to modify this behaviour by learning in response to novel demands. This capacity, of course, varies with the species, being relatively limited in animals of less complex biological (especially neural) organization and increasing progressively in more highly organized species. Learning is said by Thorpe to be 'the process of adjusting more or less fixed automatisms or patterns of behaviour and more or less rigid releasing mechanisms to the changes and chances of life in the world'.[1] This modification of innate behaviour is really the operation of its plasticity in response to different circumstances, and its tendency is towards enhancement of dynamic organization, both as regards apprehension of the situation to which response is made, and in respect of the adaptiveness of the behaviour pattern in which it issues.

That learning is not a single or a simple process is, today, generally recognized. It includes, first, what psychologists call 'habituation', the waning and dropping out from the hereditary pattern of a response that repeatedly fails to lead to a consummatory act. Thus, for instance, birds become habituated to repeated noises, which would normally excite alarm, and cease to respond with movements of escape. The process of habituation improves the organization and adaptiveness of behaviour by eliminating responses which prove irrelevant to the function and purpose of the behavioural system.

[1] Op. cit., p. 55.

Secondly, learning includes the process of 'conditioning', of which the Pavlovian conditioned reflex is a simplified version. The tendency to treat all learning as conditioned reflex in varying degrees of complexity is, however, to be deplored, among other reasons, because the cases of laboratory conditioning of reflex activity which are the classic examples are highly artificial and truncated elements within the more complex system of appetitive behaviour the rest of which has been deliberately excluded by the conditions of the experiment.[1] Moreover, much of what is often termed 'conditioned reflex' is modification of behaviour which is not reflex activity at all (in the sense of automatic nervous response independent of cortical control). That conditioning is an element in learning is, however, sufficiently well established, and it is clearly a mechanism for improving the organization of behaviour by establishing a response to one (biologically important) factor of a situation through reaction to another feature of the situation which can reliably be taken as a sign of the occurrence of the former. Further, such conditioning is never merely passive and automatic, but involves an element of anticipation, first established by Zener[2] and repeatedly emphasized by Thorpe (op. cit., Chapter IV). Anticipatory behaviour, as we shall later discover, is essentially bound up with the apprehension of a situation and its completion as a *Gestalt* or organized totality, and the anticipatory character of conditioning is thus clear indication of its significance as an element in organization.

There are two types or phases of conditioning, the first, which is possible subcortically, and which substitutes one sign-stimulus for another in activating an I.R.M.; and the second, called 'instrumental conditioning', impossible subcortically, which modifies appetitive behaviour by establishing a particular act (or series of acts) as efficacious for the attainment of an appropriate releaser. In this way the exploratory behaviour of the appetitive phase is channelled and arrives at its goal more economically and efficiently.

Both these types of conditioning, as well as latent learning are involved in the process of trial and error, but the old assumption, dating back to Thorndike, that trial-and-error learning is simply

---

[1] *Vide* Thorpe, op. cit., p. 81.

[2] K. Zener, 'The significance of behaviour accompanying conditioned salivary secretion for theories of the conditioned reflex', *Am. J. Psychol.* 50 (1937), 384–403.

M*

the 'stamping in' through reward (or 'reinforcement') of acciden-
tally successful movements in a train of random activity, has now
been abandoned as false. It has been well demonstrated that
from the start there is an element of genuine trial in this kind of
learning, and that random activity is characteristic only of the
behaviour of an animal faced with a problem the solution of
which is beyond its natural capacity. Dennis and Heineman[1]
showed that the behaviour of rats introduced into a maze was
non-random from the outset, and later work has established the
fact that the rats have a definite system of exploration, which
Krechevsky describes as 'a set of hypotheses'.[2] This hypothesis
theory has been confirmed by Cole in work on monkeys[3] and
is particularly significant in that it demonstrates the dependence of behaviour on cognitive factors and indicates the link
between its organization and the development of intelligence, all
of which will be further discussed in the sequel. It is of special
interest that this same hypothesis theory is used by Bruner (see
pp. 411–15 below) in his attempt to explain the nature of perception, a significant convergence of testimony to the character of
mental activity as a high grade process of constructive systematizing.

The fourth type of learning process is known as latent learning,
by which exploratory activity, typical of the appetitive phase of
instinct, leads directly to the apprehension of a situation to which
response must be made. This exploration need not be 'reinforced'
or rewarded by release of consummatory activity and, in some
cases, may even occur without apparent motivation. Rats introduced for the first time into a maze without food in the food-box,
will proceed to explore, and when later the food-box is charged
and they are set to find their way to it, their performance has been
found distinctly superior to that of control animals which have
not had the benefit of earlier exploration. Many animals, especially monkeys, show a tendency to indulge in exploration for its

[1] W. Dennis and R. H. Heineman, 'The non-random character of
initial maze behaviour', *J. Genet. Psychol.* 40 (1932), pp. 396–405.

[2] I. Krechevsky (1937). A note concerning 'The nature of discrimination learning in animals', *Psychol. Rev.* 44, 97–104, and 1938, 'A
study of the continuity of the problem solving process', *Psychol. Rev.*
45, 107–33.

[3] J. Cole 'A study of discrimination reversal learning in monkeys'.
J. Comp. Physio. Psychol. 44 (1951), 467–72.

own sake, both by locomotion and purely visually, and to give later evidence of retention of the information so acquired. Wasps and bees learn the localities of their nests and the lay-out of foraging areas in the same way. Thorpe argues eloquently that this type of learning involves insight (which he defines as the apprehension of relations), and is essentially related to insight learning, a position which can hardly be denied, for unless the relevant relations between objects were apprehended during exploration they could not be remembered and used in later performances.[1]

Here then is another outstanding example of the dependence of behaviour upon the capacity of the animal to perceive, and correlate into a unified pattern, a variety of objects and features of the total situation to which response is demanded.

There is, moreover, good evidence that investigation and exploration has a satisfactoriness of its own for many species of animals and in situations of novelty (especially where only one feature is unfamiliar in an otherwise familiar setting) a special drive to investigate manifests itself as 'curiosity'.[2] The effect of investigation is to make the new feature familiar—that is, to correlate it with the old so that it finds a place in the established experienced order—and, as it proceeds, the drive to further investigation decreases. 'There is implied', says Thorpe, 'a highly organized background of the familiar against which something new stands out requiring investigation. The investigation completed, this new object is "built in" to the perceptual world as something which is now familiar and which can henceforth be ignored or which can be utilized later, by "transfer of training", in a different context.'[3] From these facts and Thorpe's description and comment it is clear that the process of learning is one in which, by means of exploratory activity, the objects of perception come to be mutually related in a system by reference to which further action is regulated and organized.

The apprehension of relations within such a system is precisely the nature of insight, and insight learning (the fifth variety) is defined as 'the sudden production of a new adaptive response not arrived at in trial behaviour', or alternatively as 'the solution of a problem by the sudden adaptive reorganization of experience'.[4]

[1] *Vide* Thorpe, op. cit., Ch. V.
[2] *Vide* Thorpe, loc. cit., pp. 103 ff.
[3] Op. cit., p. 106.   [4] Thorpe, op. cit., p. 110.

The stress on organization is reaffirmed and insight learning might well be described as the modification of behaviour in consequence of the awareness of connections between the constituents of an organized scheme.

Examples of insight learning among animals are plentiful and are by no means confined to birds and mammals but are also to be found in the behaviour of fish and of insects. Among ants, bees and wasps it is displayed in direction-finding and orientation, in the circumvention of obstacles newly placed across a known path or a course which the insect is pursuing on the basis of locality study, and in the use of tools (the packing of earth to close its nest by *Ammophila* with the help of a pebble or splinter of wood). Among birds and mammals it is so common that an elaborate list of examples, intriguing though they are, is hardly called for. Recent work on tool-using and prelinguistic numbering ability in birds has proved them in some respects to rival man. The ability of rats that have learned a maze immediately to avail themselves of short cuts through freshly opened passages previously blocked,[1] and the spectacular accomplishments of chimpanzees are sufficiently well-known.

More important in its implications is Dr. Thorpe's discussion of the relation between insight learning and trial and error, so often treated as antithetical. It has long been the endeavour of behaviourists, from Thorndike to Hull, to reduce all learning to some form of trial and error. But trial and error learning depends on the 'law of effect' or reinforcement, and Thorpe, using the work of a number of writers shows that if this term is to be significant and is not to be definable in a purely circular manner it must, in turn, be recognized as involving expectancy. Stimuli which are 'stamped in' were said to satisfy and because they satisfied to reinforce the response, but the only way in which a satisfying stimulus could be identified was as one which functioned

---

[1] The very ingenious 'machine with insight' of Dr. Deutsch (*Quart. J. of Exp. Psychol.* 6, 1954) behaves in a way which only superficially resembles a rat in a maze. It solves no problems (not already solved by its constructor). It is never presented with a choice of alternative courses and each successive presentation is arranged to set its uni-selectors in such a way as to determine the order of future stimulation. This is not learning in any sense—unless one may be said, by loading a dice, to 'teach' it to fall with the six uppermost. The machine is ultimately set to reach the goal automatically without any grasp or apprehension of relations (except, again, on the part of its inventor).

as a reinforcement. The difficulty lies in the fact that the 'stamping in' of a response by the reward has to be retroactive (for the reward comes after the response which produces it). The attempt to overcome this by alleging the presence of a 'trace' was frustrated by the fact that it was in many cases inapplicable, and subsequent endeavours to meet the facts have rivalled the Ptolemiac system of astronomy in complication. The introduction by Hull of 'fractional anticipatory conditioned responses' has had this effect and, in Thorpe's words, 'the Hull theory appears to have become merely field theory in uncouth dress'. It is in any case an open admission of anticipation of the goal, for without that the fractional responses are completely unaccountable. Hebb[1] has criticized Hull's use of 'need reduction' and the definition of 'need', which he condemns as imprecise and inapplicable to many of the facts. The absence of 'commodities or conditions for survival' cannot, he points out, excite sensory receptors. Nor does the presence of hormones in the bloodstream constitute such an absence.

There is, in short, no satisfactory alternative to recognizing the expectant and anticipatory character of trial behaviour and to admitting that reinforcement follows the fulfilment of the expectation. Though it would certainly be wrong to suppose that in appetitive behaviour animals always know and expect what they are seeking, they do seem to have a vague expectancy of 'something' and, on finding the releaser of the consummatory act, often show evidence of surprised achievement—a sort of Archimedian 'eureka' reaction.[2] In consequence of this, Thorpe argues, the animal acquires an *insight* into and appreciation of temporal relations—an 'understanding' of what leads to what. Accordingly, appetitive behaviour becomes non-random to the extent that it is restricted by expectancy, and trial is based on some sort of rudimentary but real hypothesis (op. cit. p. 117). Even in trial-and-error learning the effort to connect and to construct according to 'hypotheses' is postulated and learning reveals itself, even here, as an activity of cognitive organization.

So Thorpe is of opinion that 'the work of recent years has, on the whole, confirmed many of the conclusions of Adams

---

[1] *The Organization of Behaviour.*

[2] Cf. William Craig quoted by Thorpe, op. cit., p 37 and p. 117, where Bühler's ' "ah-ha" Erlebnis' is cited as comparable.

(1931)[1] that all learning is in some degree the manifestation of a process basically identical with insight.[2] The apprehension of relations, which is the definition given of insight, and their elaboration in a system is the essential work of the mind. Without some form of perception it is inconceivable, and behaviour giving evidence of insight is precisely what we have called informed be-haviour—expressive of and dependent upon perception. The next task, accordingly must be a discussion of that topic, in which contemporary theories of perception put forward by physiologists and psychologists will be examined for their philosophical im-plications.

[1] Adams, D. K., 'A restatement of the problem of learning', *Brit. J. Psychol.* 22 (1931), pp. 150–78.
[2] Thorpe, op. cit., p. 118.

CHAPTER XIX

PERCEPTION—I PHYSIOLOGICAL THEORIES

I

To be aware is to cognize something and cognition may be taken as synonymous with awareness. That is not to say that cognition is all there is to consciousness for every cognition is, at the same time and by the same token, emotionally toned and conatively propulsive (if sometimes only incipiently); but, attending for the moment only to the cognitive aspect of behaviour, we may say that it consists in the awareness of an object of some sort or other. It is a mental activity the product of which is the appearance to the subject of an object. Appearance, therefore, entails cognition, which is the apprehension of something identifiable and character-ized. The typical verbal formulation of a report of appearance is 'This appears to be so-and-so', indicating an identifiable 'this' and characterizing it as 'so-and-so'. If no such object is cognized nothing appears, and, of course, an object may appear (or be cog-nized) without any formulation of a verbal report by the subject in communication with another person or even with himself. Obviously, if animals are capable of cognition and experience appearances, they cannot formulate verbal reports. We can only infer from their behaviour whether or not they cognize anything.

As has been explained, primitive, undifferentiated feeling is not cognition because what is felt is not identified or characterized unless and until attention has been directed to it and it has be-come an object—that is to say, unless it is, or at some time has been, selected and distinguished from the background of diffuse sensibility. Feeling as such is therefore preconscious and con-sciousness begins with cognition (though, of course, particular feelings may receive attention and so become objects of con-sciousness). With cognition and not prior to it is there any appearance.

In seventeenth- and eighteenth-century philosophy any form of apprehension of an object, every kind of cognition, was referred to as 'perception'. Thus Descartes includes under 'perceptio', 'perceptions of our desires, and of all the imaginations or other thoughts which depend on them'.[1] Berkeley uses the word

[1] *The Passions of the Soul*, I, xix.

similarly. In fact, the whole force of his argument that *esse* is *percipi* depends upon our understanding by *percipi* an activity that includes every form of cognitive apprehension[1] not only 'ideas imprinted on the Sense'. Their being perceived puts these ideas in the same case as 'our thoughts', 'passions' and 'ideas formed by the imagination'.[2] Berkeley makes this fully apparent when he argues that to imagine trees existing in a park or books in a closet though nobody is by to perceive them is only to 'perceive or think of them' yourself (in imagination or conception).[3] Much misunderstanding and misinterpretation of Berkeley's philosophy has resulted from the failure by modern critics (G. E. Moore and Bertrand Russell not the least) to recognize the comprehensive meaning which he gives to the word 'perceive'.

Today, however, we tend to restrict the meaning of the word 'perception' to the apprehension of things in the physical world by means of the senses, and to give other forms of cognition different names. But we do so unsystematically so that 'perceive', as ordinarily used, is ambiguous, along with many of its partial synonyms (like 'see', 'hear', 'feel', 'observe'). For if by 'perceive' we are to mean only cases of veridical apprehension of physical objects, we require a different term for the apprehension of afterimages, hallucinations, delusory apparitions, dream objects, and responses to intra-optical stimuli, and in ordinary language we have no such term. In common parlance we should say that we see, or hear, or perceive these objects; but they are not physical things. And it would be just as confusing to say that we only imagined them, for after-images are not only imagined and normal imagination is by no means the same as hallucination, dream and other forms of delusion. Further, when physical things are misperceived, something must be cognized which is (at least to some extent) other than the physical object. Is this other something perceived or not? With the restricted meaning of the word we should have to deny that it was, yet in what way are we to say that it is cognized?

Modern philosophers, especially those who pay homage to ordinary usage, miss this ambiguity and fall into confusion in consequence. They are led to deny the existence of dreams,

[1] An exception might have to be made for 'notions' about which Berkeley is never very clear; but even in their case *esse* is *percipere*.

[2] *Vide Principles of Human Knowledge*, Part First, § 3.

[3] Op. cit., § 23.

hallucinations and non-veridical 'perception', and examples of them that we should ordinarily adduce they explain away as cases in which we only *think* we perceive something though actually we do not. This, however, raises the questions on what grounds we think we perceive something when in fact we do not, and by what criterion we decide when we are perceiving and when we only think we are perceiving. As we shall later stress, the answer to this second question cannot be that the criterion is the actual presence of the physical object perceived, unless the person who gives this answer can demonstrate a means, other than perception, of ascertaining that actual presence.

It would be best therefore to apply the word perception to the apprehension of any form of sensuous appearance[1] whether it be hallucinatory, imaginary, illusory or veridical, and to distinguish these forms only as and when we can determine the criteria for identifying them. Correlatively the word 'object' will be used henceforward to mean that which is apprehended whether it be a physical thing or no. When it is a physical entity we shall refer to it as the physical object.

As soon as it is acknowledged that, for an organism to be conscious, objects must somehow appear to it, certain questions arise. (i) How and by what means do objects appear? (ii) Koffka's question: Why do objects appear as they do? (iii) Are the objects which appear the things of the world about us? (iv) If so, how far do they appear as they actually are? and (v) So far as they do appear as they are, how do we discover this? These questions are all facets of the problem of perception, psychological and epistemological. The first two are primarily psychological questions; and the last three are primarily epistemological, but both psychologist and philosopher must consider them all.

The objection raised by Hamlyn[2] to Koffka's question is unwarranted and arises from the ambiguity of ordinary language that we have already noticed. He asserts that it is legitimate to ask why things appear as they do only when our percepts are illusory (permitting the question in some specially complicated cases of veridical perception, when illusion would normally be expected). Their illusory (and so abnormal) character demands a causal explanation; but, so he avers, the normal character of veridical

---

[1] Cf. Plato, *Theaetetus* 152c. φαντασία ἄρα καὶ αἴσθησις ταὐτὸν
[2] *Vide* D. W. Hamlyn, *The Psychology of Perception* (London, 1957), Ch. II.

perceptions does not. The only legitimate answer to the question when perception is veridical is alleged to be that things appear as they do because they are as they are, for part of what we mean by saying that they are actually so-and-so is that they appear so under normal conditions. But the second part of this statement, if taken generally, is false and if accepted would falsify most, if not all, of our scientific theories. This will become apparent in what follows. The first part of Hamlyn's contention: that normally things appear as they do because they are as they are, is a gross assumption, commonly made, no doubt by the unreflective, and explicitly posited by the naive realist, but one which can legitimately be made only if we have and can demonstrate a criterion of veridicality *other than* their normal appearance. Without that we could not tell whether or when illusions occurred and so could not make the distinction Hamlyn so blandly assumes between normal and abnormal conditions of perceptions. We do make this distinction only because we apply some criterion, but it is by no means obvious what that is and its identification is the task of epistemology.

It is, moreover, precisely the discovery of non-veridicality in perception that raises the problems to which psychologists and philosophers address themselves. If we apprehend things otherwise than they actually are, how do they come to appear as they do? And if they do appear as they are, how is that achieved? 'Even if the popular notion were true', writes Floyd H. Allport, 'that things appear as they do because they are what they are, explaining how we could perceive them as they are, in view of all the vagaries of the stimulus pattern, would still be a major undertaking. The veridical in perception is as difficult to explain as the non-veridical.'[1] But in the first instance, he allows, it is the many and various cases of the non-veridical, that 'force the problem upon our attention'. Here again we observe that the capacity to make mistakes is what compels us to acknowledge the fact of appearance, and that fact proves crucial for both psychology and epistemology.

2

The answer to our first question: How and by what means do objects appear? is given by neurophysiologists, for the most part,

[1] *Theories of Perception and the Concept of Structure* (New York, 1955), p. 44.

in terms of neural transmission of impulses from peripheral sensory receptors to the brain. Some hypothetical account is then offered of how impulses are organized and interrelated in the brain so as to produce an appearance of objects.

Sensory impulses from various parts of the body have been traced to areas of the cortex which has been correspondingly mapped. Adrian asserts that the main function of the sense organs is to construct in the brain a map of events occurring on the body surface, so that a physiologist with sufficient knowledge of the working of the nervous system should be able, from electrical recordings of the activity of the cortex, to deduce with varying accuracy of detail, the occurrence of peripheral events and to tell what sensations are being experienced.[1]

The impulses, as they arrive and irrespective of their source, are of the same kind, and if reliance is placed on the notion of simple location in the brain of specific sensory functions, the conclusion is reached that the perception of objects is dependent ultimately on specific events in the cerebral cortex. Without these, no perception occurs and these may and sometimes do occur in the absence of their normal concomitants in the peripheral nerves and the external environment, for instance when the appropriate part of the cortex is electrically stimulated. So the doctrine is formulated, notorious for its logomachy, called by Russell Brain 'physiological idealism'. This is the position that, as the character of our sensations depends in the last resort solely upon the condition and activity of our grey matter, and as they are 'projected' by us to form a world of (apparently) external objects, we have no means of knowing their actual relation to external realities.

'Thus, according to neurophysiology, the observer is like a deaf housemaid who sits in her kitchen and watches the indicators of the electric bells. There are different bell-pushes (receptors) outside the front door and the back door and in various rooms, but similar currents travel along similar wires, and the only difference she can detect is that different indicators move. Being paralysed as well as deaf she never answers the bell except by pressing another one!'[2]

[1] Cf. Adrian, *The Physical Background of Perception*, pp. 18 and 46–7.
[2] Russell Brain, *Mind, Perception and Science*, p. 7.

The internal contradiction of this position is manifest. The indicators could indicate only to one who knew the connections between the bell-pushes and the signals they occasioned (to say nothing of the external pusher) and this knowledge is inaccessible to the housemaid of our simile. And as the physiologist himself would be related to the data from which he derives his theory precisely as the housemaid is to her indicators he should be ignorant of those relations the establishment of which constitutes his physiological theory. The theory is therefore falsified by the very conclusion which it supports.

So fatal is this objection that it may be taken as final, and it would seem anticlimacteric to mention other defects. Yet one which is almost equally serious must not be overlooked, if only because it reappears or is implicated (as will presently be shown) in so many favoured and strongly advocated hypotheses, at the present time. The board of indicators which the 'housemaid' observes is the brain itself. What in the organism represents the eye and the mind of the housemaid? To postulate a sort of manikin inside the brain who observes brain events and infers from them to events outside the cranium, is not only to presume the existence of that for which there is no evidence, but is to duplicate the phenomenon the theory set out to explain and to reset the original problem. It is no answer to the question, 'How do we perceive things?' to allege that they are projected on to a screen which 'we', or something in us, then perceives. No problems are solved by presuming the existence of a ghost within the machine.

The rival realistic theory of unsensed *sensibilia* existing independently of neural functioning and perception is no more satisfactory to the physiologist, for there are whole classes of percepta which defy the hypothesis. The perception of the colour black, for instance, involves the same kind of neural activity as that of other colours but nothing physical corresponds to it similar to wave-lengths of light. How, then, can it exist unsensed? Nor is it the result simply of absence of visual stimulation, which produces different visual effects. After-images and hallucinations give rise to similar difficulties. Apart from neural activity what ontological status can be assigned to them? Sensations of the phantom limb which occur after amputation are no different in quality from those of the real limb. They are obviously not generated where they are felt (in the limb). How can they plausibly be said to exist unsensed? If they exist in the stump they are misperceived and the problem arises of the existence unsensed of that in the misperception which deviates from the reality.

Accordingly, Russell Brain attempts to escape from the dilemmas of physiological idealism and physiological realism by accounting for the externality of perceived objects in terms of cortical functioning itself. In company with other neurophysiologists he considers the 'mapping' on the cortex of the parts of the body to form the basis of a neural schema—the body-schema—which serves as a frame of reference for the location of sensations. He argues cogently that there is no discoverable property of a neural impulse which carries, or serves as, a 'local sign'. Nervous pathways, which convey electrical potentials exactly like those going on in all other sensory areas of the brain, if taken in isolation, could have no localizing significance. This cannot depend simply upon the position of the stimulated cortical cells, for that position is not signalized by any special character of the impulse produced, but is determined only by its relation to other parts of the cortex.

For a sensation to be localized, therefore, Russell Brain concludes that it must 'irradiate to the anatomical basis of the body-image.'[1] Even the location in perceived space of visual sensa depends upon the position and movement of the body (awareness of which in turn depends on the reference of proprioceptive and other sensations to the body-schema). The perceived position, for instance, of a red patch depends upon the relation to each other of its images on the two retinae, on the accommodation of the eyes, the reflex reactions of the eye-muscles, the position of the head, and so forth. All these bodily facts are represented in the brain by neural impulses, some below the level of consciousness but others occasioning identifiable somatic sensations. 'In other words, the spatial setting of the red patch is derived from my body; and the proof of this is that when this bodily machinery goes wrong I no longer see the red patch "there". I see two red patches, or the red patch goes round and round, or though I see it, I simply do not know where it is, and cannot find my way to it.'[2] The neural basis of the perception of a red patch 'out there' is, in consequence, a highly complicated structure of activity. It is this kind of evidence that so forcefully weighs against the existence of separable sense data. Russell Brain continues: 'We may consider the red patch as an isolated sense-datum but we cannot

[1] *Mind, Perception and Science*, p. 32.
[2] *Ibid.*, p. 14.

experience it so, and, in so far as we consider it so, our consideration is remote from experience. The total experience of "a red
patch there" contains subjective somatic sense-data inextricably
mingled with it.'[1]

So, in the very nature and form of their perception, it is alleged,
our objects are external to one another, because *ab initio* they are
referred to the body-schema mapped upon the brain, the parts of
which are mutually external. The body image is intrinsically
extended and the relation of sensa from different receptors to it,
and their correlation with one another, generates our awareness
of our own bodily parts as external to one another and of other
physical objects as external to them.

As the physiologist presents it, however, this account of the
matter does not succeed in avoiding the difficulties. For how,
and by whom, is the mutual externality of the parts of the brain
apprehended (apart from the fact that it is perceived from without
by the physiologist). Whatever apprehends a relation of mutual
externality between points, cannot be confined to any one of them;
nor yet, if it were spread out over all of them, could it apprehend
their mutual relation merely by that fact. It must be able to
grasp the schema, as such, as a whole, all in one. Kant made it
clear that the awareness of a line drawn in space involves the
synthesis in apprehension of its successive points, and the same
is true for all spatial relations. How does the brain synthesize the
spread-outness and externality of its parts so as to provide a
coherent recognizable frame of reference for localization? The
transmission of electrical potentials along nerve paths, however
intricate the pattern of reticulation, is hardly a sufficient account
of this synthesis? We must go beyond that and still seem to need
an inner observer who grasps the total schema as a single whole.
If so, our machine is still haunted.

Moreover, the reference of a single item (a sensum) to the schema
as a co-ordinate system is nothing less than a judgment. No bare
sensum can (as such) perform an act of reference; nor can a
pattern drawn upon a surface, nor even a dynamic complex of
electrical transmissions through a three-dimensional network.
Reference is again a synthesis uniting in one act of apprehension
the bearing of one item upon another, or upon a system of others
taken as a whole. How does a map refer points to its own framework or locate them within itself? Must there not be a mind

[1] *Mind, Perception and Science*, p. 14.

to do this, and would that not be another visitation from the ghost?

Yet again, suppose the brain does contain a schema of the body to which it refers and in reference to which it locates sensa. This system is still confined to the brain. How does it become aware of the relation of its own mapping to the peripheral receptors, or of theirs to the causes which affect them? Are we not still committed to the predicament of the paralysed housemaid shut up in her kitchen referring signals to a schema—of what, she has no means of knowing? Even if, in these circumstances, she were to project her schematic constructions as an apparent external world, this would not amount to perceptual *knowledge*, for she would have no external criterion of possible error. In fact, on the basis of this theory we should be hard put to explain the fact of illusion, let alone the means of detecting it.

These epistemological difficulties persistently haunt physiological theories. E. L. Hutton, in more detail but with less subtlety and caution sets out a similar theory of perception.[1] Here too the body-image is made central to the theory and the author contends that neural impulses trace smaller images of external objects in the brain as well as of the subject's own body and constitute there a microcosm of the external macrocosm.[2] So, it is asserted, the brain is able to locate itself within the head and the head within the body. This would presumably involve a sort of Chinese puzzle. Within the head is the brain and in the brain a small-scale model of the body with its head and in that again a small-scale model of the brain which would presumably contain a repetition of all this on a still smaller scale, and so on *ad infinitum*. What, in the brain, perceives and relates these models we are not told. But if it were a ghost, it could as well dispense with models and observe their external archetypes direct.

In all this, no provision has been made for the brain to grasp the relation between its own internal schemata and the external things they are supposed to replicate. Physiologists are said to discover this by comparing external objects with the brains of other persons. But physiologists in doing so, if their theory be true, can but rely upon the models in their own brains. The objects they study, we are told, 'are only determined by things existing

---

[1] *Vide* 'The Relation of Mind and Matter to Personality', in *Perspectives in Neuro-Psychiatry*. (Ed. Richter.)

[2] *Op. cit.*, p. 164.

independently, their actual nature depending entirely on the temporo-spatial patterns occurring in the scientists' own cerebral cortices'.[1] It is not clear on what grounds we may be confident that the objects are determined from without, and we are once again trapped in a physiological solipsism which contradicts the pre-supposition of its own scientific evidence.

The idea of models in the brain seems to have a special appeal to physiologists, perhaps because there is special physiological evidence which suggests the hypothesis. Adrian refers with approval to a somewhat elaborate version of this view put forward by Kenneth Craik in a book,[2] so confused in its argument that, not surprisingly, it has been largely neglected by philosophers despite its appeal to physiologists.

Craik's proposal (in outline) was that the brain is or contains a diagrammatic model of the entire world of experience and that thought is an anticipatory experiment with this model by means of which we solve our practical and theoretical problems. The results of the experiments are then used in regulating behaviour which is presumably just a translation into overt action of the successful version of the internal cerebral experiment. Indeed, mechanical analogies are by no means useless for the understanding of brain activity. It is undoubtedly helpful to compare the regulative mechanisms of predictors in automata, with the systems of reflex and quasi-reflex activity in the organism which regulate and adjust muscular tensions in the service of various movements without any assistance from consciousness. These predictors do, in some sense, contain a diagrammatic model, a kind of replica, of the relevant features of the environment to which response is to be made. Even here, we shall presently see, the analogy is far from completely adequate, and it breaks down entirely where perception and judgment are involved. But if what Craik alleges, or anything like it, were true, it should follow (i) that we cannot understand our environment and the world until we understand the working of our brains, or at least that our understanding of one is identical with our understanding the other, and both these propositions are obviously false; (ii) that the easiest way to study the world would be to examine our cerebral activity—which is a model of it—and this is hardly plausible; (iii) that the subject (referred to above as 'we') is a *tertium quid* examining and

[1] Op. cit., p. 159.
[2] *The Nature of Explanation* (Cambridge University Press, 1952).

experimenting with the model which is, or is in, the brain. What and where is this third party? It cannot be the brain itself, for that is the model, and if located in some other part of the organism it will require within its own make-up another model of the brain-model in order to understand that.

A model cannot itself, by self-observation, perceive an external world, nor can it experiment on itself, nor 'understand' anything. It cannot, qua model, apprehend that of which it is a model, much less that it is a model of something other than itself. Such apprehension implies an awareness of the archetype by some direct and independent means as the prior condition of recognizing anything as a model or copy of it. It implies a separate subject (the ghost once more) who cognizes directly both the archetype and the model and can relate them as such. No model can do this for itself, and if it is incapable of knowing its own status, *a fortiori* any subject of awareness who is, as 'we' are, wholly dependent upon it for knowledge and understanding, will be equally ignorant.

This, however, is not the only form of the representative theory of perception to which physiologists (and others) fall a prey. It reappears in Eccles' account of the body–mind relationship. He postulates a 'mind influence' that produces a spatio-temporal field detectable by the brain whenever its activity is at a high level of intensity. 'No physical instrument', he claims, 'would bear comparison with the postulated performance of the active cerebral cortex as a detector of minute "fields of influence" spread over a microscopic pattern with temporal sequences of milliseconds.' So, either within the Heisenberg limits of uncertainty in the behaviour of particles in synaptic knobs ($1 \cdot 0 \ \mu$ in diameter, with a mass of 5×10^{-13} gm.), or by correlation of the behaviour of particles in neural activity, some such mind-influence could modify cerebral activity as an act of will.[1]

Conversely, cerebral activity might function as a transmitter, signals from which could be picked up by the mind in perception. Transmission from the receptor organ to the cerebral cortex is, he says, by a coded pattern quite unlike the original stimulus, and the activity in the cortex itself is yet again differently structured. This cortical activity is the only necessary condition for experiencing sensations, by whatever means it is produced and however occasioned. The perceptual world is thus a private interpretation of specific events in the brain which is made on inherited

[1] Cf. *The Neurophysiological Basis of Mind*, pp. 276–9.

and conventional principles, and is projected externally. In Eccles' words: 'We can regard the perceptual world as a map built upon the spatial relations between objects in the external world, but also giving us symbolic information in terms of secondary qualities.' By communication with other persons and by experiment we are said to correlate this private world with the real physical world, of which scientists strive to construct a conception purified from subjective symbolic elements.[1]

All the epistemological paralogisms we have already pointed out are here involved and more besides. The privacy of the perceptual world is *ex hypothesi* incurable, for communication with other observers and personal experiments must inevitably be mediated by our own brain activity and can be no more than complications in the map. There is no independent means of access to 'the spatial relations between objects of the external world' which could enable us to discover (a) that it was a map built upon them (and not by some other method) or (b) whether or to what extent it was accurate. The symbolic elements must symbolize something, yet we could discover what they symbolized by no means other than themselves. In these circumstances, we should conclude that Eccles must have special ways of perceiving and knowing other than those he describes, by which he has discovered the facts that he alleges. For if his theory were true that discovery would be impossible.

Meanwhile Eccles explicitly advocates belief in a ghostly receiver of what can hardly be otherwise conceived than brain-waves—some sort of sub-etherial wave pattern—'a field of influences'—that 'the mind' alone can detect.[2] Here at least it can be assumed that the mind may be in need of such a transmitter and incapable of direct awareness of the influences which stimulate the sense organs of the body. But if so, it would forever remain unaware of the origin of the brain-waves it picked up and at a loss to understand their significance as representatives of objects in the physical world. We mortals, who use radio to inform ourselves of distant events, have other means of ascertaining their existence and their relation to our radio reproductions. Our poor ghost relying solely on his brain-transmitter has no such check on its veracity. And thus deprived he must be unaware that its signals are derived from an external world, and he must remain devoid of science and innocent of neurophysiology.

[1] Op. cit., pp. 279–81.   [2] Op. cit., Ch. VIII.

It is no failure of physiology that leads to so deleterious a conclusion but only of epistemological speculations on the part of some physiologists. The scientifically discovered facts are not here in question. For no physiological evidence has been discovered of images in the brain which model external objects and certainly nothing to indicate the presence of an inner observer. Some neural connections and networks of neural excitation and transmission have been discovered, but such evidence as we have runs, if anything, counter to any copy theory. It is true that certain areas of the sensory and motor cortex answer to areas of stimulation on the body surface, but there is no actual map or model of the body detectable in the brain, however minutely the physiologist has succeeded in identifying and correlating these areas. Still less is there evidence of an internal mapper or map-reader. The shapes of excited cortical regions are quite different from the peripheral stimulus-patterns which give rise to them. There is, in short, little or no physiological evidence for the epistemological theories advanced by some physiologists; and this is hardly surprising since, as we see, the theories are such as to contradict any physiological evidence that may be claimed as their support.

The source of such representative theories of perception is, in fact, not physiological evidence, although the findings of physiology may have prompted them. It is the tacit presupposition that our knowledge is somehow bestowed upon us ready-made by transmission from the external world through the medium of sensation. It is assumed that the physiological machinery of perception must be the device for transmitting this ready-made information to the brain, so that it can provide us with infallible data from which an awareness of the world is built. This tacit presupposition is metaphysical and when elaborated into explicit theory it is called Empiricism. There is however no empirical evidence to support it and physiology gives no warrant for it. On the contrary, if it were true, neither physiology nor any other science would be possible at all. All the evidence we have runs counter to the belief in the reception of data which are not themselves the product of the integrating and constructive activity of the receiving organism. That they constitute signals of events in the external world is a gratuitous assumption. That there is an internal observer who recognizes them as such and interprets them is at best a superstition. That our knowledge, scientific and other, is acquired in this way is a metaphysical theory, for which in contemporary science there is no foundation whatsoever.

3

The fundamental misconception which leads to disaster and against which we must guard is that the nervous system is an instrument for receiving, processing and transmitting ready-made information from the receptor organs to some internal recipient. On this assumption, we shall find, no satisfactory theory of perception ever emerges and a completely different pre-supposition (already adumbrated in the foregoing chapters) is required. But this is the assumption commonly made by physiologists, and not all psychologists and philosophers are free from it. The application to the problems of perception of contemporary cybernetics, fruitful and suggestive though its theories have been for physiology and psychology, leads to conclusions which are still infected and vitiated by the same fallacy. For cybernetics makes the same assumptions, that peripheral sense organs receive and encode information about external physical objects, much as a telegraphist receives and encodes messages passed to him from some extraneous source, that these code messages are transmitted by the nerves, possibly transformed en route according to definite and discoverable rules, and delivered to the brain where they are decoded, read and understood in the form of perception.

Cyberneticians invent mechanisms for performing these functions, which they offer as analogues of brain mechanisms and brain processes and suggest how they might be constructed from neural elements. Their theories of perception are based on the principles of communication engineering governing the various devices for transforming and transmitting symbols, as well as on those on which computers and various complex automata are constructed.

There are two kinds of problem, both involving perception, in attacking which the cybernetic approach has been used. The first are problems of regulated movement adapted appropriately to environmental stimuli, the second are problems of transmission and of recognition.

In the first type the notion of feed-back is used as the main explanatory concept—that is the return of some portion of the output of a machine and its use to regulate the amount of its input. That this occurs in some form in the co-ordination and adjustment of bodily movement there is plenty of physiological evidence to show. The control of bodily movement is by this means effected so as to be smooth and accurate, and failure of the nervous mechanism, as of the feed-back devices in artifacts, results in oscillation of movement about a norm. So, when I reach out to pick up a pencil the movement of my arm is regulated by a constant feed-back of its changes of position to the muscles concerned so that the hand is directed steadily towards the object and does not waver, or fall short, or overshoot the mark. The changes of position fed-back are usually referred to as 'information', and its content is the continually diminishing discrepancy between the actual position of the hand and the intended (final) position. In analogous mechanisms in artifacts, this final position is something to which the machine is set by its operator, and the movement is directed to it by a device which registers any discrepancy in aim and is so designed as to affect the movement of the parts in a compensatory manner, which progressively decreases the discrepancy.

But in the case of my arm movement, the information fed back must contain the position of the pencil as well as of my arm. The latter is registered in proprioceptive sensation and need not be consciously perceived, but the former is consciously perceived and its apprehension must be separately explained. Cyberneticians often overlook this fact and assimilate the organic process too easily to mechanical forms of feed-back which are strictly not of information but only of energy. Precisely what is meant by 'information' we shall presently consider, but whatever it is, it is something more complex and less elementary than energy. In a steam-engine input and output are both forms of energy and the governor, which is the servo-mechanism involving feed-back, does no more than return a proportion of the energy output, via the servo-mechanism, to regulate the input. This mechanism can be set so as to establish equilibrium at a determinate running speed, but no 'information' strictly speaking is involved in the mechanical process. Though more complicated, the same is true of a thermostat which is not regulated by the precise difference between the temperature of the outside air and that to which the thermostat is set, but by *any* difference. Temperature registers access or decrease of heat energy in a given volume of matter. This may be taken as the output of the system, and the thermostat uses some of this to throw a switch or activate some similar device which regulates input so as to counteract the discrepancy irrespective of its precise amount. Information as to the amount of the discrepancy is not fed-back but only as to its existence. And this is not strictly information but merely the change of energy that produces the discrepancy. In the case of the regulation of muscular movements when I pick up a pencil, what all the time influences the operation of the servo-mechanisms is information in the proper sense—i.e. my perceptual awareness of the pencil and its position relative to my hand—and this is what has to be explained.

There are, no doubt, automata in the working of which 'information' (at least in the sense given the word by communication engineers) is fed back by servo-mechanisms to regulate input. But even in such cases caution must be exercised in their description, for the 'information' is coded and fed into the machine in the form of a notation—usually digital—and its operation may be no more than the release, or restriction of energy flow in mechanically adjusted amounts. We might, for instance in the example used above, treat the retinal image of the pencil as a sufficient stimulus to the servo-mechanisms. It is conceivable that the retinal image might be the starting-point of impulses transmitted through the brain structures to the arm muscles. The mutual relation on the retina of the images of hand and pencil might be the information fed back to regulate movement. It is possible to assume that the portion of the brain to which the neural impulses go has topological correlation with the retina itself, and that the brain contains a computing mechanism which can calculate the co-ordinates of stimuli in this field, with reference to axes of which the fovea is the origin, and so can estimate the distance between images and integrate its rate and direction of change. This information may then be fed to the servo-mechanisms regulating the flow of nervous stimulation to the muscles and so their movements are directed and co-ordinated.

Such a description omits all reference to perception and the process described could go on in its absence. But in actual fact this does not occur. I cannot direct my hand to the pencil unless I see it, and the mere occurrence of retinal images is not sufficient for vision nor is the activity of any portion of the brain acting simply as a computer. That this is so may be easily demonstrated. A computing mechanism is an arrangement of parts such that their movement represents certain mathematical relations, which can be made to correspond to similar mathematical relations between external objects. This is true of all calculating machines from the abacus to the slide-rule and from that to electronic computers. The relations of the moving parts of the mechanism may replicate or represent in an analogous way those of the objects the quantitative properties of which are being calculated. But that they are so analogous, that they do represent external objective relations, is a fact which is not included in the computation. Any such reduplication in the brain of the structure of the external situation would be similarly exclusive of this fact (that it is the reduplication of an external situation). If then perception were, or were dependent solely on, such a reduplication, it would necessarily exclude the apprehension of an external object as such. It would, in short, just not be perception.

Servo-mechanisms of this kind, therefore, cannot account for perceptual awareness; and all arguments are fallacious which attribute 'consciousness' to machines on the ground that they are able to construct within themselves a representation, coded or otherwise, of an external situation.[1] Whatever our awareness may be, it cannot be simply a representation in the brain of external things, whether pictorial or merely diagrammatic and symbolic.

In relation to the second type of problem, cyberneticians have had recourse to a different device, but one which falls foul of similar epistemological snags. Neural discharges are all of the same kind and (overlooking subliminal processes) are of the all-or-nothing variety. They occur, moreover, in temporal sequence. The obvious problem presents itself how spatial facts and very different qualities can be transmitted by such means from physical objects to the brain, and there be converted into a veridical representation of the external scene. What seems to be required is some way of encoding information, of transforming the elements of the code when necessary, and of transmitting it to a centre where it is decoded in some manner. Cyberneticians point to the way in which speech and music are transformed into electrical impulses in a telephone system, and light patterns, which are spatial, translated into electronic wave patterns, which are serial, and then reconverted by a scanning mechanism (on a television screen, for instance) into light patterns similar to the originals. Ingenious models have been suggested following these analogies, most of

[1] Cf. D. M. Mackay, 'The Mind-like Behaviour of Artefacts', *B.J.P.S.*, II, 1951.

which have since been abandoned as they have been discredited by later neurophysiological research.[1]

Epistemological reasons for rejecting the proposed models are perhaps even stronger than neurophysiological. A scanning mechanism, for instance, elicits a pattern from serial impulses suitably arranged, but the pattern as such is not picked out by the mechanism but by the eye observing it. The sweep of the wave to and fro across the area scanned produces the elements of the pattern seriatim. In this temporal order they do not constitute a spatial pattern, but if the sweep is very rapid, and if the whole area can be apprehended at once, the pattern emerges. Thus it is not the electron beam in the television tube that sees the picture, but the viewer who observes the screen from without. One may arrange mosaics serially in horizontal rows, and so select their colours as to produce a two-dimensional pattern; but it is not the rows of mosaics that 'pick out' the pattern, only the person looking at them from above. Even a temporal pattern like a melody has to be appreciated as a whole (or as a series of consecutive 'passages'), for each note (or chord) passes and is gone before the next occurs. It is only an agency capable of synthesizing the series that can apprehend it as a tune. If (as was suggested by McCulloch and Pitts) the cortex were a kind of three-dimensional screen swept by the α-wave, and if this produced neuronal discharges, in conjuction with afferent impulses, which constituted specific patterns, the *recognition* of these patterns could not be attributed either to the rythmic sweep or to the individual neurones. If it is to be 'picked out', it must be by some other agency. Again the tacit assumption seems to be involved of a mysterious manikin in the brain who observes the screen and recognizes the patterns. Once more the ghost stalks upon the battlements.

Not only is cybernetics powerless to exorcise this persistent spirit, his services are actually demanded in yet another connection. Neural discharges are regarded as the elements of a code by means of which information is transmitted. The information in its original character is (presumably) that particular state of affairs in the world which has to be perceived. The nervous system is conceived on the analogy of a digital computer—and the organism

[1] Cf. especially D. H. Hubel and T. N. Wiesel, 'Receptive fields, binocular interaction and functional architecture in the cat's visual cortex', *J. Physiol.*, 160 (1962), pp. 106–54.

as a whole as a machine, though it is admitted that in its working it combines the principles of both digital and analogue mechanisms. Such machines cannot accept input in any given form. The information fed into them must first be reduced to symbols which are elements of a system and can be processed in accordance with its rules. When the information fed in has been processed it issues as output still in coded form. Artifacts are operated by human beings who can encode the input and decode the output; but the living machine must do this for itself. How is it achieved? The process of encoding presents no great problem for it seems to occur automatically as external influences on the exteroceptors (be they physical or chemical) are transformed into the all-or-nothing firings of neurones in various relays. But how are these symbols (if such they be) decoded?—where and by whom?

The image of a pen is projected on to my retina by the lens of my eye, it excites impulses in my optic nerve which are transmitted to the brain. There the neural discharges are still all-or-nothing firings of particular cells—no doubt in a highly complex and intricate pattern. At what stage are they reconverted into the likeness of a pen? Or if they are never so reconverted, what agency receives and interprets them as indicating the presence of a pen before me? Who does the decoding? We seem once more constrained to mumble the incantation and summon up the spectral presence—but, alas, in vain! For if there were a ghost available to decode the message, it would only be the ghost of our paralytic housemaid imprisoned in her cerebral kitchen without access to the code book.

As perception is cognitive, there can be no question but that it conveys information of some sort; and so far as it is a medium of knowledge the information will be about the world at large—the environment in which the perceiving organism behaves. In short, percepts have *meaning* for the organism and present it with recognizable objects. To speak of recognition apart from meaning is to use words without precise reference. What meaning is has been much discussed and no attempt will be made at this stage of our discourse to elaborate a complete theory. We have insisted from the first that perception is appearance, and appearance involves cognition of an object, which is at least in some degree definite and has some predictable character. For our present purpose it will be enough to say that to be such an object for

N

cognition is to have meaning. In the psychology of perception what constitutes meaning has been and remains a perennially unsolved problem, to which some attention will be given in the next chapter. Can cybernetics, in the use it makes of communication theory, contribute anything to our understanding of this matter?

'Information' in cybernetics is a technical term, and much of its use helps very little in the formation of a theory of meaning, because the mathematician and the communications engineer explicitly abstract from meaning in its usual sense. When they speak of 'message' one would normally expect them to mean something which conveys some meaning—and so they do. But for the purposes of their theory the particular meaning of the message is of no consequence and is neglected. It is the symbol only which conveys the message with which they are concerned and if it had no significant interpretation at all, it would make no difference to their theory. Nevertheless, their technical use of 'information' is not without its suggestiveness.

The object of the communications engineer is to transmit through some medium a recognizable symbol which *can* convey meaning. Such a symbol must be an organized or patterned effect of some physical process which can be distinguished from those inevitable effects of the process that are devoid of organization. This disordered product is called 'noise' as opposed to 'message'. The primary distinction between noise and message (or 'information'), therefore, is that between disorder and order. We have met this before in the physical theory of entropy, which is precisely what communications engineering has to deal with. 'Information' accordingly is defined as negative entropy and its mathematical measure is:

$$K \log \frac{1}{D}$$

(where K is the Boltzmann constant and D a quantitative term expressing the degree of disorder). Information thus becomes synonymous with organization and we are given a pointer to the true account of meaning and perception.

In physics, we have learned, entropy always increases, ordered arrangement always tends towards disorder. So the physicist will tell us that by ordinary physical processes 'noise' will always tend to drown out 'message', and the engineer's problem is therefore to find a way to minimize entropy. The physicist also will assert that to transmit information, one must begin with order and expect some of it to be lost in transit. Message will always tend to break down into noise, and by no means, he will say, can noise be converted into message.

The biologist, on the other hand, finds that living organisms are systems which succeed in minimizing entropy, and sometimes even in decreasing it. J. B. S. Haldane has described natural selection as a method for converting noise into message, and the bulk of biological evidence supports the view that evolution is a process of increasing integrity of complex organization. Thus the organism not only succeeds in doing what the communications engineer strives after—minimizing entropy—it has even found ways of converting noise into message. Photosynthesis, and all the endergonic reactions that take place in metabolism are surely cases in point. The living system is thus a mechanism (if so we must call it) for imposing order on relatively disordered matter; for extracting message from noise; as well as for transmitting it (which it does in self-reproduction). At that pitch of organic activity, that degree of intensity or organization which is feeling,[1] a critical point is reached; and the next stage in the creation of message is consciously apprehended *meaning*, the cognition of a more or less definitely qualified object. This is perception. If we think of the brain and nervous system as the organ for the creation of meaning (or information proper), for extracting 'message' from, or conferring significance upon, *less* organized material in the environment, and not simply for transmitting it from an outside source to some unknown and mysterious recipient, the problem of perception may prove more tractable. In cognition—as cognized—an object acquires significance for the first time. It *becomes* information extracted from a relatively confused and indefinite source of 'noise'. Perception is the activity of organization that gives it meaning, not one which receives the message ready-made from elsewhere. Considerable support for this hypothesis can be derived from psychological theories of perception—the subject matter of the following chapter.

[1] Cf. Susanne K. Langer, *Philosophical Sketches*, I, quoted above.

CHAPTER XX

PERCEPTION—II PSYCHOLOGICAL THEORIES

I

Because psychologists address themselves, in the main, to the second of the questions listed on p. 369 above: Why do things appear as they do?—the epistemological fallacies we have been discussing are less noticeable in their theories. Even when they propose physiological hypotheses the fallacies do not necessarily arise. Hebb, for instance, advances his theory of cell assembly, not as an account of how physical objects are repesented in the brain, but as a description of the neural mechanisms which subserve phenomenal appearances. He does not say that the cell assembly and the phase sequence assures us of the nature of the physical stimulus, or that they constitute our knowledge of the external object. The hypothesis has another and much more fruitful implication for epistemology. Similarly Köhler's theory of cerebral fields aims at discovering a process in the brain isomorphic to the phenomenal object. The question whether either of them are, or how they could be the vehicle of knowledge of physical events is not raised. It is no more epistemologically fallacious, therefore, than the well-attested theory that images of external things are projected upon the retina of the eye, for nobody suggests that they constitute for us a knowledge of the things projected. Köhler's detailed description of the cerebral field, however, is not well supported by evidence, and such as there is seems to disconfirm it rather than otherwise.

There are nevertheless some psychological doctrines which present serious epistemological difficulties, though it is not immediately obvious that they are fatal. The psychologists themselves do not face them but for that they may be excused, for such questions fall outside their special field. Koffka, for instance, distinguishes the behavioural from the geographical environment and this distinction, we have noticed, corresponds to that between appearance and reality. He defines behaviour as movements which occur in a behavioural field (as opposed to such as occur only in a geographical field).[1] But the criterion for distinguishing the two

[1] *Principles of Gestalt Psychology*, p. 32.

fields is not specified. His example is that of a mountaineer stepping on a snow-bridge and falling through into a chasm. The use of the snowbridge and the action of walking upon it are behaviour in the sense defined, but the fall is not. The victim may make efforts to prevent or break his fall after the snow collapses, but the fall itself is not a response to anything in the behavioural environment, for it is not a response at all.

How are we to identify the geographical environment in which the unobserved weakness of the snow-bridge exists, before it gives way? For the mountaineer it does not exist until the bridge collapses and the psychologist knows of it only by hindsight after the accident has been reported. Then it has become part of the behavioural environment of both of them. It is not satisfactory to say that all movements which are not responses to anything in the behavioural environment are *ipso-facto* in the geographical. The apparent movement of an electric sign, in which a series of stationary lights appearing in quick succession produce the phi-phenomenon, occurs in the behavioural environment, but *qua* movement it is not a response, and it does not exist in the geographical world. It would seem that the distinction under discussion is always made in retrospect, unless it corresponds to that between the behavioural environments of two different subjects (as when one sets a trap for a mouse whose behavioural environment contains only cheese).

Koffka says that every datum is a behavioural datum whereas 'physical reality is not a datum but a constructum'.[1] Presumably, it is constructed out of behavioural data; yet, as we are explicitly told, it affects the behavioural environment and in some measure at least determines what the data shall be. It also determines the results of behaviour, which, so far as they take place in the geographical environment, are called its accomplishment.[2] Is this relationship between the two environments plausible? Can a construct out of phenomena causally affect those phenomena as well as the behavioural response to them? There seems to be some paralogism here and how it may be resolved is not obvious.

This problem raises questions (iii) and (v). We may resume consideration of it, therefore, when we come to discuss them in the sequel. First let us attend to question (ii), which Koffka asks: 'Why do things look as they do?' Koffka refers to visual appearances but the question may be considered generally of all

[1] Op. cit., p. 35.   [2] Op. cit., p. 37.

sensory forms. The numerous psychological theories of perception which bear upon this question fall into two main groups: (i) those which, like Koffka's, answer it in terms of organization, whether of the sensory field, of neural excitation, or of behaviour. And (ii) those which answer it in terms of the set of the organism, whether emotional, or muscular or dispositional and habitual: that is, the way in which its complex functionings are organized. There is no necessary incompatibility between these two types of theory. The organization of the field, of neural firings and of behaviour may well be dependent upon the dispositional and habitual set, muscular or emotional or both, of the total organism. In fact the plurality of psychological theories reflects the complexity and many-sidedness of the problem rather than any insuperable disagreement between theorists.

The first group includes the old and now out-dated core-context theories, as well as recent and current views: gestalt theories generally, sign-gestalt and Lewin's theory of topological field, Hebb's hypothesis of cell assembly and phase sequence, and some more behaviouristic views appealing to neural organization. The second group includes theories of transactional functionalism, motor-adjustment, adaptive level, sensory-tonic field and directive state. But for our present purpose the important point to notice is that both types of theory account for perception in terms of organization; the first attributes it to organization of the sensory field; the second to the organization of emotions, dispositions, muscular tonus or the like. In both cases what determines and shapes perception is the organization of activities reflected in or constituting some form of feeling. This is well brought out by Floyd Allport summing up his discussion of thirteen major theories:

'We could say that the perceptual aggregate, according to fairly general consensus, is to be conceived as composed of inter-related and interdependent parts, that it is assembled in space and through time, and that it is self-delimited and self-closed in its ongoings or operations . . . it manifests an operant energy-ratio or weighting among its parts, a summing or averaging of their energies, a flexibility and yet a stability of certain inner relationships or proportions. . . . Stated in this manner the picture begins to take on more unity and form. What does it signify? . . . What the writer sees [is] the clear evidence that the perceptual act is really a dynamically operating *structure*, that it presents the very picture of a self-delimited and self-contained structuring of ongoings and events.'[1]

The perennial dispute between nativists and empiricists, which cuts across the division of theories we have made, is relatively unimportant from the point of view we have adopted, for we are maintaining that mental activities are but a higher phase of organization of organic activities and that there is a continuous process of increasing integration which links the successive phases. We have also alleged that the gradation of integrated levels in the individual organism is paralleled, more or less, in the process by which the individual organism itself has developed and in that by which the species has evolved. If then the forms of perception were innate they must nevertheless depend upon factors in the organism which have developed gradually in the course of evolution. Thus if, with Koffka, we say that things look as they do because of the organization of the field and maintain that forms of organization are innate, it may still be held that they are a development of less organized forms of organic functioning and have evolved from simpler forms. If on the other hand we say that they are the product of experience and depend upon some process similar to learning, we say no more than that in the course of its development the organism generates more elaborate forms of order, which at a certain stage constitute the perception of objects. The same is the case with set theories. If the set is innate, it must nevertheless have evolved. If it is developed in the course of experience, it nevertheless determines the percept in accordance with the structure of the organism's functioning. Both sides of the argument contain obvious truth and we need not spend much time, in this study, trying to adjudicate between the disputants.

Earlier theories were relatively atomistic in their approach to perception, viewing it as an aggregation of sensations on principles of association. But some form of order and sequence of combination was always seen to be necessary. So arose the context theory of meaning, due to Tichener, who regarded meaning as central to perceptual experience. The percept, according to this theory, was a group of sensations consolidated by the activity of attention and forming a core within a wider context of associated images derived from past experience. This context gave meaning to the core which

[1] *Theories of Perception and the Concept of Structure*, p. 612.

was the percept proper. The theory has obvious defects, particularly its regressive explanation of meaning—for if context gives meaning to core what gives meaning to context? and if each elucidates the other the explanation will be circular. But this early attempt at explanation does recognize the fact that perception is not just a matter of sensing, nor a mere colligation of sensa, but a structure of elements in some systematic relation, and a structure brought about by an activity of integration through attention. As many of the associated sensations and images were held to be kinaesthetic and meaning was derived largely from centrally supplied elements, it was also realized that how things are perceived depends as much on the contribution of the organism and the past accumulation of experience as it does on any peripheral stimulation.

This idea was developed by Helmholtz and the functionalists, who attributed the combining activity almost wholly to the perceiving agent and regarded perception as an 'unconscious inference' from sensations to objects. The theory has been criticized for postulating what *ex hypothesi* is undetectable either by the subject's own introspection or by observation of the subject's behaviour, and also because the alleged inference can be attributed neither to the incoming stimulus nor to the neural organization in the cortex; for neurones and synapses do not infer. So it is objected that a manikin in the brain must be presumed to observe or experience the sensations and then to make inferences from them. Neither of these points is very well taken. The first has been fully and ably disposed of by Blanshard,[1] and the second overlooks the fact that neural organization in the brain is a matter of structure and not of individual neurones and synapses. It need not be, and almost certainly is not, confined to the purely sensory level; and just what in neural organization corresponds to inference is as yet undecided. Our immediate purpose, however, is not to give a detailed examination of outdated theories and we may say of this one, that whatever defects it may display, it does, in common with more modern views (some of which have revived it in modified form), recognize and accentuate the existence of a combining, integrating, 'interpreting' activity that goes beyond immediate sensing.

The same general notion is stressed by set theory, that the

[1] Brand Blanshard, *The Nature of Thought*, Vol. I (London, 1948), Ch. II.

perception is a selection from, and construction out of, presented data by the perceiver in accordance with the tonus of his musculature, his emotional or dispositional orientation, or other directive factors in his active organic make-up.

2

Perhaps the most influential and spectacular advance in the psychology of perception in the present century has been made by *Gestaltteorie,* which insists above all upon organization and structure. The gestaltists argue insistently against the old mosaic type of psychology, against the notion of separable stimuli producing effects collectively either in the cortex or in the phenomenal field, against the 'constancy hypothesis', 'that the result of a local stimulation is constant, provided that the physiological condition of the stimulated receptor is constant'. Their persistent advocacy is of holism of both physiological and psychological activity which they regard as isomorphic. Physiological processes are to be taken 'in extension', as wholes, and phenomenal are likewise totalities, which cannot be dissected, nor yet constructed out of parts that remain unaffected by their mutual association. They are *Gestalten,* configurations, within which the parts, if they can so much as exist alone, are different and behave differently as elements in the whole. Their contention is, and their experimentation is designed to prove, that what is perceived is always the inclusive effect of the pattern of stimulation as a whole. 'Things look as they do,' declares Koffka, 'because of the field organization to which the proximal stimulus distribution gives rise.'[1]

Forthwith, laws of organization are sought and 'forces' of organization are identified; not physical forces but dynamic principles governing the way in which phenomena group themselves into patterns and parts are drawn together into wholes. So an inhomogeneity in an otherwise uniform field is constituted as a unity, not simply by the differences between stimulation from it and its surrounding, for these may be ineffective in producing the phenomenon (e.g. colour difference apart from difference of luminosity[2]), but as a result of definite dynamic principles. Shape and structure are shown to be produced by similar dynamic laws and principles of organization.

[1] *Principles of Gestalt Psychology,* p. 98.
[2] *Vide* Koffka, op. cit., pp. 126–9.

N*

What in every case are organized are sensory elements, the effects of sense-stimulation, feelings of some sort, to which attention is directed. Sometimes this direction is specified in advance as when subjects viewing an ambiguous shape through a tachistoscope are asked to try to see it first in one form (e.g. as a kite) and then in another (e.g. as a square sail blown by the wind). By such experiments the 'forces' of organization are discovered,

simplicity of form, continuity of line, closure of figure, segregation of figure from ground, and so on. And these are made to account for our perception of unity, shape, spatial depth and other characteristics of perceived objects. In every case what emerges is a whole with a character which is imposed upon its elements in the sense that, if they exist at all apart from the configuration, they lack the properties which they acquire within it. Thus two lines may be seen as intersecting units each continuous within itself, but if their ends are joined, two closed areas form subwholes in a single pattern in which the continuities are altogether different and the segments of the original lines are differently segregated.

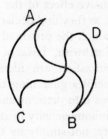

Gestalt theory has been criticized for its alleged 'nativism' and its minimization of the role and importance of learning. It is understood to maintain that the percept owes little or nothing to past experience, since, as a unity which derives its properties and general character from its wholeness, it could not possibly have been built up piecemeal. If and so far as any gestalt psychologists allege or imply the complete irrelevance of experience, they are surely wrong. But in the main it is not their intention. Koffka says: ' . . . we shall dischard the empiristic theory as an ultimate explanation of our framework, without, however, raising the claim that experience can have no effect at all upon it. Such a claim, in the present state of our knowledge would be unwarranted.'[1] Allport, also, referring to this critique, admits that it would be incorrect to attribute to gestaltists a doctrine of strict nativism. But as he goes on to point out, what is insisted upon is that perception is organization from the beginning and that whatever may be provided by experience is already an organized whole which is either further elaborated into a new configuration or is absorbed with others (perhaps similarly provided) into a wider structure. What is denied is that experience delivers the pieces singly each intact in itself and that we 'learn' to put them together in ways which leave them severally as they were originally received.

This is the essential contribution of Gestalt theory, and it has been copiously supported by experimental evidence; nor is it contradicted by theories which demonstrate the role of experience and practice in building up our skill (for such it does seem to be) in perceiving. In fact this process itself may be viewed as one of progressive organization of our experience, continuous elaboration of configural or systematic connections between elements which are themselves systems and configurations on a smaller scale or at a less complex level.

There is surely little doubt that the apprehension of ambiguous stimuli is affected by experience, however true it may be that it is also governed by forces of organization such as Koffka claims to demonstrate. The well known rabbit-bird outline will appear more readily in one guise to persons who have had more experience of and are more interested in birds, and in another to those more familiar with rabbits. In many of Koffka's examples the rules of organization apply almost as easily to one appearance as to the other, and the determination of how the object will appear will then depend largely upon the habit of mind or perceptual disposition of the perceiving subject. The Gestaltists admit what they call the influence of trace in such cases. When, for instance, what first appears as a jumble of lines is later seen as a face, it cannot thereafter be seen again in disorganized form.[1]

Hebb's alternative theory is, therefore (as he himself in part admits) not in principle incompatible with *gestalt* theory as his critique is of detail rather than principle. He protests that in the perception, for instance, of a triangular shape, the capacity to see the points may have been separately acquired and the perception of the complete shape built up by stages. Having cited supporting evidence from the work of von Senden and Riesen, he elaborates an hypothesis of cell assemblies corresponding to elements of the stimulus pattern, which become linked and facilitate one another reinforcing some connections and weakening others (by omission). These processes he calls 'recruitment' and 'fractionation'. So the assemblies become organized variably yet systematically into larger structures and operate serially ('phase sequence') and in conjunction. But Hebb is quite clear in his assertion that the work of Lorente de Nó and modern neurophysiologists has revolutionary implications for psychology, that the notion of linear sensorimotor connections is now altogether obsolete, and that the neural mechanism of autonomous central processes must be structural. He further admits the inexpungeable contribution of *Gestaltteorie*, maintaining that 'Köhler and Koffka and Lashley have unquestionably slain the dragon of pure learning theory, in the field of

[1] Cf. Koffka, op. cit., pp. 173 and 554.

perception, and no one today would argue that perceptual organization is wholly acquired.'[1] His contention, moreover, is not against the holistic character of perceived objects. Primitive unity, figure and ground organization, and certain simple elements of form he is prepared to attribute to sensory dynamics alone, and these he regards as primary in visual perception. Nor are the elements, out of which (he maintains) more elaborate figures are built, bare simples. He begins with the cell assembly, not with a single cell or even a single synaptic link, and what is throughout hypothesized is a progressive organization and integration. Whether or not the neurophysiological hypothesis is confirmed (and recent research has already shown it to be in need at least of revision), there is good reason to believe that some phenomenal counterpart to the alleged neural process occurs in young infants as well as in the congenitally blind whose sight has been restored. There is indeed further evidence that perceptual objects and structures may be, not only acquired, but also modified and readjusted by experience and practice in adult life. To this we shall return anon.

Further, Hebb himself maintains that the final stage in the achievement of the percept of a particular form is a total configuration. The assemblies corresponding to the various elements (a, b, c) having frequently been activated in sequence, reverberations may produce simultaneous activity of two or more. This would result in mutual facilitation with consequent recruitment and fractionation leading to a new composite whole, which is not just the sum of the former assemblies, abc, but a modification of them in combination. The participating assemblies, however, need not thereby be altogether abolished, and can still, to some extent, function apart though never again quite in their original form. The new composite, which may come into being by stages, he calls, the superordinate perception and denotes it by the symbol t. This he explicitly identifies with the *Gestalt*.

Hebb's theory is consequently no less organismic and holistic than either Lashley's or Koffka's. He claims to give a neurophysiological schema (hypothetical, no doubt) which will explain the clinical and experimental facts, and allow for supersummation as well as equipotentiality (demonstrated by Lashley and others). The implication is none the less that perception is an activity of organization and Hebb declares it to be dependent upon attention

[1] *The Organization of Behavior*, p. 22.

(in the sense of central facilitation of activity) and to provide a basis of explanation for set and expectancy.[1]

A second criticism of *Gestaltteorie* is that the whole is hypostatized and made to transcend the parts as if it were something independent of them, and even pre-existent. Allport makes this complaint against the components of the theory and alleges that it is the fruit of a metaphysical presupposition which has no foundation in the evidence.[2] If it is true that gestalt-theorists do tend to treat 'the whole' as if it existed alone and apart from its constituents like some Platonic idea, the criticism is justified. But it seems a little harsh and may not be altogether fair. Allport states what he accepts as the facts: (i) that a percept is a phenomenological aggregate of items of direct experience; (ii) that this aggregate is self-contained, self-delimited and experienced as a more or less segregated whole; (iii) that the appearance of the parts is different when they are observed together from their appearance when observed separately, and the whole presents a different appearance from any of the parts; (iv) that elimination, change or addition of any part produces a change in appearance of all the rest and of the whole; and (v) that the aggregate observed as a whole has certain whole-characteristics such as unity, continuation, articulation, closure, tendency towards symmetry, and a 'requiredness' among its relationships.

Yet Allport persists in speaking of an 'aggregate' of phenomenal items though the facts described make it plain that they do not appear or behave in perception as an aggregate but as an articulate unity. All that need be conceded to satisfy the gestaltists' demands is that the parts when perceived in the whole are different from what they are in separation and that the whole has characters of its own to which those of the parts are subordinated and in which they become absorbed. This is not to hypostatize anything. There is no need to allege a new and separate entity over and above the parts-in-combination. That *is* the whole and any separate entity would not be—for it would lack the requisite constituents and articulation. What is being stressed in the theory is the fact, to which Allport's list testifies, that the character of the so-called 'aggregate' depends primarily upon its form and organization, factors which do not belong to any of the parts in isolation nor even to all of them lumped together as a collection (or mere aggregate).

[1] Cf., op. cit., pp. 100 ff.   [2] *Vide* Allport, op. cit., Ch. V, pp. 141–7.

But, Allport objects, 'the whole' cannot be 'denoted'; that is, pointed to or touched, as such. All that we can contact (so to speak) is one or other of the parts. This indeed is true and proves how futile it is to imagine that any explanation can be reached through 'denotation'. In touching parts, whether singly or in succession we never reach the way in which they are organized together. 'Denotation' cannot grasp the principle of order, the pattern or the form, and so is powerless to indicate those very facts that Allport has enumerated. We cannot discover by denotation even that an aggregate is self-contained for we cannot 'denote' inclusion within a boundary, as such. We cannot discover by 'denotation' how appearances change when element are brought into conjunction, or when changes are made in the form and inter-relation of the parts of a configuration. The whole-characteristics that Allport acknowledges can none of them be 'denoted' in his sense. Moreover he himself insists on structure as the essential explanatory factor and concludes his examination of the various theories by contributing a general theory of structure that he considers fundamental. But structure is no more a denotable entity than wholeness—they are, in fact, mutually implicated. Without wholeness there can be no structure and if the former cannot be identified the latter disappears.

Allport objects further,[1] that the separate parts themselves have meaning and structure prior to their incorporation in a whole, so that their character cannot altogether be the result of their place in the organization. But he admits that it is changed by association with other parts, and is incorporated into the whole so that its character *as participant* is explicable only by the form of the totality and not, or not entirely, by its former aspect. There is no need to deny all character to the parts of a whole. On the contrary, to do so is to make the constitution of the whole impossible for each part contributes something of its own. Furthermore, there must be some components to be organized. One cannot make a right triangle out of curved lines, but three straight lines do not constitute a triangle unless organized in a determinate way. The operative contention is not that the parts in isolation have no character, but that, once formed, the whole takes precedence and supplies the primary principle of explanation, and the participating factors may be so changed by their membership, that they can never again become what they were before incorporation.

---

[1] *Vide* op. cit., Ch. 19, pp. 545 ff.

This is especially true in perception, for an object seen naively in isolation may become so modified when seen as an integral part of a larger organization that it can never again be seen in its pristine simplicity. If Hebb's theory of recruitment and fractionation is correct this should always be the case.

That the elements of a percept may exist prior to their inclusion into the larger whole (as lines may exist prior to the formation of a linear figure) and may later become separated from it is not in all cases denied, and that in such relative separation they have a character of their own is obvious. But then they are themselves *Gestalten*, though relatively simple, and have their own peculiar internal structure. Strictly it is true, however, that any apparently simple element is an integral part of the sensory field; and it is the total organization of this field which, in the last resort gives character to its distinguishable contents.

3

The lesson of Gestalt psychology is that the percept is always an articulated unity, an integration of sensory elements into a whole systematically structured to form a succinct object; and that this whole is produced by an activity in the perceiving subject the effect of which is organization. That stimuli from the outside world play no part in this process is never, of course, alleged. But they are no more than starting points which set the internal processes of organization going, and it is essentially of these that the percept is the product.

This is especially evident in the phenomena of constancy in visual perception. Though, as we move about, the retinal images of objects change perpetually both in shape and in size, and, with variation of illumination and reflection of light, the colours of objects are variable, the objects appear to us within limits to be constant in size, shape and colour. Virtually every theory that tries to cope with this phenomenon explains it in terms of the activity of the subject, and, indeed, as it is manifest that the appearance of objects does not follow the vagaries of the stimulus pattern, it is difficult to see how else the phenomena could be explained.

Not only perceptual constancies are explained in this way, however, but also the size, orientation and general structure of appearances. A large body of psychological theory today, supported by an abundance of experimental evidence, attributes the perceptual appearance of objects to what has been called 'autistic' factors—that is the effects of the perceptual activity itself.

This brings us to the second main type of explanation of the way things appear, which includes a number of different but often closely related theories, all of which explain the appearance of objects as consequent upon the way the organism is set to perceive. The term 'set' may be given a narrow or a wide connotation. It may be limited to the muscular tonus of the body preparatory to the reception of more or less expected stimuli, it may be made to include motor adjustments preparatory to overt behavioural reaction, or it may be widened to include emotional attitudes, perceptual dispositions, and personality traits. A brief review of some of the more remarkable theories will show that the general consensus is towards the view that perception is an activity, in varying degrees subconscious, of ordering and interpreting sensory material; but creative rather than merely receptive, and constructive rather than merely transmissive of data or reflective of external physical things. In the words of Gardner Murphy, 'the perceived world pattern mirrors the organized need pattern within'.[1]

The work of Werner and Wapner[2] demonstrates the effect of tonic equilibrium upon the orientation of visual percepts. The authors claim that tonic effect—the tonus of the musculature— are equivalent to and combine with sensory effects to form an 'equilibrial axis' determining body balance, and that changes in this will affect the subjective assessment of verticality and of the median plane of visual perception. The position of objects seen will thus be displaced according to the distribution of the sensory-tonic field, or organismic balance between the body and the object.

The theory is supported by experiments in which subjects were required to rotate a luminescent rod into what they considered to be a vertical position. The chosen position always diverged from the true vertical. The subject was then submitted either to a sharp sound or to electrical stimulation of the neck muscle on one side of the body and required to adjust the rod again while under the effects of this assymetrical stimulation. It was found

[1] G. Murphy, *Personality* (New York, 1947), p. 351.
[2] H. Werner and S. Wapner, 'Sensory-Tonic Field Theory of Perception', in *Perception and Personality*, Ed. J. S. Bruner and D. Krech, (Duke University Press, 1949).

that the perceived vertical was displayed towards the side of increased muscle tonus or of sensory stimulus, in each case.

The theory is somewhat limited in its scope but would permit of extension with further experimental investigation. H. Helson, for instance, has developed a theory of perceptual norm providing a frame of reference for the judgment of size, weight and other perceived dimensions of objects. This, he finds varies, not only with the perceiver, but with reference to the range of comparison within which the judgment is being made. He therefore concludes that the norm is determined by an organismically established level of adaptation to the range of the quantitative character perceived.[1] This is reached by an unconscious process of 'pooling' in which the organism establishes a sort of average of its experiences of the magnitude under inspection.

G. L. Freeman[2] has gone further and attributed perceptual appearance to the integration of motor and other organic adjustments. He defines a set as the covert tensions in the skeletal muscles and the effects of proprioceptive 'backlash' from these as facilitating reaction to exteroceptive stimuli. Accommodation of the peripheral receptor organs and its maintenance enter into this complex and so also may impulses from the vestibular receptors, glandular activities and other autonomic functions. Both peripheral and central factors are involved so as to form a single cyclic structure of interacting parts. Such a set exerts a selective influence in perception, facilitating and prolonging specific stimuli; it facilitates the entry of those stimulus patterns to which it is preparatory and inhibits others to which antagonistic sets are appropriate. Long-standing sets may be established which will determine definite perceptual dispositions, as when, for instance, a distant dust cloud is seen by a general as the movement of troops, by a herdsman as a movement of cattle. Freeman maintains that the organization of visual excitation into meaningful patterns depends more upon reactions made to objects, the residual effects of past reactions, acquired and habitual ways of looking at or

[1] Cf. H. Helson, 'Adaptation-level as a frame of reference for prediction of psychophysical data', *Amer. Jour. of Psychol.* LX, 1947; 'Adaptation-level as the basis for a quantitative theory of frames of reference', *Psychol. Rev.*, 55, 1948; *Theoretical Foundations of Psychology*, New York, 1951, Ch. 8.

[2] Cf. 'The Problem of Set', *Amer. Jour. of Psych.*, 52, 1939; *The Energetics of Human Behaviour* (Cornell University Press, 1948); *Physiological Psychology* (New York, 1948).

moving in connection with them, than upon the intrinsic nature of the objects themselves.

Perception, Freeman points out, is always a matter of integration of several sensory modes, though proprioception is a common factor in all; it is always selective, motor adjustments accentuating one group of sensory impulses at the expense of others; one modal excitant can take over the effects of others that have, in the past, formed part of the perceptual totality (as when velvet 'looks' soft or ice looks cold); empathic elements may be contributed by past motor responses (e.g. the appearance of a hill as 'rising', or a road as 'winding'). Thus the general set or adjustment of the organism determines the way things appear and emphasis is placed upon the active integrative and organizing process involved.

A doubt however may be expressed whether these theories are in full measure explanations of why things appear as they do. Clearly workers like Werner, Wapner and Freeman have pointed to factors of organic structure and functioning which undoubtedly *affect* the way objects are perceived. But have they done more than that? The claim is, or seems to be, especially in Freeman's case, that these factors determine the percept and that the effect of the stimulus pattern is at most to provide the material which is given specific form by autistic influences. But the evidence produced leaves room at least for the argument that there may be much more to perception than the factors listed. For instance, though the sensory-tonic equilibrial axis may determine the orientation of objects it hardly seems to determine their character as recognizable things in the world. So also, the set of the muscles and the readiness of the organism to receive specific stimulation may decrease reaction time, may contribute sensory factors additional to those supplied by the distance receptors, may exclude some stimuli and favour others; but does it fully determine the content of the object perceived? The readiness of the sprinter on his mark to hear the report of the gun may increase the apparent intensity of the sound or even alter its time relations to other percepts, but it does not radically affect its quality. The meaning of perceived objects may well be modified, but is it constituted, by these elements in the organic set of the perceiver? When one includes past experience, perceptual dispositions and personality traits the view becomes more plausible that the total set determines the percept, but even then there is room for the argument of nativist opponents of the theory that past experience must also be perceptual, and it may be asked what determined that and whether an infinite regress is not implied. So also perceptual dispositions are presumably developed as a result of perceptual acts and must these not be explained independently?

For the moment we shall postpone consideration of these questions, for there is another group of theories leading to a further development of the notion of set which is much more far-reaching and which puts its authors in a stronger position *vis-a-vis* such objections.

The study of the problem of perceptual constancies has led a group of thinkers to a notion of set (though they do not use the term) which is less physiological and much more cognitive in its nature. Egon Brunswik[1] addressed himself to the question how the organism is able to attain a perceptually stable world despite the almost infinite variations and transformations of stimuli. The facts of perceptual constancy are well-known but their explanation is not easy. Why do visual percepts not vary as the visual image changes in size with distance, or in shape with the angle of vision? Why are objects seen roughly in their natural colours despite wide variations of illumination and reflected light? The percept is not absolutely constant but tends towards the veridical in defiance of the vagaries of the stimulus.

Brunswick maintains that a number of factors (to which he refers as 'cues') contribute to this result besides the exteroceptive stimuli. The muscular reactions involved in convergence and accommodation of the eyes, the disparity of the two retinal images, the appearance of intervening and occluding objects, atmospheric effects, brightness and many other factors serve as 'distance cues' which enable the subject to determine relationships between objects in the environment and himself. These cues are 'weighted' according to their reliability which is variable owing to the inconstancy of environmental conditions. It can be estimated, therefore, only with probable accuracy. Thus the perceiver arrives at a sort of statistical average of the probable relations between himself and the perceived objects, in terms of their apparent relations among themselves, as a result of an automatic and

---

[1] Cf. Egon Brunswick, *Die Zugänglichkeit von Gegenständen für die Wahrnehmung. Arch. ges. Psychol.*, 88, 1933; 'Psychology in Terms of Object', *Proc. 25th Anniv. Celebr. Inaug. Grad. Stud.* (Los Angeles: Univ. of S. Calif. Press., 1936); 'Organismic Achievement and Environmental Probability', *Psychol. Review*, 50, 1943.

subconscious summation of the various cues provided by the sum-total of stimuli. The combined result is the perception of magnitude—is, the author claims, the object as perceived. So the organism keeps its reactions free from control by the variations of the proximal stimulus by combining its effects with those of distance cues into a single *Gestalt*, which is the percept.

Brunswick calls the theory 'probabilistic functionalism' and a not unrelated view has been elaborated further under the name of 'transactional functionalism' by Ittelson, Kilpatrick, Cantril and others on the basis of spectacular experiments performed by Ames.[1]

The thesis maintained is that perception is (or is part of) a process of adjustment involving participation in a transaction between the organism and the world. The transaction is regarded as a single activity the contributions to which of subject and object cannot be sharply distinguished. It is a transaction within which perceptual objects are discriminated by the activity of the perceiving subject, on the basis of past experience and probabilistic weighting of cues. These once again are the means alleged for the production of percepts, and the theory is explicitly admitted to be a development of Helmholtz's notion of unconscious inference.

The proximal stimuli in visual perception are notoriously equivocal in their relation to distal stimuli. This is not exceptional, as is commonly believed, but almost invariable, the exception being rather when distal and proximal stimuli are uniquely related. A round object seen at an angle looks elliptical but so does an elliptical object at right angles to the line of vision; and objects in different degrees elliptical at various different angles to the line of vision will all produce retinal images of the same shape. This ubiquitous ambiguity of visual stimuli is vividly illustrated by Ames' experiments. A rotating trapezoidal window frame, appears, when monocularly viewed, to be rectangular, and does not appear to revolve but to oscillate about an arc of

[1] *Vide* Adelbert Ames Jr., 'Visual Perception and the Rotating Trapezoid Window', *Psychol. Monogr.* 65, No. 7, 1951; 'Reconsideration of the origin and nature of Perception', in *Vision and Action* (Ed. S. Katner), Rutgers University Press, 1953. W. H. Ittelson and H. Cantril, *Perception, a transactional approach*, Doubleday, Garden City, 1954; W. H. Ittelson and F. P. Kilpatrick, 'Experiments in Perception', *Scientific American*, 185, No. 2, 1951. H. Cantril, 'A Transactional Inquiry concerning Mind', in *Theories of the Mind* (Ed. Jordan Scher), New York, 1962.

100°. A small cube attached to one corner appears to revolve round it, floating loose from it at some stages of its course and reattaching itself at others. A paper tube thrust between the mullions appears to rotate for some part of the way in the opposite direction from the frame, to bend and to straighten in the course of its revolution. Even with binocular vision completely veridical perception does not occur, but a shifting mixture of appearances some more illusory than others. In the same experiment, however, a rectangular window frame attached to the same spindle is seen veridically all the time and its attached cube and paper tube appear to behave 'normally'.

Similar bizarre effects are produced by looking through a peephole into a room distorted in shape, with sloping ceiling and trapezoidal walls. To the viewer the room appears rectangular and normal, but ordinary objects placed in it, or faces looking in through the windows appear disproportionate in size. Veridical perception in this case may be recovered by acting in relation to the walls of the room (by bouncing a ball against them or tracing an outline on them with a wand), but the distortion may then be transferred in perception to rooms and objects of regular shape. Such perceptual changes cannot be due to the stimulus pattern, for it remains the same in each case, and is attributed, therefore, by the authors of the theory, to changes in the perceivers' so-called 'assumed form world'.[1]

The perceived properties of objects are thus the result of a 'transaction'[2] between the objects and the perceiver. The subject's perception of them depends on 'assumptions', made on the basis of past experience, as to the most probable occurrences. The assumptions are formed, are combined and operate unconsciously and may change with experience. Which assumptions are adopted depends upon their usefulness as 'prognostic directives for action' and that again is decided by experience. Failure of the assumptions to prove prognostically efficacious is experienced as a 'hitch' or incompatibility between different perceptive interpretations in the course of action. A hitch of this character may be removed by training—that is, by repeated readjustive activity in reference to the objects. In this process of readjustment the body of

---

[1] *Vide* Ames, 'Reconsideration of the Origin of Perception', *Vision and Action*, p. 254.

[2] The term is due to J. Dewey and A. F. Bentley. Cf. *Knowing and the Known*, Boston, 1949.

assumptions becomes modified, and as a whole it constitutes the 'assumptive world' of the perceiver.

4

At this point it may be well to pause and take stock. Set-theorists found it necessary to introduce the hypothesis that past sets, or long-established sets, produced perceptual dispositions, so making the percept in some degree dependent on the form of organization built up in the past within the perceiver. With probabilistic and transactional functionalists, this idea is further elaborated and is not confined to muscular habit or sensori-tonic equilibrium. Now we have come to speak of 'cues' and 'assumptions' and their organization into systems.

A cue is not just a physical thing or physiological event, it is a sign or an indication of something other than itself which it signifies or indicates. To speak of cues is to imply an activity of referring beyond the cues as presented. The word, therefore, has epistemological implications. Brunswik maintains that in perception the effects of the stimulus together with those of the distance cues form a *Gestalt*; but that would suggest some kind of combination between physiological factors and epistemological. This seems hardly feasible and the only apparent alternative is to regard the entire percept as constituted from cues—that is, as an act of interpretation. But then the question naturally arises: interpretation of what? It seems difficult to find any other answer than interpretation of sensory material at the level of feeling.

On the other hand, there are some who maintain that 'cues' and the like are to be taken only on the psychophysical level. J. J. Gibson writing of the perception of the visual world[1] asserts that 'there is always some variable in the stimulation (however difficult to isolate) which corresponds to a property of the spatial world'; and he goes on to elaborate a theory of visual ground against which objects are seen, involving, like Brunswik's, the incorporation into the stimulus pattern of 'cues' and 'clues', which indicate, surface, depth, distance and the other properties of the visual scene. The approach is asserted to be strictly 'psychophysical', and its object is to find a physical variable as counterpart for every psychical characteristic of the percept. If, however, we regard the aggregate of such variables purely on the physical or

[1] *The Perception of the Visual World* (New York, 1950), p. 8.

physiological level, what have we?—a highly complicated collection of diverse elements: a pair of two-dimensional perspectivally
distorted retinal images, the neural backlash from the movement
of eye-muscles in focusing and accommodation, proprioceptive
backlash from muscular movements of head and neck, vestibular
stimuli, the neural effect (whatever it is) of the incongruence of the
retinal images, heterogeneities in the retinal stimulation that are
not copies but only correlates[1] of properties of the physical object.
All this taken together merely as a physical or physiological
aggregate is an indefinite conglomeration of heterogeneous and
diverse elements none of which bears any resemblance to an
object and which, as a collection, has none of the properties that
the visual world presents. The members of this aggregate can be
relevant to perception only as *symbols* or (as they are called) clues.
In other words, they cannot function unless they are *interpreted*;
and that can occur only if they somehow become features of an
awareness within which they can be systematically interrelated.
On the physical or merely physiological level they cannot serve as
cues, but only if apprehended in some epistemological process
of referring, comparing, hypothesizing, and judging. Unless they
can somehow be viewed as functioning epistemologically they
offer no explanation of such puzzling perceptual phenomena as
constancy, visual depth, discrimination of figure from ground, or
for that matter of perception at all as the apprehension of an
objective world.

When we talk of assumptions the epistemological and interpretative character of the process is inescapable. Strictly an
assumption is a proposition, but of course it may be operative in
behaviour without being formulated. That perceiving is a kind of
behaviour is an assertion dear to the hearts of some psychologists,
but that it is the kind which interprets sensory cues in accordance
with formed assumptions is not always what they mean. The
account given by functionalists, however, is certainly of a form of
activity—not just of a passive receptivity of data. This activity
involves the assessments and weighting of probabilities, which
inevitably involves past experience, and involves it not just as
having occurred but as having significant bearing on the interrelation of sensory and motor events. The past experience here
useful must be organized experience of objects in spatio-temporal
and causal relations, which can provide evidential foundations for

[1] *Vide ibid.*

the estimate of probabilities. This is a highly complex body of already acquired knowledge, and it is the bearing of this upon the immediately presented sensory clues that constitutes the percept. Such a process of reference of clues to a system of interrelated objects is precisely what is meant by interpretation, and it is small wonder that the functionalists see themselves as the inheritors of Helmholtz's theory of unconscious inference; for what is all this activity if not the activity of thinking.

The question still remains, how past experience is acquired—for this too is perceptive. But now it seems obvious that the answer must be given in terms of degrees of organization and comprehensiveness. Perceiving seems clearly to be the process of organizing, and at the start (in infancy) sensory experience may be assumed to be largely chaotic and vague. Experience gradually gives it structure, as the child comes to distinguish objects, relate them, and to build up an idea of the world as the context in which to behave[1] and which can form the conceptual basis of 'assumptions' governing the future course of the perceptive activity. What is perceived thus depends upon what the mind of the perceiver, as a body of organized experience, brings to the act of perception. The percept is 'in the eye of the beholder'.

How far is this position supported by experimentally observed fact? Some would say that it is not, and that the processes alleged are not perceptual, for perception is something instantaneous and in the words of C. C. Pratt 'stimulus-bound'.[2] Further, the contribution of past experience has been minimized and facts have been adduced (e.g. the occurrence of certain percepts in the very young of different species) as evidence against its efficacy. These we may pass over, for if past experience is only a prior phase of organization it makes small difference of principle where the process is said to begin. What the experimental evidence leaves beyond dispute, however, is that the percept is seldom if ever 'stimulus-bound'. The phenomena of constancy and the Ames demonstrations make it obvious that, at least for vision, perception of a stable object world would be impossible if it were. It is notorious that auditory stimuli can be as ambiguous as visual; and tactual, in themselves, give little precise indication of determinate objects.

---

[1] Cf. J. Piaget, *La Naissance de l'intelligence chez l'enfant.*
[2] 'The role of past experience in perception', *Jour. of Psychol.* 30, 1950.

Hearing and feeling *objects* are always processes which go far beyond the bare stimulus patterns, and hearing or feeling anything less or other than objects is something less or other than perception.

5

Further evidence of autistic influences upon the percept is produced by a group of experimenters who concentrate upon emotional and evaluative attitudes in the subject. These factors may also be regarded as elements contributing to a set of the organism which disposes it to single out certain stimuli and react to them in specific ways.[1]

A range of experimental work has been undertaken by a number of investigators the results of which have inspired a theory of what is called directive-state, that the purposes, drives and emotional states of the organism combine to select, direct attention to, and even modify the appearance of objects. The theory has been summarized by Allport into six theses as follows:

(i) Bodily needs tend to determine what is perceived.

(ii) Reward and punishment associated with the perceiving of objects tend to determine what is perceived, its apparent magnitude and the speed of recognition.

(iii) The values characteristic of the individual (the habitual scale of values he adopts) tend to determine the speed with which words related to those values are recognized.

[1] *Vide* R. Levine, I. Chein, I. and G. Murphy, 'The relation of intensity of a need to the amount of perceptual distortion', *Jour. Psychol.*, 13, 1942; R. Schafer and G. Murphy, 'The role of autism in figure-ground relationship', *J. Exp. Psychol.*, 32, 1943; H. M. Proshansky and G. Murphy, 'The effects of reward and punishment on perception', *J. Psychol.*, 13, 1942; K. R. Smith, G. B. Parker and G. A. Robinson, 'An exploratory investigation of autistic perception', *Amer. Psychol.*, 5, 1950; M. K. and W. K. Rigby, 'Perceptual thresholds as a function of reinforcement and frequency', *Amer. Psychol.*, 7, 1952; L. Postman, J. S. Bruner and E. McGuinnies, 'Personal Values as Selective factors in perception', *J. Abnorm. Soc. Psychol.*, 43, 1948. J. S. Bruner and C. D. Goodman, 'Value and need as organizing factors in perception', *J. Abnorm. Soc. Psychol.*, 42, 1947. W. R. Ashley, R. S. Harper, D. S. Runyan, 'The perceived size of coins in normal and hypnotically induced economic states', *Amer. J. Psychol.*, LXIV, 1957; J. S. Bruner and D. Krech (Ed.), *Perception and Personality* (Duke Univ. Press, 1950).

(iv) The value of objects to the individual tends to determine their perceived magnitudes.

(v) The personality characteristics of the individual predispose him to perceive things in a manner consistent with those characteristics.

(vi) Verbal stimuli that are emotionally disturbing or threatening to the individual tend to require a longer recognition time than neutral words, to be so misperceived as radically to alter their form or meaning, and to arouse their characteristic emotional reactions even before they are recognized.

Each of these theses has been submitted to elaborate experimental investigation[1] and the last of them is by far the most intriguing as well as the most controversial, for it includes the much criticized conception of 'perceptual defence'.

The experimental evidence for this is that when words with emotionally disturbing associations were exposed tachistoscopically to subjects, the exposure being progressively increased from ·01 second until the word is recognized, galvanic skin responses (indicating emotional reaction) occurred before the words were recognized, preliminary misperceptions (or 'guesses') were dissimilar in form and meaning from the actual words, and the recognition time was longer than for words without disturbing connotation. In the case of non-critical words galvanic skin response was consistently smaller and misperceptions had some similarity of form or sound to those actually presented. The implications of the experiments were not always univocal. Just what was being repressed, whether recognition or merely the overt reaction is difficult (if at all possible) to establish. But the suggestion is strong of some form of sub-liminal organization of sensory material which can evoke emotional response at a stage prior to that at which it can evoke perceptual response. This emotional reaction then seems so to affect the perceptual response as both to distort and to delay it.

Be that as it may, a new body of evidence is here presented for autistic influences contributing to a process of self-organization of feeling-content into meaningful objects.

Finally all the various forms of set theory are implied and combined in a new elaboration of the doctrine known as cognition

---

[1] *Vide* op. cit., and p. 410 n above. None of the experimental evidence is fully conclusive. At best it may be described as suggestive and stimulating.

or hypothesis-theory.[1] Perception is now conceived as a process in which hypotheses are generated, applied to incoming stimuli and confirmed or disconfirmed. Bruner and Postman have adopted the idea that all cognitive processes, perceptual or other involve expectancies or hypotheses set up by the organism in the course of its activity or aroused in a particular setting. The hypotheses are not consciously entertained but, as it were, condition the receptivity of the organism, they demand further experience to confirm or disprove them. For this purpose 'input of information from the environment' is required. If the information is congruent with the hypothesis, it is confirmed; if not a shift or modification of the hypothesis is made, partly on the basis of personality and experiential factors and partly as a result of the conflict between the initial hypothesis and the new input. This gives rise to a modified, or what Bruner calls a consequent, hypothesis. In either case the process ends with the confirmation of an hypothesis, even if in its course others have been modified or abandoned, and this confirmation is the percept.

Bruner explicitly identifies the hypothesis with 'cognitive disposition' or 'set'[2] and this is determined by all the factors we have hitherto discussed under that heading, but in particular by emotional, evaluating tendencies and personality traits. He describes it as a sort of 'tuning' of the organism to receive a certain type of information and it is always in such a 'tuned' organism that perception takes place.

The hypothesis may be strong or weak in accordance with the influence exerted by these factors. If it has been frequently confirmed in the past it is to that extent strengthened; if it is not subject to competition, or is supported by other related hypotheses (or both), it is so far strengthened; if it is germane to the needs of the organism, its strength will be increased, and if it agrees with the hypotheses of other people. The stronger it is the more easily aroused it will be and the more readily confirmed by evidence, which need not be very appropriate or reliable. The weaker it is, the more easily it will be disconfirmed, or will require more evidence, both appropriate and reliable, for confirmation.

The reliability and appropriateness of the evidence is assessed

[1] *Vide* R. R. Blake and G. V. Ramsey (Ed.), *Perception—an approach to personality*, New York, 1957, Ch. 5; J. H. Rohrer and M. Sherif (Ed.), *Social Psychology at the Crossroads*, New York, 1951, Ch. 10.

[2] *Vide* Blake and Ramsey, op. cit., p. 125.

by the experimenter and not by the subject, who under the influence of the hypothesis may take as satisfactory evidence which the experimenter judges to be inappropriate or unreliable or both. And the criterion by which the experimenter judges is his own 'knowledge about how people, in Brunswik's terms, correctly attain objects in their environment'.[1] The subject, on the other hand accepts (or rejects) as evidence what his general set or complex of hypotheses inclines him to. What he perceives, therefore, may well from the experimenter's viewpoint 'be all wrong'.

The theory is well supported by experimental evidence, which we need not here describe in detail. Every aspect of the theory has been experimentally tested: the dependence of hypothesis-strength on frequency of past confirmation, on the absence of competing hypotheses, on motivational and social consequences; the manner of confirmation and its relation to these features of the hypothesis; and applications to sociological and anthropological situations have been made and are shown to lend it support.

Much of the material used for experiment consists of relatively ambiguous or unstable stimuli which give more play to 'subjective' factors. Pictures or letters are presented under ground glass or are tachistoscopically exposed for brief periods. Does this, asks Bruner, imply that learning and personality affect perception only under poor conditions? He confesses that perhaps it does, or rather that there are limits imposed by the stimulus, which in certain simple cases may reduce these effects almost to zero.

Despite this concession, as we shall shortly see, the effect of this theory is to make perception completely autistic, for the stimulus is no more than incoming information and if the evaluation of this as confirmatory evidence, as well as the hypothesis to be confirmed depend on the general character of the set, everything will ultimately be subject to central determination. That different criteria (as used by an experimenter) may give different results is not to the point. Superior knowledge of how people usually confirm their hypotheses will no doubt give one a more sophisticated outlook. But that is not enough to exempt even the psychologist from his own theory of the nature of perception, for that, to be valid, must be completely general. There can be no privileged observers. We should have to say, then, that if this theory is correct, the evidence for confirming hypotheses is assessed, as to its reliability and relevance, according to the set of the perceiver,

[1] Op. cit., p. 131.

which is, if not the hypothesis itself, at least the body of past experience and dispositional tendencies which support and give rise to it. Thus both factors contributing to perception, the hypothesis and the information by which it is confirmed are determined by autistic influences, and what specially pertains to the stimulus pattern, the so-called autocthonous element, is reduced to zero.

Bruner's admission, however, that the stimulus imposes limits and in simple cases, where the evidence is appropriate and plentiful (i.e. under good conditions of perception), may reduce the autistic effects to a minimum, appears to contradict this conclusion, for he seems to be introducing an element antagonistic to set which limits and reduces its effect. He does not explain precisely what this element is, but it could be held against him that *this* is the perception proper, independent of autistic influences, which at most is modified by them in varying degrees according to circumstances. Perhaps after all perception is stimulus-bound.

The evidence produced by the transactionalists, on the other hand, runs directly counter to any such belief. 'Our perceptual awarenesses', writes Ames, 'are not determined by the characteristics of our physiological stimulus patterns, peripheral or central, which can be thought of as completely "heiroglyphical", but are our own interpretation of these stimulus patterns in terms of our past experiences, personal and inherited.'[1]

The solution of this dilemma seems once more to lie in regarding the stimulus not just as an isolated pattern of neural excitation but as an element in the felt complex of organic activity. The percept, on the other hand, will be, as Ames alleges, the interpretation of this element in the setting (or 'set') of past inherited and acquired organization of feeling. The process of ordering is a continual on-going activity of which the present percept is a contemporary stage or feature. It grows out of past experience (as a bud grows out of a meristem) in response to modifications in the feeling matrix. But these cannot limit the activity or its results. What restricts the judgment, in cases where the conditions of perception are good, is the insistent crowding of hypotheses frequently confirmed in the past—the mass of established knowledge—supporting it.

The formation and verification of hypotheses is an epistemological process—one might say, without undue risk of error, a logical process. At least it depends on logical relations, though

[1] *Vision and Action*, p. 254.

in practice these may be mistakenly conceived. What, in this theory, is offered as an account of perception is unmistakably an activity of organization, and an activity which is nothing short of thinking. For not only must hypotheses be entertained, but the evidence in their favour or against them must be assessed for relevance, appropriateness and reliability. It must then be, presumably, considered in its bearing upon the hypotheses, which in its light, are either corrected or accepted in the form of a perceptual object.

The result of this highly complex activity is accomplished with great rapidity, but that need not arouse our suspicions; first because the funded product of past efforts (which may well have been slower and more laborious—e.g. in the infant), are immediately available in each new perceptual act, and secondly because the implications of evidence may well flash upon the mind with a minimum of time-lapse. If the available supporting knowledge is plentiful perception may occur at once. If the presented material is vague and the evidence ambiguous it takes longer. But the percept (e.g. a jumble of dots and lines seen as a face) can spring to mind after an initial period of hesitation, just as the solution to a problem can suddenly occur to one after a long period of cogitation.

6

Though somewhat digressive and anticipatory it would be well to observe, at this point, the implications for scientific method of the theory of perception which has so far emerged. Observation is universally and rightly held to be of first-rate importance in scientific investigation, and observation is throughout perception. On the basis of observation, we are often told, hypotheses are formulated and these are then checked by new observations (often involving experiment). But psychologists contend that perception (or observation) itself is always the confirmation of hypotheses and presupposes them. More unsettling still is the assertion that the very evidence sought and found, the acceptance of it as relevant and the assessment of it as reliable, depends upon the assumptions from which the hypothesis itself arises. In what sense, it may be asked, can observation be a check upon hypothesis under conditions of this kind. Is not the question always being begged and the argument perpetually circular?

The psychologist himself appeals to experiment to validate the very theory he is propounding. How are we to view these experiments? Are they and their results merely the fruit of preconceptions which have prompted the theory itself? It may be the case that they are, and that this is true of every theory and its supporting evidence. That indeed need be no detraction from its value, and whether or not it is will depend upon the scope and nature of the presuppositions not upon their mere existence. For by what right do we assume that pure observation is the infallible touchstone for establishing the truth of theories? This is itself a gratuitous assumption suggested only by the idea that valid information comes into the mind ready-made from some outside source through the senses, and then sits in judgment over all internal theorizing. And this idea, we have seen, leads only to disaster. All the evidence at our disposal points in the opposite direction, to the view that there is no such thing as 'pure observation', that all perception is saturated with and governed by the set of the organism and that this is for the most part a product of its past activity. This has been and persists as a process of organizing sensory material, which is itself the sublimation into feeling of the organism's complex physiological and behavioural adaptation to the world. The percept is already the fruit of an interpretative activity. There are no unprocessed data free from all theoretical taint by reference to which hypotheses can be confirmed and no method of checking theories against bare sensa (or primitive feeling). The actual method used, when carefully examined, is very different.

7

That perception, however else one may wish to view it, is at least and in essence an activity of organizing and structuring is the common conclusion to which all psychological theories lead, and is not the peculiar teaching of only one or a few. Allport's monumental review, critique and extension of the various theories leads precisely to the notion of dynamic structure as the underlying and unifying concept. It is in terms of structure that quality, form and figure, three-dimensionality, constancy, quantitative assessment, object character and meaning are all ultimately to be explained. Consequently it seems fair to say that the body of physiological and psychological evidence that has been reviewed weighs heavily in favour of our general view of mental activity as one of organization and integration at the reflexive stage. The brain is not an instrument for conveying information nor for receiving it either ready-made or in code. It seems rather to be an organ for the extraction of information from less organized processes (neural and other)—an organ, in short, for decreasing entropy and extracting message from noise. To put this in other terms, our nervous system seems somehow to perform the function of integrating the entire interrelated system of organic functions into a felt whole, and further of organizing the contents of this 'whole of feeling' (to use Bradley's phrase) into a dynamic system of interrelated percepts.

That this is so is evidenced by the fact that perception is never 'stimulus-bound' but that the stimulus pattern is always transformed and interpreted in conformity with the structure of acquired knowledge. The Ames demonstrations gave examples of this, and yet more striking are the proven effects of wearing spectacles which invert or otherwise distort the image. Within a relatively short time the subject sees objects normally oriented and in correct spatial relations, in spite of the pattern of stimulation. In one experiment the subject wore spectacles for five days which reversed right and left. After that he wore them only for half of each day. He then found that whether he wore them or not no change in the perception of objects occurred.[1] The removal of cataract involves the removal also of the lenses of the eyes. The patient must then wear glasses which focus the light on to the retina, but the focus can never be made perfect and the image at the periphery of the field is always distorted. Nevertheless, after a few days it is no longer seen as such, and in perception it regains its normal shape. Clearly in such cases the brain, through its neural organization, is able to extract 'message' from the incoming stimuli however they may be deranged, as long as the distortion is consistent, the system into which they are to be integrated is intact, or the means of constructing a system are available. So to regard the brain, is moreover, not to forget that it functions only as an integral part of the entire organism. It is therefore the organic system as a whole that converts noise into message; or rather, raises the level of organization to the point at which its complex activity becomes self-reflexive, aware of its own content; and discriminates within it meaningful objects. That is done by selecting, distin-

[1] *Vide* Taylor and Wolpe, in *Theories of the Mind*, (Ed. Scher), p. 232.

O

guishing and setting in relation the elements of its self-awareness. To be so set in a context within a self-conscious experience is what constitutes meaningfulness. It is the total organism that is involved in this total activity. Even if some parts may contribute only indirectly and all in varying degrees, they function organically and in inextricable conjunction. Thus it is the total organism that becomes aware, in and through its integrant activity, and there is no call for any ghost or special percipient manikin within the brain to observe the effects of physiological processes.

This reflexive activity, bringing feeling to full consciousness is perception. To perceive is to be aware, and that is *ipso facto* to be aware of one's own awareness. So in perception the organism, which is acting as a whole in this process, can take account of elements of its own feeling and relate them to one another systematically. It is this activity of systematic relation that provides the basis for cues, assumptions and hypotheses and the method of verifying them. It issues in the ascription in an act of judgment of a property or nexus to the world as actual. Every phase in the process is a stage of integration. Each percept is itself a whole (a *Gestalt*) into which are fused lesser configurations and which itself relates to others in a wider organized field. Each percept is a moment in the progressive construction of the system of knowledge —of assumptions and hypotheses—built up gradually on the basis of past experience. The percept is a focal point in a ramifying network of references and contains an implicit judgment riveting them all in a single predication of a property to some feature of the real world.

This predication represents to the perceiver the confirmation of an implicit hypothesis and its validity depends on the comprehensiveness and consistency of the system of judgments to which the perceptual judgment conforms. Our system of hypotheses is real for us—is the only world we know. Their ultimate truth consists only in their mutual systematic consistency—coherence among themselves and with those of other people with whom we communicate meaningfully, and on communication with whom the construction of our system is in large measure dependent.

8

So the answer given to the question, Why do things look as they do? is, Because of the way the subject organizes his sensory experience to form objects, in the course of his total activity. The further questions (which may be taken together), Are the objects that appear those of the real world? and Do they appear as they really are? cannot be answered apart from the final question, How do we discover whether they are real and appear veridically? The answer to be offered will be justified more fully in a later chapter; here it will be baldly stated that we can make this discovery only by continuing the process of systematization and interpretation already operative in perception—that is, by scientific investigation. The discovery of the nature of the real world and the extent to which appearances approximate to it is not the starting-point but the goal of the cognitive process of which perception is an early phase. Whether or not perception is veridical cannot be given in perception but only through further investigation of the perceived objects. But perception is not so rigid that it does not become modified in this process and may not change in consequence of scientific understanding.

Koffka is therefore right to say that the geographical environment is a constructum and not a datum. But we have seen that the behavioural environment is no less a construction. The data, such as they are, are relatively chaotic feeling-contents from which the subject constructs an object world. But the apparent paradox of relating the geographical to the behavioural environment, as a cause to an effect and as the determinant of the accomplishment of behaviour, is overcome when it is realized that both of these are constructed within the behavioural environment of the psychologist. The geographical world of the subject he observes is his constructum and the subject's report and behaviour generally is part of that same construction, and so, therefore, is the postulation of a behavioural environment for the subject; and the two are related causally and otherwise within one constructed system. For the subject himself the behavioural environment and the geographical are one and the same—they are his constructed world. The distinction affirmed by the psychologist and the relations between the two distincta cannot be known by direct perception but only in retrospective reconstruction. For the climber in the example, the snow bridge is real and firm until he steps on it. It is on that hypothesis that he does so. The collapse of the bridge and his fall are experienced as much through perceptual dispositions as the earlier appearance of strength. They are disconfirming experiences but, as we have seen, their evaluation as such is equally dependent with the original hypothesis upon the perceptual and interpretative disposition (or set) of the subject. It is conceivable, though not of a sane mind, that these evidences could be so differently viewed as to confirm different hypotheses not inconsistent with the original one (e.g. that some malicious demon had purposely destroyed the bridge, or that to fall was the natural consequence of the intended act and the proper way to descend the mountain). But the result of normal experience would be a hypothetical sub-set interpreting the fresh evidence in a way which conflicts with the former sub-set, and it is the subsequent adjustment of these conflicting sub-sets of hypotheses that is formulated in terms of the contrast between appearance and reality. The appearance was a judgment made on incomplete evidence in terms of a sub-set that did not exhaust the implications of the acquired perceptual dispositions. The incorporation of the new experiences interpreted brings to light the omitted implications—for instance, the known effects of the sun's warmth on snow, or of the movement of the ice in a glacier—and develops a reality by reference to which the appearance is recognized as such.

Is not the new experience here a datum? Yes, as sheer indeterminate feeling, it is. But not as a significant *quale*; for it could be interpreted otherwise if the hypothesis-set were different. It is an access of feeling, the integration of new adaptive adjustments between environment and organism, which has to be assimilated into the ordered constructum of the experienced world. The systematic character of the constructum defines reality, but always only provisionally, because the cognitive activity is a continuing endeavour to define it ever more adequately—or coherently. This as it proceeds is the work of the intellect and it reaches beyond the common-sense world to the development of scientific theory.

A NOTE ON MEMORY

The dependence of sensori-motor learning, perception and intelligent action upon some form of memory and imagination is obvious, and no study of mind can be complete without some examination of these two aspects of mental functioning. If this were a serious psychological treatise, or an attempt to elaborate a complete philosophy of mind, the omission of a thorough treatment of these topics would be inexcusable; but the object of this book is different. It is to frame a general view of the world as presented by the sciences, physical, biological and psychological, in the twentieth century, and to discover the place in it of the human mind and its efforts to comprehend the world in science. To this end a review has been made of the main deliverances of physics and biology, and if the survey of modern psychological teaching is now to be concluded with some account of prominent theories of the nature of thinking, though much of interest and importance will have been neglected, enough material will have been marshalled to make apparent the general outline of the contemporary world-picture. Nevertheless, it is hardly possible to pass over the topic of memory in complete silence, and it might be well at least to indicate the direction which a fuller discussion might take.

Recent efforts (both psychological and philosophical) to explain the phenomena of memory have made use of one or more of a group of concepts none of which is adequate by itself, nor all of them taken together, to account for the essential achievement of remembering, namely, the recall and identification of an individual occurrence experienced in the past. Memory, of course, includes much more than this; it includes the awareness that a present experience is not new but is being repeated; it includes recognition of individual things, places and persons; it includes the awareness that certain classes of events (e.g. meals, train journeys, sunsets, and what you will) have been experienced before, and it includes the recall of facts, poems, names, numbers and formulae learned in the past. That these abilities involve some method of storage of information is obvious; that they require some mechanism for recording and reproducing patterns of neural activity is indisputable; that such mechanism includes some kind of association and affinity between different mental occurrences is an assumption that common experience seems to warrant; but the recall and identification of a definite event as one that has been experienced at a definite time in the past is more than can be explained in terms of storage, or neural traces, or mere association of 'ideas'.

That storage is not enough is obvious, for the retention of an experience is by no means the same as its recall, still less does it explain identification and dating. Storing wines in a cellar makes them available when required but does not ensure that they will be taken out at the right time, nor determine which shall be taken, still less does it establish the date of their vintage. When the witness is asked if he was at the scene of the crime at the specified time, it is indeed necessary that his brain should have stored the information but that will not of itself insure that he can reproduce it with any degree of accuracy. Filing cabinets are useful commodities but of little help without a skilled clerk who understands and can operate the filing system.

Mental processes may very well—in fact, to account for our experience, they must—leave some sort of trace in the brain. Some kind of neural mechanism is demanded to account for the retention of information, whether it be the growth of the synaptic knobs, or the connection of neural pathways, or the activation of reverberatory circuits, or something different from any of these. But none of these explain recall. For this recourse is usually taken to some theory of association, by means of which a present experience revives a past one—a present neural discharge over-flows (by virtue of some mechanism like those listed above) into a path or circuit previously traversed. But the most that any such theory can provide for is there appearance in consciousness of a past experience (or if one insists on 'objective' description) the repetition of some past pattern of behaviour. It cannot explain the recognition of it as past, still less the identification of it as the particular experience which occurred at a particular past time. (The precise 'objective' description of that must be left to more expert writers).

Storage, traces, association can at most account for retention and resuscitation of past mental processes; they are obviously involved in the formation of habits, verbal and other, and may go far to explain the recall of information learned at second hand. But memory proper—the awareness that a particular event was experienced at a definite time, and an awareness enjoyed directly in the present, not merely inferred from present evidence—such recollection requires other explanatory principles, whatever they may turn out to be.

Images may well be instrumental to memory; but images cannot constitute memory. To have an image of the house where one lived as a child is not the same as to identify it as the image of that house, or to remember having lived in it. That involves an ability to relate the image to the actual house experienced in the past (which may long since have been demolished). The image is a present experience, and the past experience is long gone. How can the two be related and the relation apprehended in the present when only one of them is available? What substitutes *now* for the past experience with which the present image must be compared and identified? The answer is that nothing can substitute for it, because anything which did would be a present experience and the problem would arise afresh.

It helps little to postulate, with Bertrand Russell,[1] a feeling of familiarity (whatever that might be), for no feeling is an awareness of relation or identity and any feeling can be felt only in the present, whereas memory is an awareness of a relation between the present and the past. The familiarity of sights and sounds, faces and situations does undoubtedly arouse characteristic feelings; but they are consequent upon recognition. They do not cause or constitute remembrance. That something is familiar is a judgment, not a feeling, and even when it is made it falls short of recollection and may be illusory. Memory, it is true, is not infallible. One may mis-remember, and when one does so one judges falsely that some event, as recalled, was actually experienced. But simply to recognize an experience as familiar is not to remember it, even if the feeling of familiarity is justified. At most it is one feature of remembrance.

The fact that memory can err is the best clue to its essential character. Only propositions can be true or false, and the assertion (or denial) of a proposition is a judgment. That memory requires this at least, therefore, cannot be gainsaid. Nevertheless, the epistemological problem remains how a judgment involving the awareness of a relationship between present and past experience can ever be made. For the judgment must be made in the present and must therefore lack direct access to one term of the relation. This is what was meant earlier by saying that memory itself must be 'transcendent'—it must somehow transcend the present moment—and the alleged transcendence of consciousness in general cannot be explained away by means of 'memory traces'.

Perhaps the solution of the problem is to be found in the realization that memory is a process of the same kind as, and is indeed an extension of, perception. For in perception there is no immediately given object, nothing that is not constructed by the selective and relating activity of attention and set in a context— nothing, the significance of which does not depend upon implicit

[1] Cf. *The Analysis of Mind*, Ch. IX.

interpretation by reference to a wider field of experience. Perception is the point at which the organized experience of the world is actualized in present awareness. This organized experience includes spatial and temporal structure which is never as a whole 'given' as an immediate sensum. The past therefore enters into every experience of the present and is implicity related to it. Memory may well be nothing other than the explication of this relation, the development in imagination and thought of the temporal structure of experience. This, of course, is intelligent activity and involves thinking, but that memory proper is an aspect of the functioning of intelligence is not an extravagant suggestion. Piaget (1960) asserts with some firmness that intelligence is the development of what he calls 'assimilatory schemata' of structured experience. In reference to Duncker's theory he remarks: 'An act of intelligence is doubtless determined by past experience. . . . But this relationship involves assimilatory schemata which in turn are the product of previous schemata, from which they are derived through differentiation and co-ordination. Schemata thus have a history; there is interaction between past experience and present act of intelligence, not uni-directional actional of past on present as empiricism demands. . . . It is even possible to formulate these relations between present and past by saying that equilibrium is reached when all previous schemata are embedded in present ones and intelligence can equally well reconstruct past schemata by means of present ones and vice versa.'[1]

If this be so we may pass at once to theories of the intellect, presuming with some justification that memory is related to it in the same way as perception and sensori-motor learning; in short, that memory is one of the forms of inchoate activity of the intellect. The key to the problem of memory may lie in seeing it as yet another aspect of the organizing function of consciousness, operating through implicit judgment in the activity of recollection.

The development of a theory along these lines would require detailed investigation of psychological research and careful exposition in order to carry conviction, and this is a task which cannot be undertaken here but must be attempted in another context.

[1] J. Piaget, *Psychology of Intelligence*, p. 66.

CHAPTER XXI

INTELLIGENCE

I

The work of the mind *par excellence*, at least in some sense, is intelligent action. When one speaks of the evolution of mind one thinks primarily of the development of intelligence, and the claim of man to superiority over other living beings is based essentially on intellectual superiority. The range of evolutionary forms is viewed as an ascending scale largely because the successive phyla are represented as a series of increasingly complex structures functioning with increasingly versatile adaptability, each of which is an ostensible step towards human beings capable of intelligent action. As in our own intelligent behaviour we are most acutely aware, and cannot consistently deny the existence of our own conscious activity, it is in the operations of the intellect more than anywhere else that we confidently assert the presence and effectiveness of mind.

That intelligence however is something separate and apart from other psychological functions—a Cartesian *vis cognoscens*, a pure spiritual light bathing in effulgence the merely corporeal products of the senses and the *phantasia*—we shall find ample reason to deny, as we have already found reason to assert that consciousness is nothing apart from the organic and neuro-muscular processes of which it is the form of integration.

Whether or not intellectual capacity constitutes superiority has been questioned not only on biological but also on moral and religious grounds; and, apart from this, some philosophers rank the intellect as no more than second best in the scale of mental forms. The question, whether posed in a biological or in a philosophical context, is meaningless except in the light of a theory of value, for with it immediately the demand asserts itself for definition both of intelligence and of the criterion of superiority. In discussing the biological question we maintained that the value judgment was forced upon us by the deliverances of biology themselves which made 'survival value' a criterion of success in evolution, and showed, at least by implication, that this was consequent upon auturgic wholeness. If now intelligence is

o*

identifiable as that form of activity which is specifically directed to the construction, elaboration and operation of dynamic wholes, in practical behaviour, in social interaction and in theoretical formulation, the claim of intelligent action to be a mark of biological superiority must surely be well founded. It would remain to show that moral or religious superiority rested upon a similar criterion of value before decision could be made about the status of intelligence in those spheres, but the investigation of moral and religious criteria falls beyond the scope of this volume. Enough, however, may come to light in our discussion of the nature of intelligence to give pointers towards answers to questions belonging more properly to moral philosophy, and our conspectus of the deliverances of the sciences and the resulting world-picture will suggest lines of thought more appropriately developed in a philosophy of religion.

That intelligence is the highest development of the adaptive capacity of the organism—the condition of its biological superiority—is clearly upheld by Piaget, for whom this virtually constitutes its definition. 'It is the most highly developed form of mental adaptation', he asserts, 'that is to say, the indispensable instrument for interaction between the subject and the universe when the scope of this interaction goes beyond immediate and momentary contacts'.[1] But, he goes on to say, that an exact definition of intelligence is difficult precisely because it is not a separable and unique function but is continuous with sensori-motor and biological adaptation of which it is the development. He refuses to separate intelligence from instinct or to oppose it sharply to trial-and-error learning, declaring in agreement with Claparède and Stern that 'problem, hypothesis and control, whose combination is the mark of intelligence . . . already exist in embryo in the needs, the trial-and-errors, the empirical test characteristic of the least developed sensori-motor adaptations'. The copious evidence collected by Thorpe makes it clear that this is sound teaching and it further corroborates the theses we have all along been maintaining: (i) that there is in nature a continuous trend towards more elaborate, more coherent and more labile organization displayed in a continuous scale of developing forms, and (ii) that consciousness and the activity of mind constitute a section of this scale in a late phase of its development, continuous with the lower phases, and are not attributable to any separate influence

[1] Op. cit., p. 7.

or entity mysteriously impinging upon material structures from
without.

Piaget proceeds to define intelligence, again in conformity
with our general position, by reference to 'the direction towards
which its development is turned' and by contrast with lower
phases in the scale. Behaviour becomes more intelligent as its
objects become more distant from the behaving subject and their
relations to it more complex. In contrast with instinct it is neither
rigid nor stereotyped. In contrast with perception it is less simple
and can cope with matters not immediately in contact with the
organism. In contrast with both perception and habit, its organization is more supple and can be elaborated by reversible processes;
in short, it is capable of more thorough analysis and more complete
synthesis. It forms 'mobile structures' of 'progressive reversibility',
and is thus defined as the most versatile and yet the most stable
form of equilibrium to which organic activity tends. In other
words, if we follow out the logical direction of Piaget's argument,
we come to the conclusion that intelligent action is the completest
and most adequate exemplification of conscious living activity, to
which other exemplifications are, in varying degrees, less developed
and less satisfactory approximations. This conclusion may,
however, need amplification to allow for the scope of intelligence
so defined. If the definition is taken along with what was quoted
earlier, if intelligence is seen as the indispensable form of interaction between subject and object which goes beyond immediate
and momentary contact, it will be realized that all the highest
activities of the human intellect are included in its scope, so that
what has been said above about the supremacy of the intellect can
be accepted without further cavil.

2

What the theories of perception outlined in the foregoing chapter
revealed, that perception essentially involves an activity of interpretation and judgment, an activity of ordering objects and placing
them in a coherent context elaborated in the course of experience,
Piaget confirms by approaching the topic from the other side and
tracing back the typical activity of intelligence to its developmental sources in perception. In a critical review of past and
contemporary theories, he stresses the importance of the organization of wholes but, while agreeing with the Gestaltists that the

perception of configurations is not subsequent to the apprehension of separable sensa, he insists also upon the possibility and occurrence of progressive assimilation of wholes none of which individually is analysable into separate primary elements. He attributes the phenomena of perceptual constancy to what he calls 'transportation' and 'decentralization', by which he also explains the proved ability of percipients to counteract common visual illusions with familiarity and practice, an ability which has been shown to increase in children with their age and mental development.

The significance of these two terms must not be overlooked. Perception is defined as 'the totality of relations given immediately and simultaneously with each centring'.[1] This affords *Gestalten*, some of them illusory. But by subconscious transportation of (what in effect amounts to) attention from one part of the *Gestalt* or 'totality of relations' to another, by implicit comparisons and automatic sensori-motor adjustments and co-ordinations, a process of decentralization takes place, which compensates for illusory and perspectival effects, and corrects them in a new synthetic grasp of the presented relationships. 'However elementary and dependent on sensori-motor functions these decentralizations and regulations may be', Piaget asserts, 'it is clear that they all constitute an activity of comparison and co-ordination which is allied to intelligence.' Such 'transportations' take place both in space and in time, and the growing capacity to make them in the developing infant produces progressively increasing awareness of constancy of shape and size. The recognition of individual objects follows, but none of these features of the environment is originally given, as such. They are the product of a process of construction in which spatial and temporal relations are singled out within the sensory field and stable connections learned and co-ordinated.

The more direct and primitive type of perception is marked by 'centralization', relative immediacy and inability to distinguish. This centralization is a manifestation of that enhanced 'centreity' attributed by Tielhard to mind as a typifying characteristic; but as Piaget applies the term it is one of limitation. The decentralization characteristic of intelligence on the other hand (though Piaget fails to emphasize this point), is not a dissipation of unity, but is the capacity to transfer attention, without losing hold upon the mutual relevance of the successive foci. It is an analytic capacity

[1] Op. cit., p. 79.

which is at the same time correlative to a higher and more articulated synthesis. 'Centreity' is therefore far from being lost through 'decentralization'. The former term (in effect) refers to what Kant called the synthetic unity of apperception, while the latter corresponds to the self-differentiation of that unity into relational 'categories'. Whereas Kant's terminology is epistemelogical and refers to the form of developed perception, Piaget and the psychologists view the matter genetically and recognize the fact that ready-made categories are not provided *in vacuo* subsequently to be imposed by the mind upon a sensuous manifold (as some misrepresentations of Kant would have us believe he held), but emerge through a process of active development, in which what is innate is only the ability to form them—the capacity to distinguish and relate, to analyse and synthesize, to explicate the implicit articulations of a diversified totality. It is, in short, capacity to develop and explicate, to distil out, the principles of organization which differentiate and at the same time unify (by interrelation) the elements within a systematic totality or polyphasic whole.

This, as we shall presently find, is the essential function of intelligence, and its contrast to perception resolves itself into that between subjectivity and objectivity. This is clearly demonstrated by Piaget.[1] The characteristic centrality of perception is subjective centrality. Perception is conditioned and limited by the organic, neuro-muscular conditions of sensibility and the spatio-temporal circumstances of the percipient. Its deliverances are relative to these. Many perceptual illusions are due to subjective exaggeration of objective difference, and others are the consequence of subjective neural and psychological idiosyncracies. The relativity of perception is relativity to the subject and his singular viewpoint. Decentralization and the correction of this subjectivity is effected through the establishment of a different kind of relativity: the relativity of the intellect. Here the word is used in a new sense, that of relativity to an objective or absolute standard. This second relativity is the basis of comparison and measurement; of those compensatory comparisons which effect correction of distorted appearances; of co-ordination and co-variance. It is the relativity inherent in, and sustainable only on the basis of the organization of systems in which corroboration of converging evidence can establish invariants, and which is consequently indispensable to

[1] *Vide* op. cit., pp. 75 ff.

the construction of a stable world. It is, in sum, the foundation of objectivity.[1]

The distinction between appearance and reality corresponds to this opposition of subjective to objective, what appears, appears to a subject and *qua* appearance is subjective. It is conditioned by the circumstances of perception and the special limitations of the subject's point-of-view. Reality is not so limited, but transcends immediate and momentary perspectives, as well as the possibly distorting influence of organic and physiological processes. But this contrast, and the relationship between the real and the apparent, cannot be perceived; it does not appear, but can only be discovered, by the 'decentralizing' and objectifying activity of intelligence, comparing, correlating, co-ordinating and systematizing the deliverances of sense-perception in the construction of a coherent objective world. Reality is never 'given', in sense or otherwise. What is 'given' is at best appearance. Reality must be sought and discovered. In the last resort it can only be inferred.

The common beliefs, that the real is immediately given in sensation and that what is objective is independent of the mind, are not only incompatible but false; and it is so much the more astonishing that philosophers have so often and so pathetically subscribed to them. Objectivity does indeed entail detachment and liberation from the limiting conditions of perception, but it is essentially the product of intelligence and thinking. This is not to say that perception is altogether void of objectivity. We have insisted that thought is inchoate and already working in it and intelligence grows out of it by continuous development. There is a stage in this process which Piaget explicitly calls 'intuitive thought'—thought based upon perceptual appearance— just prior to its emancipation from perceptual immediacy. The opposition is that of successive phases in a continuous scale and is intensified or mitigated, as the degree of difference is increased or diminished. If perception is appearance it must not be forgotten that 'only the real can appear', and we must proceed to investigate the actual operation of intelligence in its construction of an objective world and the stages through which it works towards the scientific discovery of reality.

[1] The spatio-temporal relativity of modern physics is, as we have seen, of this kind. It is not the abandonment of all absolute quantities but the recognition and establishment of invariant laws and objective constants. It is (*pace* Eddington) the very antithesis of subjectivity.

3

It is not to be forgotten that perception is only the phenomenal aspect of behaviour and that intelligence is essentially an activity —one characterized by a specially high degree and kind of dynamic structure. The construction of the objective world is, accordingly, at once a matter of practical experiment and perceptual development. In this two-sided process, perception and sensori-motor habit are freed from subjectivity and are refined into the activity of thought proper.

The development of the infant proceeds by the assimilation of new factors into innate schemata of reflex action (which Piaget, however, does not regard as crassly mechanical).[1] In this way habits are evolved, which are described as higher-order schemata. These schemata are essentially assimilatory. They grow by mutual incorporation and the addition of new constituents into an already systematic structure to form more comprehensive and at the same time more adaptable systems. The utilization of innate sucking mechanisms (for instance) improves with practice and becomes adapted to different objects. These activities are then combined with head and arm movements and manipulation, affording means of more elaborate and efficient responses to environmental stimuli. Further innate activities such as following a moving object with the eye until it disappears and turning the head to fixate the source of a sound, initiate the practical recognition of objective permanence, so far as perceptuo-motor anticipations and expectancies are involved.

The germ of intelligence is detectable when the child begins to co-ordinate vision with manual prehension (e.g. accidental pulling of a string attached to a rattle), and his attention is attracted to a novel result, which stimulates him to repeat the action. The development of perceptual skill continues as the child becomes able to move his head to follow visually the contours and motions of objects, and displays active interest in the examination of perspectival distortions. This leads to the awareness of shape and size constancies, manifesting itself in the pursuit and search after objects which move out of the field of vision behind obstructions. Secondary schemata thus become co-ordinated, and the practical relationship of means and ends becomes established. A period of trial-and-error learning develops the practice of deliberate experi-

[1] Cf. quotation in p. 337 n 4 above.

ment, as when a desired object is reached by pulling on a cloth or other base upon which it is resting.

Out of these activities, proceeding from the recognition of shape and size constancy and the formation of the concept of a permanent object and its movement, the schemata of space and time are elaborated—again a matter of the assimilation and union of schemata. This involves differentiation between change of state and change of position, which, again, must depend upon co-ordination and correlation of spatial and temporal sequences, the distinction of internal and external changes, and the emergence of the antithesis between self and not-self, effecting a new degree of decentralization from the subject and a definite step towards objectivity. Here the importance is evident of the distinction between subjective and objective succession, so strongly emphasized by Kant, and the implications which it holds of temporal relation and spatial co-existence.

In the course of this development co-ordination of the deliverances of different senses is essential and is possible only on the basis of the gradually emerging objective schema to which such deliverances can be referred. The schema is not given in sensation and cannot be provided by any one sense modality alone. It must be supplied by the structuring activity of thought developing from concurrent perception and motor activity as a logically prior condition of co-ordination. Strict Empiricism which takes sensation as prior to construction can never account for this process consistently; and empiricist theories of perception inevitably commit *petitio principii* in the attempt.[1]

Trial-and-error learning is a factor in this developmental process; and Piaget insists that it is not sharply distinguishable from intelligence. He cites Claparède, Tolman and Krechevsky in support and in this contention he is in full agreement (as we have seen) with Thorpe who bases his opinion on the evidence of widespread experimental investigation. According to Piaget, trial and error involves real elements of problem, hypothesis and test. The problem arises out of a presupposed, pre-existing structure in which some element is lacking and some gap demands to be filled. Even the infant's need to suck presupposes the physiological apparatus of sucking and ingestion and its adaptation to a source

[1] Cf. Bertrand Russell, *Our Knowledge of the External World* (London, 1914) and, for criticism, E. E. Harris, *Nature, Mind and Modern Science* (London, 1954), Ch. XIV.

of supply, the lack of which creates a need, and failure to connect the complementary parts of the system sets in train the first movements of trial and error. Piaget maintains that in trial-and-error learning success depends upon the subject's awareness (however inchoate) of the implicative relations of the elements of the system which demands completion.[1] This dependence of question and answer, hypothesis and confirmation upon construction of a system becomes of vital importance for the understanding of the much later stage of development constituting scientific investigation.

4

The final stage is that of insight proper: the sudden experience of illumination and relevant reaction effected by comprehension of the situation as a whole with its constituent relations and the connections of its salient and (for the problem to be solved) essentially relevant factors. This again depends on organizing activities of a rather special kind specific to intelligence, to some account of which we shall presently turn. It is already apparent that the stage of insight proper is correlative to a high degree of elaboration of an objective system. At this stage a body of systematized and co-ordinated experience must already have been evolved, the bearing of which upon the presented problem must be directly apprehended to effect an immediate solution. Insight is precisely this direct grasp of the inter-connection of relevant factors.

Awareness of the bearing and relevance of a body of organized knowledge upon the particular nexus to which attention is directed was early discovered to be characteristic of thinking in the researches of the Würzburg school. Under the influence of Külpe they attacked the hitherto dominant belief that thinking was primarily a product of random associations. Their impressive and largely pioneering experimental investigations definitely disproved that doctrine, and they were at pains to provide some alternative principle of explanation. In this they were hardly successful, for they were able to suggest nothing better than the indefinable and indescribable '*Bewusstseinslage*', with which they later became dissatisfied, yet for which nothing more explanatory was ever provided than Ach's '*Bewusstheit*' and Bühler's

[1] Op. cit., pp. 93 ff.

'*Gedanken*'. They did, however, succeed in establishing (concurrently with Binet) the existence of imageless thought, for which at first they tried to account by postulating the notorious 'states of consciousness' (*Bewusstseinslage*) which defied description. There is no need to go into the detail of their work nor to recount the stages of development of their theories, all of which has been admirably done by George Humphrey. Some points, however, may be noted which are of outstanding interest here.

First, Marbe, though he could discover no psychological concomitant peculiar to thinking, found reason to assert that all conscious processes can be resolved into judgments.[1] Next, Ach found it necessary to postulate the existence of an impalpable 'awareness' (*Bewusstheit*), or 'knowledge', operative in the performance by his subjects of a required act of thinking. This 'knowledge'. he found, was often very complex but seemed to be present all at once—'a lightning-like momentary illumination of a complex-content, which can only be expressed verbally by several sentences, an event which because of its short-lived existence cannot possibly be given by inner speech'.[2] He identified three main types of such *Bewusstheit*: awareness of meaning, awareness of determination (knowledge of the way in which the mental act is proceeding with reference to the task set and the objects under attention), and awareness of relation (between a result attained and a prior expectation or set). Humphrey draws attention to the support given to Ach's thesis by Mozart's description of his own ability to 'hear' the entire course and structure of a musical composition 'all at once', 'so that I can survey it like a fine picture or a beautiful statue—at a glance'. (Op. cit., p. 53.)

Thirdly, Dürr and Külpe when acting as subjects for Bühler reported the monentary and instantaneous operation in their thinking of whole trains of reasoning and systems of knowledge, Dürr describes how, without verbal presentation the following train of reasoning mediated the answer 'No' to the question whether the future is just as much a condition of the present as the past: 'That sounds like something correct . . . men are determined by thoughts of the future . . . the thought of the future should not be confounded with the future itself . . . such confusions, however, constitute a frequent dodge in philosophical thought.' Külpe answered the question, 'When you think of purpose, must you

[1] *Vide* Humphrey, *Thinking*, p. 35.
[2] Quoted by Humphrey, op. cit., p. 49.

also think of chance and folly?' with the single affirmative 'Yes', and reported that this was mediated by an involved complex of thinking bringing the terms of the question into relation with Darwin's theories. The whole complex, he asserts was 'an immediate, quite clear knowledge'. (*Ibid*., p. 58.) On another occasion Külpe reported the instantaneous presence in his awareness of 'the whole picture of the pre-Socratic philosophy, its relation to Socrates, how Plato fought against it'; and on yet another occasion, the whole development in three phases of the ancient scepticism. (*Ibid*., p. 50.)[1] These examples testify that, in spite of experimental methods which would today be considered defective, these Würzburg pioneers did discover some impressive evidence of the operation in thought of entire organized systems, and this, according to the general trend of later opinion, is the distinguishing mark of insight.

Selz, the immediate successor of the Würzburg school maintained that thinking consisted essentially in the construction or completion of wholes. Developing the work of Watt who laid stress upon the regulating and directing influence of the set task (*Aufgabe*), Selz found that task and stimulus affected one another to form an indissoluble whole. The stimulus is apprehended as a complex relational fact (*Sachverhalte*)[2] and the subject, determined by the total *Aufgabe*, strives to complete the structure of the presented data. So Franklin, attempting to bring the electricity of the thundercloud to earth completed the system by supplying the needed link between earth and cloud—the kite. The insight which leads to the solution is derived from what Selz calls schematic anticipation, which enables a means to the desired aim to be abstracted from the apprehension of the structural principles of the complex.

This theory is a forerunner of *Gestalt*, for which thinking consists in structural reorganization and recombination of presented data with mnemonic traces, to bring about a new configuration revealing new properties, the grasp of which is insight. For Köhler this is a sudden illumination, but for Duncker something which may be achieved by successive steps. But whereas for

[1] How these examples could consistently be explained by proponents of a peripheral theory of thinking—one which equates thought with incipient or latent muscular movement—it would be interesting to speculate.

[2] A term later adopted by Wittgenstein.

Selz the final solution is implicit in the schematic anticipation, for the Gestaltists the work of thought is the construction of a new whole that completely transforms the significance of the presented material.

Despite Humphrey's strictures on Selz's theory—to the effect that no truly constructive thinking is possible if the solution is implicitly given at the outset—and his preference for Gestalt, something may be said in the defence of the former. Obviously if the whole were explicit from the start there would be no problem; but equally, if there is no implication of the solution in the data at all, the problem must remain intractable and incapable of solution. We are faced here with something very like the problem of the *Meno*. If the combination of data with mnemonic traces were haphazard, the emergence of the new *Gestalt* would be purely accidental and the *Gestalt* theory would be no more than an obscurer form of Thorndike's view of learning by random 'trial' and failure. Insight would then be simply chance or magic. Nor can it be maintained that the construction of the new *Gestalt* is arbitrary, for the solution of a problem may not be invented, it must be discovered—it must 'fit the facts'. Accordingly, the new construction must be based upon implications already present in the data and if these are insufficient the problem will remain unsolved until the original schema has been suitably augmented.

There is a sense, moreover, in which every presented situation holds implicitly everything that thinking can extract from it, for the organism is always integral to a system of organic relations with an environment which ultimately includes the entire universe. The whole of this is sublimated into feeling and its detailed explication is the task of thought. But it must not be forgotten that thought is practical and combines awareness with movement and manipulation. Experimental trial and error are part of its operation. It is this process that elaborates and explicates the patterns of structure and which reveals the relations between component elements of the total system centred in and focused by the integral organic activity which is felt. It is, as Thorpe declared, the apprehension of relations that is insight.

5

Piaget regards the aim of intelligent activity as a state of equilibrium of the mind, or a system of such states; and though the term is not wholly felicitous, it is not altogether misleading, inas-much as an equilibrium is a condition which supervenes upon the rounding off or completion of a system. In mechanics it is the closing, and so the stabilizing of a system of forces. The idea, however, suggests a static condition which belies intelligence. There are, of course, states of dynamic equilibrium and open systems which suggest a more appropriate concept. The activity of intelligence might be described as the most highly developed form of dynamic equilibrium between organism and environment; but this too falls short of what is required, for it suggests an opposition between two factors, alien to each other, which is only partially true of the highest products of the mind. What the intellect seeks and in large measure achieves is a coherence or perfection of a system comprehending both organism and en-vironment and its method of operation is nicely assimilated to that end. Piaget recognizes this fact when he writes:

'In fact every relation between a living being and its environ-ment has this particular characteristic: the former, instead of sub-mitting passively to the latter, modifies it by imposing on it a certain structure of its own. It is in this way that, physiologically, the organism absorbs substances and changes them into something compatible with its own substance. Now, psychologically, the same is true, except that the modifications with which it is then con-cerned are no longer of a physico-chemical order, but entirely functional, and are determined by movement, perception or the interplay of real or potential actions (conceptual operations, etc.). Mental assimilation is thus the incorporation of objects into patterns of behaviour, these patterns being none other than the whole gamut of actions capable of active repetition.'[1]

In this way the intellect gives its objects its own structure, yet by so doing elucidates the nature and construction of the object itself, for the reason that the structure and working of the intellect (not two things but two aspects of one and the same function) is no more nor less than the fuller development of that same principle of synthetic organization which has been operative throughout the *scala naturae* and is thus inherent in the environ-ment equally with the organism. Its realization and explication, in fact, is effected only through that development which culminates

[1] Op. cit., pp. 7–8.

in intellectual activity. Rational understanding, in other words, is nothing other than the fullest possible explication of the inherent structure of the matter understood.

To this end the operations of the intellect evolve and apply certain schemata of relationships (by Piaget called 'groupings') which make possible the most searching and versatile analysis concurrently with complete closure, or rounding off, of system. The result is that fully articulated unity typical of mathematical elegance. The groupings which Piaget lists are, in fact, the forms of logico-mathematical relationships, and their characteristics those of combinativity, reversibility, associativity, identity and tautology. On the basis of illuminating experimental evidence, he describes very fully and with great lucidity the way in which the capacity to perform formal operations by the use of these categorial 'groupings' develops in the growing child. It proceeds from sensori-motor and perceptual organization, through imagined representation in symbolic preconceptual thinking and intuitive (perceptual) thought, to concrete operations requiring the combination of actions into a unitary schema and the recognition of reversible serial order.

In the course of this development it is observed how a young child presented with two similar glass vessels will place an equal number of beads into each by simultaneously dropping one bead at a time with each hand into each glass. The equality of the numbers is then recognized perceptually and as the result of sensori-motor behaviour. If then the child is made to pour the beads from one of the glasses into another of different shape, he judges the numbers to be different because the levels have changed. At a later stage this error is corrected by a process of decentralization in which the child sees the compensating effects of shape on volume and capacity; the situation is more adequately analysed and reconstructed in his mind and more objectively assessed. This is but one of a rich variety of examples, assembled in the work of C. Bühler, P. Janet, A. Rey, Piaget himself and his associates, and illustrative of the gradual emancipation of thought from perceptual fixity and subjectivity towards the suppleness and coherence of logico-mathematical order.

Logico-mathematical operations thus emerge as the most characteristic and refined form of intelligent behaviour. Their detachment from personal and subjective influences is the most complete and they are objective in the highest degree. The extent to which the methods of the other sciences approximates to them is the measure of their advancement. The process of discovering the objective structure and the actual nature of the world consists accordingly in applying these methods of rational systematization to the objects of perception and the work of discovering the nature of reality is that of scientific research. The way to discover and correct illusion and error is to think, not (if that were possible) passively to observe.

Thinking, moreover, is the activity of organizing; and, unlike psychology which traces the genesis of this activity and investigates the process of its performance, logic seeks the abstract principles of organization—the formal schemata of thought. To do so successfully it may not disregard the nature of the process, but must analyse it. To say that its task is rather the analysis of the *objects* of thinking than the form and structure of the process itself would be to confuse logic with the other sciences; though of course it is not to be denied that in logical analysis the intellect is active and makes the schemata of thought themselves its object. Nevertheless, the proper subject matter of logic is the form and principles of thinking and its total disregard of the psychological process can only defeat its special purpose. The effect of the contemporary divorce of logic from psychology (due to the current desire to avoid psychologism in philosophy) has been to divert logicians from their proper business. Abstracting altogether from the process of thinking they are left with its alleged object, the proposition. As its subject matter is not their concern, they abstract from that as well, to consider only its form. But its form is the product of the interaction of the process of thinking with its subject-matter, so the residue, when abstraction is made from both, is an empty shell giving no clue to its living character. Thus the proposition, which in living thought is not an isolable unit, is treated as if it were one; and a purely atomistic, exclusively extensional logic has evolved, devoting itself to the elaboration of calculi which do not reveal the principles of organization of any thinking, not even that which goes to make them. Whatever may be value and virtues of modern symbolic logic, it still leaves room for a science (the need for which is clamant) of the form and principles of thinking as the activity of organization.

Further, if the findings of the psychology of thinking are to be trusted, this much-neglected science should be a logic of wholes and of dynamic structure. It should elucidate the principles of coherence and integration and should be a discipline not only of analysis but of synthesis as well. The logical atomism that set the fashion in modern philosophy launched it upon the wrong tack. Thus the evidence of contemporary psychology corroborates the evidence of contemporary biology in pointing to the need for a kind of philosophical discipline different from what currently claims to be scientific.

6

Even in mathematics and logic the work of the intellect is always a doing; it is always action, and the essentially practical character of thinking cannot be overstressed. Yet it is perhaps a tendency to exaggerate this point that has led some thinkers to put forward what has been called a peripheral or motor theory of thinking, according to which it is identified with muscular tensions and incipient movements.[1] Evidence is not lacking that such tensions and movements do (perhaps always) accompany thinking and that internal problem-solving and reasoning are sometimes assisted, though at other times hindered, by them. Evidence is also forthcoming, however, that some thinking occurs even in the absence of specific muscular tensions, when the musculature is completely relaxed and also when the muscles alleged to be involved in thinking are otherwise occupied.[2] It may be admitted that there is a sense in which we think with our whole bodies, but it is because thinking is the organization of total behaviour, not the functioning of special organs. It is organized and organizing activity, and this must be molar; it cannot be identified with such occurrences as the suppressed or incipient movements of the tongue and larynx. Variants of the motor theory allege that the muscular movements, kinaesthetically and proprioceptively felt carry symbolic reference to other experiences and constitute thinking in so doing. This, however, does not escape the difficulties and is either a return to crude sensationalism and associationism or a tacit admission of a form of thought that cannot be reduced to muscular movement.

[1] Cf. The views of Watson, Dunlap and Washburn reported in Humphrey, op. cit., Ch. VII.

[2] Cf. R. Pintner, *Psychol. Rev.* 30 (1913), pp. 129–53 and A. Rizzolo (1931) reported by Murphy in *Briefer General Psychology* (New York, 1935). Also Humphrey's comment on the work of Jacobson (1929 *et al.*), loc. cit.

If the activity of thought is not to be identified with molecular functions, it is equally not confined exclusively to the sciences and so-called intellectual pursuits. Behaviour as a whole is the medium of its expression. We have observed that instinctive behaviour is innately organized in systematic relation to the animal's environment; but that organization is relatively unvarying. Through learning it becomes more plastic and adaptable, and learning in all its forms was seen to involve some measure, if only germinal, of insight. As this develops behaviour becomes deliberately purposive, and purpose is the practical expression of rationality. What constitutes rational purposive conduct is the imposition upon innate patterns of reaction of the analytical-synthetic insight of the intellect, relating means to ends in its appreciation of the situation in which action is taken.

The internal motivating influences of instinctive activity impel to appetitive behaviour, and this we have seen is variable and adaptive, but it is not self-conscious. In the more developed mind insight, which is the apprehension of relations, discerns the relations between instinctive impulse and the objects which it seeks, and intelligence turns appetite into conscious desire. But this is a late stage of development which probably belongs exclusively to the human mind, and which presupposes the organization of the behavioural field into ego and non-ego, and of the internal structuring of both in intricate ways. The detail of this has been set out by psychologists, the Psychoanalysts not least in importance, but it is not our immediate business. It will be sufficient to observe that the organization of the ego involves the combination, correlation, and co-ordination of perceptual, affective and conative dispositions into complexes or enduring interests (called 'sentiments' by McDougall) any one of which may display itself in widely different activities, all, however, relevant and directed to a single purposive determination. This is the characteristic of dispositional behaviour—relevantly varying, or polyphasic, unit. So love may express itself in tender care and gentleness towards its object, or in jealous anger towards rivals or disloyalty, or in violent attack upon a threat to the safety of the beloved, or languishing depression in her absence, or in gay delight in her possession. All these behaviour patterns despite their vivid contrasts are mutually consistent and subject to the regulating influence of the organizing interest. In all this, in proportion to its insight, the subject is aware of his own relation and that of other things and persons, to the object of his desire, and his actions are ordered in accordance with his awareness. Desire, though often set in opposition to reason, is nevertheless the manifestation of thought (as insight) in the regulation of conduct.

But purposive action, like behaviour at lower levels, is subject to hierarchical order, for desires, deriving (as we have seen) from natural needs and appetites, at times conflict, and the decision between them depends on choice. This is not just a matter of stronger and weaker forces, but again one of organization. The subject, conscious of his own desires and their mutual relation is constrained to express a preference. Here again the intelligence comes into play, desires are schooled and disciplined in accordance with the principles of choice which are adopted, and mutually compatible and supporting desires are approved while those which frustrate dominant interests are excluded and suppressed. So desires fall into the hierarchical order of the more and less desirable, determined according to their compatibility with a pattern of living which is, as a whole, satisfactory; and a structure of ordered conduct develops that forms the basis of judgments of approval and disapproval. The result is a pattern of life so organized, in accordance with experience of successive choices, as to give maximum satisfaction in the long run; not just the fulfilment of single desires, but the satisfaction of the self as a whole and the realization of a harmonious personality.

Purpose, therefore, the conscious pursuit of an object of desire, is once more organized activity, and as in the case of instinctive behaviour, its aim is no isolated or single event, but the maintenance of a complete system of activity with specific bearing upon a selected object—it is not so much a goal as the resourceful pursuit of an enduring interest.

This description, however, is much foreshortened, for the environment in which a person acts inevitably contains other people, also with desires and purposes. Conflicts are not confined to separate individuals and one is called upon to choose probably more often between one's own satisfaction and that of others, than between conflicting tensions in oneself. In fact, the two forms of conflict are not separable but are mutually involved.

The upshot of these conflicts and their reconciliation is the regulation of conduct by rules both self-imposed and socially required. The process is essentially rational and purposive, consisting in the intelligent adjustment of interests, the co-operative ordering of activities in the supply of social needs and the consequent determination of mutual responsibilities in the performance of social functions. So arises a system of rights and duties, a moral and political order, at once the natural outcome of the development of life and mind and the consciously devised artifact of human intelligence. The obvious *raison d'être* of this social and moral order is the maintenance of a total way of life embracing an entire community; and the measure of right and wrong, of good and bad, within this system is the harmony, coherence and ultimate satisfactoriness of the system itself.

No rational conduct is attainable, either moral or intellectual, in isolation and apart from the mutual interaction and influence of persons. The organization of conduct thus becomes a social matter. Its developed and rational phase is the organization of a society, and enlightened social action is in a paramount sense the work of the intelligence. Nor is this a development subsequent to that of intelligence in the individual, for the 'operations' that Piaget describes are almost wholly dependent for their performance upon social factors. Symbolization is an obvious condition and language an indispensable medium. The learning of established conventions and procedures, of norms and of rules, are all involved, and all imply social interaction possible only with a high degree of intelligence and likewise the condition of its development.

Adequate treatment of all this would require a study of the social sciences and provide material for moral and social philosophy, but the limits of this essay preclude the exploration of those fields. On the evidence already assembled it should now be possible to form a sufficient impression of the concept of mind entertained or implied by modern psychology, to round off our account of the contemporary scientific world-view, and to consider the philosophical doctrine which it might justify. Before we do so, however, there is one final comment to be made on the nature of intelligence.

Once again, it is remarkable to note, how the general pattern of the macrocosm repeats itself in microcosm. It is not really so surprising to find that intelligence displays itself in the construction and operation of dynamic systems, and that its higher activities issue in mathematical operations such as afford the very examples we chose in Part I to illustrate the meaning of our new term 'polyphasic unity', for it is to the intelligence that we naturally look for the elaboration of such structures, and we less expect to find them elsewhere. What is more significant is that the pattern of a scale of continuously developing forms should here again appear in a theory like that of Piaget. Intelligence specifies itself into sensori-motor thinking (manual and bodily skills) representative and symbolic thinking (typical of mechanical skills), intuitive or perceptive thinking (involved in the solution of visual and manipulative puzzles), concrete reasoning in the practical comprehension of serial order, and formal abstract theorizing. These are the specific forms of intelligence, but they are also phases in its development and characterize degrees of intellectual capacity. They stand in mutual contrast and yet, in sequence, lead continuously up to the paradigm case. That in itself, though it is the *example par excellence*, is not the whole and concrete nature of the intellect, for the comprehension of which only the complete scale will serve as adequate.

7

We may now proceed to sum up our findings concerning mentality, to check our provisional definition of mind and to consider how far it has been justified and how far it needs modification. That definition was that mind comprised all such activity as was conscious or liable to emerge into consciousness; and we have argued that consciousness is not a separate entity, or an illuminating effulgence emanating from some extraneous source and playing upon material objects (whether within or without the organism), but essentially an activity of articulating and integrating distinguishable elements inherent in the already highly organized and integrated open system of the living being.

The first phase of this integrating activity that exceeds the merely physiological we identified as feeling, which by some little known method of self-reinforcement is concentrated into the directed activity of attention—a channelling of the organic energies in the direction required by the demands of adaptation. Attention selects and distinguishes elements in the mass of feeling, which now constitutes the psychical field. The consequence of its activity is to bring into relief particular patterns of relationship and to concentrate the mutual bearing of the constituents of the field upon a particular focus. This setting of elements in a relational context, grasped as a whole or *Gestalt*, is consciousness. It is not the apprehension by a mind of an external object, but the appreciation by the organism of a nexus of elements in relation which are elements of its own activity in response to its surroundings. In the language of Existentialist philosophers, borrowed in the main from Hegel, the living activity of the organism comes to exist not only in itself but for itself—as self-awareness. This is by no means immediately awareness of an ego, but the self-reflection of the organic unity within which that awareness develops later.

What attention effects and brings to light is system and order—in a word, information, or negative entropy of a high degree. It effects the appearance of objects which constitutes perception, and that enables the organism to respond to complete situations by means of informed behaviour. The continued refinement of the organization of behaviour, the clarification and increase in scope and comprehension of its information, its fuller and more perspicacious systematization, gives intelligent action. So it seems possible to give a consistent account of consciousness, in the forms of perception and intelligent insight as an activity of distinguishing, relating, systematizing and ordering; and indeed the description of the living organism as a device for the conversion of noise into message has no little justification.

Mind is now seen as that phase in the process of continuous increase of integrated systematization at which the dynamic totality comes to be *for*, or conscious of, itself—at which order and structure become information in the true sense—the sense of awareness of a state of affairs, or *Sachverhalte*—in a word, knowledge. That process, which when discussing the nature of life we described as moving upstream in the physical tide of increasing disorder, culminates in mind, which is the antithesis of entropy and the consummation of coherent order. It is not, of course, as we know it, the *perfection* of such coherent order; and in reply to those who point sceptically at the derangements of mental abnormalities, at the blunders and confusions in the conduct of human affairs, and the enormities of human wickedness, we must draw attention to the staggering complexity of the activities which pertain to mind. Their organization, while it surpasses anything at lower levels in the natural scale, is so excessively complicated, that relative breakdowns and derangements when they occur are the more impressive. *Corruptio optimi pessima.* It is only at this very high level of organization that such aberrations as insanity and vice can occur at all. They are the price (possibly unavoidable) of the realization of the higher values.

Having given this account of mind, it can occasion no surprise that in its structure, both in whole and in constituent parts, mind should display the now familiar pattern of a scale of forms. This time it is a double scale as the activity of mind is two-sided, behavioural and phenomenal. On the one hand, there are sensori-motor activity, instinctive behaviour, learning and intelligent action; on the other are feeling, perception, insight and formal reasoning. Each is a specific case of mental activity, and successively they constitute degrees of realization of the generic character of mind (systematic order). Each, in its own internal make-up displays the same general scalariform structure. Nevertheless in some contexts they stand to one another in mutual opposition. Intelligence is opposed to instinct, reason to emotion, theory to practice. Yet each is a moment within every other and all together make up the single unity of mind which comprehends them all.

Further, mind displays a propensity, similar to physical activity and life, to constitute itself into a single world-wide unity. Its activities on the level of intelligence are social and are rooted in the mutual dependence of individuals. This does not stop at the boundaries of single societies, for societies too are interdependent. Just as the relations between individuals, being relations between active subjects (agents) demand regulation into a system of conduct, moral and political, so the relations between societies call for inter-community regulation and organization. The claim of humanity upon its members is world-wide and there is no limit to obligations of morality. On the intellectual side knowledge is a single system. It is not all known to every person, but the discoveries of every scientist and the findings of every discipline determine those of every other so that the world of knowledge is one. The same is true of art and literature and if it seems less so of religion that is mere superficial appearance. Not only do religions generate one another and influence one another, but they are all, in the last resort, alternatvie symbolizations of the same ultimate truth. There is ample justification for the idea expressed (if some ground for cavil at the terms used) by Tielhard when he refers to the nöosphere as well as to the biosphere. The terms are objectionable because, on the analogy of 'lithosphere' and 'atmosphere' they suggest spatial regions filled with a particular kind of matter, whereas neither life nor mind are either. Yet each does constitute a single cosmos, life as the overall biocoenosis and mind as the world of human enterprise.

There is a further sense in which mind embraces the universe as a whole. It is only in consciousness that the universe is a whole *for itself*. As the organism sublates in feeling its total reaction to an environment that has no fixed limits, so the mind by degrees brings to consciousness the total world. The process is long and arduous and its completeness is relative to its degree of development. Nevertheless, however incomplete, its tendency is constantly towards the whole. Though there are all kinds of qualifications to which the aphorism is subject, that the mind is 'the world come to consciousness' states a very defensible doctrine. But here we become involved in the metaphysical theory to which the whole of our investigation leads us, and it is time to draw more explicit conclusions as to its general character.

PART IV
OUTLINE OF A METAPHYSIC

CHAPTER XXII

RELATEDNESS AND SYSTEM

I

It is now possible to consider the general world-view arising out of the sciences we have discussed, the type of philosophy which the evidence best supports, and the metaphysical theories which it tends to validate. What is most obvious is that nothing in contemporary science supports or gives evidence of the truth of logical atomism or empiricism, for the facts of science are not logically independent one of another nor are the propositions stating them devoid of mutual entailment, and the modern scientific accounts of perception and intelligence are not consistent with the roles assigned to these functions in the empiricist theory of knowledge. The Anglo-Saxon philosophy of the first half of the twentieth century which has grown from these two roots has accordingly been out of keeping with the trend of scientific development. On the other hand, everything from physics to psychology emphasizes the holistic character of the reality studied, as well, at the same time, its fluidity and persistent developmental trend. The kind of philosophy which made the same emphases was that which contemporary empirical and linguistic analysis superseded. The British Idealists followed Hegelian lines, advocated dialectical logics and a holistic metaphysics; Samuel Alexander, J. C. Smuts, Lloyd Morgan and Henri Bergson, partly in reaction against the Idealists, expounded theories of process and evolutionary pluralism. Whitehead in large measure combined all these features and, like Hegel, attempted to reconcile pluralism with monism and process with holism. For each of these philosophies some counterpart can be found in modern scientific theories. To this type of thinking philosophy must return if it is to be consonant with contemporary science, and this is the direction it must take if it is to aspire to and to deserve the epithet 'scientific'. A synthesis of the ideas severally explored by each of these philosophies which will remedy their several deficiencies is what must be sought. The Idealists (though not Hegel) tended to concentrate too exclusively upon consciousness and its attributes. Alexander and the Emergent-Evolutionists stressed a holism which still left emergence an inexplicable mystery. Bergson's *élan* was equally mysterious and though immaterial contrived to propel evolution endlessly onward, endlessly progressing towards no assignable end. Even Whitehead's impressive synthesis leaves the status of mind uncertain and the nature of concrescence obscure. These unsolved problems need fresh attention from a new philosophical movement that will redirect thinking into the channels so long dammed (as well as damned) by analytic philosophers.

Analysis, however, has obviously not been without its positive influence and effect. It has cured philosophers (one may hope) of the obscurities (and at times pomposity) in which Hegel and many of his followers delighted to indulge. It has put a premium on accuracy and clarity (if it has not always itself been clear as to their requirements); and it has issued a caveat against linguistic pitfalls, which, no doubt, do beset the unwary, even if analysts have been too apt to explain away all problems as due purely to false linguistic analogies.

To develop the system which would result from this synthesis is the work of the future. I shall attempt here to suggest in very brief outline only such features of it as I am able.

2

The conception of the world which contemporary science offers is in one aspect, undoubtedly monistic, whether or not this is explicitly realized by practising scientists. The sciences present the world as a single system, and its unity is, moreover, four-dimensional, both temporal and spatial. This is not only the outcome of modern physical theories, for which space-time is a closed, finite but unbounded, seamless structure, but also the conclusion forced upon the philosopher who traces the transitions from physics to chemistry, from chemistry to biology and from biology to psychology and finds no break in the continuity of forms or in the process of development. Further, not only is the process and the system of dynamic relationships, unbroken, not only is transition from one form or phase to the next smooth and gradual, but the series of forms and systems which evolve tend continuously towards complexes of greater cohesion and comprehensiveness, fuller completion and (in the original sense of the word) perfection.

The total and ultimate fulfilment of this whole transcends

the limits of science and can, at most, be postulated by philosophy It lies beyond the capacity of human reason to explain in detail, or even to conceive with more than a minimum of clarity and articulation. But the whole body of scientific theory testifies to the need to postulate it, and every ramification of scientific research reveals new examples demanding a holistic interpretation of its subject matter.

But there is another side to this discovered holism of the world and of its multifarious contents. The unity is never blank or featureless. It is never abstract unity devoid of internal differentiation. The whole is one, is coherent, is integral, only by virtue of the multiplicity of parts, the interrelation of distinguishable elements, and the structural features of its internal diversification; whether it be the entire universe or any selected system within it; whether it be the spatio-temporal field of physical events, the wave-packets of elementary particles, the leptocosm of crystalline forms, or the dynamic systems of living organisms.

Moreover, this inexhaustible diversity is not given all at once, but proliferates in a continuously changing process. Physics, if it does not actually reveal, nevertheless gives ample reason to presume a primordial matrix of the world, which though *mater*, is not *materia*, because it is prior to all matter. The matrix is in no way static but is some form of perpetual activity, in essence process. No elementary particle nor any so-called atom is composed of hard impenetrable substance, but all can be resolved into energy the essential property of which is a perpetual flowing. Nor is this aspect of the real confined to physics. The living organism is an open system in continuous flux and the history of living species is one of constant change and evolution. Wherever one may look one finds activity, and function prevails over and determines structure.

Pluralists and relativists like Bergson, Dewey, Capek or Hartshorne have good grounds for their views—but not quite good enough. The reason why one cannot rest in pluralism is that one is bound (if the facts are to be respected) to recognize the intimacy of relationship between the elements of the plurality and so to recover the system which gives completeness to the manifold. Or if one postulates a continuous but unending process tending ever onward but to no assignable end, one is nevertheless constrained to indicate a direction of development (or concrescence), which contradicts the alleged absolute relativity. The penalty for doing otherwise is the dissolution of the connections between the elements and the degeneration of the theory into a crude and unmanageable atomism, without a vestige of coherence and consequently devoid of intelligibility. The theories of all of the philosophers mentioned above are in danger of this denouement and are saved from it only by the insight and better judgment of their authors. Hegel and Whitehead, whom some of them claim to follow, avoided the error of relativism; but they were well aware of the two-sided character of the whole on which the absolutism of the one and the process-philosophy of the other were equally founded. Accordingly they have been variously misinterpreted by those who have missed the significance of either aspect.

The scientific conspectus of the world is of a continuous process of activity progressively elaborating more complex and more highly integrated systems; yet the world itself, as a whole, is a totality systematically diversified and integrated in the same way. Physical space-time is such a whole and its self-involution constitutes energy and matter. The forms of matter are systems of energy increasing in complex structure from elementary particles to atoms, from atoms to molecules, from molecules to crystals, from crystals to polymers. Throughout this series nothing is static, except in superficial appearance; physical and chemical interchange is constant and ubiquitous. But the organization of chemical processes into cyclical, self-maintaining and coherently structured systems of activity carries the scale into a new phase, distinct from and contrasted with the foregoing phases yet none the less continuous with them. This is the sphere of life. Living forms evolve and the process of complexification, increasing coherence and integrity continues, until at a pitch of intensity which defies description this integrity issues as feeling and initiates the processes of mind. Again the biotic sphere is a totality organized on similar principles to those which govern the integrity of each organism. The same pattern is to be found in the world of the mind. The spheres of activity of intellect, art, politics, morals and religion interfuse into a single noëtic or experiential totality, each within itself and all together, within which individual personalities are distinct and distinctive, yet indisseverably linked. The entire structure is one of wholes, within wholes, within wholes, each expressing in its own character the general principle of unity that is immanent throughout.

Within the over-arching totality, the progression is in the direction not only of greater complexity but also of more intricate and elegant organization, more variable and adaptable equilibrium, and more intense and indissoluble unity. This last is not indissoluble in the sense that it is indestructable or incapable of degeneration, but in the sense that its distinguishable constituents are not separable and have no independent existence apart from their synthesis in the organized totality, so that they are indissolubly united because their dissipation destroys, not only the coherence and arrangement of the complex, but the very character of its components.

Increase in the integrity and indissolubility of the whole, in this sense, is the chief mark of progression up the scale. It is never true at any level that the parts of the recognizable entities are merely juxtaposed or conjoined in their construction, for at the most elementary physical stage the energy system was found to be prior to the individuation of particles, which exist only in mutual relation. Nevertheless, atomic particles have a greater degree of separability from the more complex groupings in which they form molecules, and molecules are more easily separable from crystalline compounds, than are the cycles of chemical activity and the diverse functions which together maintain the living integrity of the organism from the system in which they are interwoven. Still less are traits, which together make a human personality distinctive, separable entities, however different and distinguishable they may be, and however changeable its successive moods and interests.

3

Throughout the gamut of natural forms the scientist finds system and structure prior to individuation. There are no particles except in energy systems, and in these systems the individuality of elementary particles is altogether inseparable from the structure of the system.[1] There are no separable molecules within the structure of the crystal, but the atoms are so arranged in the lattice that the whole may be regarded as a single giant molecule.[2] There are no organs apart from the organism, and the cycles of physiological functioning do not occur in isolation, for each is dependent on the rest and organic structure is only the static manifestation of dynamic function. There is no percept apart from an organized

[1] See Ch. VI above.
[2] Cf. Rinne, quoted above, p. 166.

sense-field or isolable from a growing body of systematic experience, and no meaning without context.

We must notice that this priority of structure to individuation is not just an empirical discovery but is essential to any and every principle of individuation. What distinguishes and defines individuals is their relations to one another; and every relation of whatever sort presupposes a background system appropriate to it. The relations between points in space (or events in space-time) presuppose the metrical field in which they are determined, and the relations of number presuppose the system of natural numbers. Family relations presuppose both a biological system and a social system. It is true that such systems are constituted by relations, but not by relations which pre-exist or could survive independent of the system. The moral of all this is that relations between distinguishable individuals are incurably 'internal'. The attempt to externalize them by separating the individuals, by whatever method whether physically or in theory, destroys the terms. The proper understanding of the nature of relatedness is thus crucial to the conception of whole and part.

So much has been written on this topic in the past that it might be considered exhausted and further discussion might seem merely tiresome. Before F. H. Bradley's classic critique, the obvious existence and simple character of relations was accepted without question, and even after Bradley's incisive argument, Bertrand Russell declared that relatedness was so patent a character of the world that no mere logic could shake his faith in it. He then proceeded himself to give a logical account and classification of relations of great acuteness and usefulness. But Russell is a mathematician, and if instead we were to consult an artist he would tell us that relations are mere fictions and that he sees 'no lines in Nature'. Apparently there are two sides to this question.

Russell assumed that all relations were external to their terms and that Bradley had argued the opposite. But Bradley's argument proves, not that all relations are internal, but that neither if external nor if internal can relatedness be made intelligible. If the relations fall between the terms they fail to relate them and give rise to a vicious infinite regress, but equally if they fall within the terms, those terms are pulverized, for the infinite regression breaks out amid the internal complexity that results.

It seems as though relations are merely a logical device, like the co-ordinate systems of the mathematician, a sort of mesh-work superimposed upon reality for the purposes of measurement, classification, or convenient arrangement. Nothing exactly corresponding to them seems to exist in fact; and as they are made sharper and more precise, both they and their terms disappear. For instance, the path of an electron is (or should be) a number of points in precise relation to one another occupied by the electron at successive instants in time; but as soon as the physicist tries to sharpen the spatio-temporal relations, to discover precise position or the rate of its change, the relations and the electron disappear into a cloud, or wave-packet, or set of probabilities. Not only is this sort of thing true at the infra-microscopic level but also at the macroscopic. The measurement of macroscopic objects is their precise relationship to a chosen standard; but it is always more or less approximate. The more exactly we try to determine it the more we are reduced to averaging readings and to statistical assessments. There is no such thing, Professor Henry Margenau has assured me, as *the exact* length of a given rod. But to conclude that relations were wholly fictional on this account would be rash and would leave us committed to the belief in a chaotic reality artificially ordered only by human intellectual endeavour. This conclusion however is incoherent, for as human beings are part of the world, it would leave the possibility of human intellectual activity altogether inexplicable, and is incompatible with the scientific account so far given both of the intellect and of the world.

The dissolution of particular relations when sharpened beyond a certain limit is however to be expected if the distinguishable and relatable characters of the world are always factors within wholes or contexts and are dependent for their distinguishable character upon the complete structure of the wholes. The general effect of this dependence of the distinguishable part on its place in the whole and in the consequent mutual dependence of distinguished factors is that, in any relation, the related terms either themselves overlap or involve the overlap of intermediary terms. Where such overlap occurs no sharp line can be drawn between the terms and they merge into one another.

In the molecule of hydrogen the orbiting electrons of the two atoms are interchangeable and the atoms overlap. Valency bonds between atoms of different elements turn out to be a similar sharing of electrons, or overlapping of atoms. In the crystal of common salt the atoms of sodium and chlorine constitute molecules

P*

of NaCl interchangeably—the molecules overlap. In catalytic reactions, the chemical changes between one compound and the catalyst overlap with those between the catalyst and the second compound. Again, the physiological functions of the organism overlap. Respiration, the digestion of food and the utilization of carbohydrates are interlacing and overlapping cycles. There is no precise determination of where one ends and the other beings. Even in mathematics the relation between the angles of a triangle depends upon their sharing arms in common and between the sides of the triangle upon the common space which they enclose. The diagonal of a square forms two isosceles right-angled triangles whose mutual relation depends upon their having a common hypotenuse. In fine, the distance between two points is but the intervening space which is the same for both.

4

To understand this overlapping propensity of terms in relation we must seek for its necessary and sufficient conditions. A sufficient condition is that they should be the parts of a continuum for it is precisely the merging or overlapping of parts that constitute a continuum. The retort might come that points in space are parts of a continuum but that they do not overlap. Indeed, that they do is powerfully demonstrated by Whitehead and Russell's definition of them, by extensive abstraction, in terms of overlapping regions. Alternatively, if points are taken as the limits of lines they are always common to adjacent lines and so inevitably overlap. It is precisely this that is meant by the infinite divisibility of space. And so for all continua. Their adjacent parts overlap and parts that are not adjacent can be mutually related only through the medium of the intervening adjacent portions.

If this is a sufficient condition of overlap, is it a necessary condition? It would seem that it is; for unless two entities participate in some way in some form of continuum overlap between them is impossible. Overlap may be spatial, or temporal, or numerical, or may occur in any continuous series; but where there is no continuity, it is obvious, overlap can never occur.

Is it then the case that all relations are between terms that are parts of a continuum? At first sight this seems implausible, but on scrutiny it transpires to be true. Relations between the sizes of things, for instance, might at first seem independent of continua;

but they are not. They are intimately dependent on the number continuum and the spatio-temporal. All quantitative relations are continuous in this way. What then of family relations? To what continuum do they belong and how do the terms (individual persons) overlap? To suggest that they do is surely preposterous. Again *prima facie* one would think so, but more detailed analysis proves otherwise. The fundamental family relationship is that of husband and wife, and this may be regarded either biologically or legally. Biologically it rests on sexual intercourse which pre-supposes the continuous genetic process—the continuum of the development of the germ-plasm. The overlap of the individual gametes takes visible shape in the offspring. Regarded legally, marriage is an institution in a continuous series of institutions well demonstrated by Aristotle in the first book of the *Politics*. The series is continuous both in history and in social structure. The family becomes the clan, the clan the tribe, the tribe the kingdom; or alternatively and concurrently, the clan forms one or more village communities, and these develop into a state. Our own systems of social institutions are more complicated but they involve similar continua, which are no less so because they ramify and the branches sometimes diverge.

But there is another way in which personal relations involve overlap of personalities, already adumbrated in the previous Part. There is psychological overlap—where more marked than between lovers, whose mutual influence produces a partial identity of ego-organization. There is, besides, an overlap and interplay of social function cogently and copiously illustrated by Bernard Bosanquet in the seventh chapter of *The Philosophical Theory of the State*. That society is a continuum of personal relations and an inextricable overlap of personalities has been recognized since Plato, and is supported by the evidence of social psychology.

To return to our main theme, we have found no example of relationship which did not imply a continuum; but an essential connection between relation and continuity must be demonstrated before it can be established that the overlap of terms is universal. A relation is the way in which one term stands to another; but they cannot stand to each other in any relation unless there is some matrix, some context, some 'respect' in which they are related. Moreover they must be part of this common matrix or context. If it is not continuous the relationship is broken and cannot hold. In fact, to relate A to B is no more nor less than to trace the extent of the intervening continuum of the relevant matrix. For spatio-temporal and quantitative relationships this is obvious, and also for many qualitative relations. Colours and sounds are related through a continuum as are all other sensuous qualities. Causal relations are the tracing of continuous connection of successive events and conditions from cause to effect, as is witnessed by the refusal of scientists to tolerate action at a distance. The quantum jump, as we have seen, is no exception. The relation of substance to attribute is closely linked with causality and presumes the continuity in space and time of the substance in which the attributes inhere, as well as a continuity of substantival manifestation in and as the attribute. This relationship, however, has certain mystifying features which have troubled philosophers who, since Kant, have tended more and more to reduce it to one of event-sequence akin to causation. So Whitehead transforms it to process and explains it in terms of the prehension by actual entities of one another and of 'eternal objects'—essentially a continuous process of successive occasions.

The question whether this same continuity and overlap applies to logical relations is peculiar, for it might be held that all relations are logical, that they are the schemata of organization by which the intellect grasps the structure of the world, and that logic formulates them *in abstracto*. But it would be wrong to assume that, therefore, the world in itself has no structure and is unarticulated. The truth is rather that logical relations are all derived from the relations between realities, in which case what is true of relations in general should also be true of them.

Relations such as that of ground to consequent imply a continuum of logical implication—a continuous identity represented by the middle term of the syllogism. Negativity and opposition are, as will later appear more fully, the relations between different phases in a continuous series. Not-A includes all the other letters of the alphabet—the members of the series proceeding from A. 'Not-red' is what you reach if you proceed continuously away from one end of the spectrum. 'Not-circular' is any figure reached by continuous regression from the circle through the various degrees of curvature. The relation of disjunction, which might appear more troublesome, may be represented as the indication that two parts of a continuum are sufficiently diverse to be alternatives; and as expressed in symbolic logic by the symbol V, the continuous character and possible overlap of the terms is allowed for in the interpretation 'either p or q or both'.[1]

Objection may be raised that this argument is somewhat strained and could hardly be made to fit accidental relationships. My paper-knife and my shoes are mutually related by both being my property; how does this make them parts of a continuum, and in what sense can they be said to overlap? If I gave them away to someone else, surely they would both remain unaltered. Again, this objection is most plausible, yet again careful examination of the case proves it to be ill-founded. The relation of 'belonging to me' means that both knife and shoes are part of my behavioural environment which is a continuum. They are what they are because of the uses to which I put them. The shape of my feet and peculiarities of my gait mould the shoes. My personal tastes and habits of dress make them continuous with other garments in a *tout ensemble*. The paper-knife has associations for me which it could have for no other—it was a gift and a memento of past experiences. Its relation to the shoes is meaningful only in the light of a continuum of experiences and activities which are mine and constitute my personality. Given away to others these objects would not be the same. They would enter new structures and be modified (perhaps even physically) in consequence.

5

The terms of a relation are thus always parts of a continuum and are always liable to overlap. Collingwood discovered this tendency among the species of a genus[2] but he restricted it to the specifications of philosophical universals, professing himself incompetent to pronounce upon the behaviour of scientific genera, and merely accepting the tradition that their species are mutually exclusive. Closer examination of scientific genera, however, reveals a similar overlap among their species and in contemporary biology taxonomists have found reason to modify the tranditional system and to advocate one in which species overlap.[3] The reason for this overlap was also rightly discerned by Collingwood. It is that the species constitute degrees in a continuous series of embodiments of the generic form, and in biology it is, in the main,

---

[1] This, however, is not a fair example because, in symbolic logic, p and q are assumed to be atomic propositions.

[2] *Vide Essay on Philosophical Method* (Oxford, 1934), Ch. II.

[3] *Vide* C. D. Michener, op. cit.

because species are phylogenetically continuous that overlap occurs. Gradations in any continuous series, in the nature of the case, merge into one another, and so always overlap. The relation between the species of a genus is at first sight only one sort of relation differing widely from many others; but, if what has been said above is true, the genus (or universal) and the kind of system which is prior to individuation will tend to coincide. The contextual background which is the condition of relationships and makes individuation possible has now transpired as a continuum and the relata within it as overlapping phases in a continuous series. So the nature of system and the nature of continua will prove to be in principle the same.

The view that there are two kinds of continua, homogeneous, in which all parts are alike, and heterogeneous, in which the parts vary continuously, is the product of abstraction. Space and time might seem to be the obvious examples of homogeneous continua —amorphous, mathematical space especially—but, if there is no difference whatever between the parts, they must be indistinguishable; and if altogether indistinguishable, identical; and if identical then not spread out and continuous. There can be no continuum without extension of some sort, and there can be no extension without distinction of parts. It is only when, like the pure mathematician, we abstract from the differences that we allege homogeneity; but it is only a pretended homogeneity assumed for special purposes and if we take it to be real we become victims of a fallacy. This I propose to call the fallacy of spurious homogeneity. It should not, therefore, be surprising that physicists have found space-time to be persistently heterogeneous (or curved), even when empty of matter.[1]

If, then, the parts of a continuum must differ from one another, they can do so only continuously and they must in consequence constitute a series or scale. The overlap of terms in a relation will, therefore, reveal itself as the sequence of serially diverging forms in a continuous scale. This is precisely what Collingwood found to be the character of overlapping classes in a philosophical universal. That universal, he demonstrated to be a scale of forms, each of which, as the sequence was followed, expressed more fully and adequately the generic nature of the universal. If the argument so far has been correct, this should be true, not only of philosophical universals, but of every system within which

[1] *Vide* above, page 59.

relational structure is discernible; for every such system has proved to be a continuum and every continuum a scale of forms.

That these forms should always be successive manifestations of the structural principle of the whole series progressively increasing in degree of adequacy, remains to be shown. At this point, however, we may notice that any such series presented temporally will constitute a process, and the primordial activity that physicists descry behind the various manifestations of energy, and Whitehead's postulation of a primordial process of creativity have a demonstrably rational basis. If now it can be shown that process is implicitly and essentially creative in the sense that the scale is necessarily a progressive unfolding of a principle of order, we shall be on the way to explaining the ubiquitous tendency in nature, that the sciences reveal, towards wholes of increasing complexity, coherence and integrity.

6

The belief that process can be continuous *ad infinitum* without progressive development—that it can be successive change without determinate direction, is just another form of the fallacy of spurious homogeneity. For if the changes are mere changes all of equal significance—or, what amounts to the same thing, of none—the process becomes a homogeneous series, which is no series at all. This would be the case if the changes were random, and that is the presumption of continuous, unproductive, non-directional process. Purely random changes though they imply difference and distinction in the short run, are in the long run all equivalent and their procession thus becomes homogeneous. Their differences in the short run would, on the basis of the foregoing argument, constitute a scale of forms; but if this is not to be progressive, its direction must be reversed in the succeeding section of the process, and this reversal must be constantly repeated. The degree of randomness of the process will vary with the frequency of these reversals, and to be wholly random the short runs would have to be reduced to infinitesimal length. At the limit we have homogeneity, so that utter randomness and total homogeneity coincide. If then there can be no totally homogeneous continuum, there can be no utterly random process of change, and random activity, where it appears, can only be relative to structural order. In such relatively random series, each short section would be a system, the structural character of which must somehow be revealed in the course of its progress.

Here, then, we have the key to our problem. A structural whole revealing itself seriatim must somehow preserve the earlier stages as it progresses and amalgamate them with those subsequently appearing; otherwise no structure or order comes to light. Single instantaneous events present no order—even if they are not simple but have internal complexity. If each as it passes were utterly obliterated, no order could ever emerge. In some manner, therefore, for an order to be constituted, the earlier elements must be retained sublated in the succeeding events. A tune cannot be heard as such if the earlier notes are lost as they occur; a sentence cannot be understood unless the first words are retained in mind until the end—and the end is not the last note, or the final word, it is the tune, or the sentence, apprehended as a whole. Mozart's description of his experience of a new composition was thus only an exceedingly high degree of that same capacity which we exercise when we hear a simple melody.

In these cases it is the experience of the hearer that preserves the earlier phases and integrates them with their successors, and the developing whole is one of experience. The development of experience is dependent upon the activity of a mind. What, if anything, can do the same for serial structures which are not experienced? One can only presume that it is some similar principle working at lower levels of integration. For minds themselves are a product of just such a process of progressive organization, and if the same principle of synthesis and concrescence were not operative at lower levels it is difficult to conceive what it could be from which mind continuously develop. For it is true of every serial order that to be a whole—that is, to be an ordered series at all—the phases must progressively, in increasing degree, manifest the whole, the earlier ones doing so with least adequacy and the later ones with continually greater fulness. Further, if there can be no homogeneous continuum, every series must have structural order and its unfolding will be a scale of forms. Consequently, every scale of forms must be a progression and every process a creative development.

Reversal of progression, or degeneration, presupposed inevitably in random activity can, therefore, occur only relative to progress. First, there must be an already constituted whole from which to regress. Secondly, the regression itself will be a form of serial order equally manifesting a whole. Piaget made clear that reversible operations more lucidly reveal the nature of a relational schema (or grouping) than irreversible. Thirdly, the total series, constructive plus destructive, will constitute a single whole and there must therefore be some way in which the earlier progression is maintained sublated and further developed into a symmetrical pattern even through the later. There are various ways in which this may be effected. The degenerative phase may contribute to and be absorbed into subsequent development, or the whole process may require a balance between breakdown and reconstitution of substances, as in the metabolism of organic activity. Where natural processes are concerned, we must never forget that the totality to which they belong is ultimately the whole universe and that degenerative processes are but partial phases.

7

It follows from all this that every process is the process of realization of a whole, and that the totality being generated is immanent in each successive phase. The degree of inadequacy of the phase fully to realize the whole will constitute an imbalance or disequilibrium the tendency to rectify which is the nisus towards greater fulfilment. Completion is thus foreshadowed and implicit in the incomplete. Moreover, each phase is a phase of a particular process, only by virtue of the fact that it is a stage in the unfolding of a particular whole. If it were otherwise the process would be something quite different. Its special character consists in its being the progressive unfolding of just that totality which gives it its special character. The whole is thus immanent in the part so characterized, and this immanence of the whole in the part gives the part the status of a specific manifestation of the general principle of order. The general principle accordingly takes on the role of genus or universal and each phase in the scale that of species. The upshot is the specification of the universal as Collingwood presented it, and the nature of the universal is revealed as structural order. This is the essential character of system—a scale of forms progressively realizing a structural principle—and is what, throughout, I have been calling polyphasic unity. The unity is the whole and its polyphasic character is its varied manifestations in specific forms, in each of which the whole is immanent, and which successively constitute a developing scale.

Is it not possible, it may however be asked, for a polyphasic system to be other than successive? Is not a spatial pattern also a system though it displays its principle of unity in disparate co-existent spatial forms? Undoubtedly this is so, but it is not to be forgotten that co-existence is correlative to succession and distance dependent upon temporal lapse. Our discussion in Chapter IV of Alexander's theory brought this interdependence to light and the theory of relativity rests upon it. Relations of spatial distance are always physically dependent upon causal transmission and the design of a spatial pattern is, in consequence, traced out and sustained by the occurrence of successive events, however static they may appear to our grosser senses. The picture on a television screen is only one, rather outstanding, example. Even in the case of our perception, the physiological events in the nervous system are successive and the co-existent pattern which is revealed in sense is built up by successive integrations. The perception of form constancy (as Piaget demonstrated) depends on 'trans-portations' and 'comparisons'—successive mental activities. The difference between co-existent and successively revealed systems is thus only apparent, and in most cases the appearance is the result of the rapidity of the succession.

A scale of forms progressively realizing a totality will in conse-quence be hierarchical. Not only is the whole immanent in each phase, but each successive phase must sublate its predecessors, if it is to be a fuller realization of the totality to which they all belong. Consequently the later phases will include and integrate the earlier ones into more complex structures. In this way the consummation of the series is not and cannot be confined to any one particular and must somehow be at once both species (or final phase) and genus, both particular and universal. It must sublate the entire scale and so must comprehend the total sequence. It must thus be, *par excellence*, a union and reconciliation of opposites. For, as the consummation, it is opposed to, and contrasted with, every partial manifestation; as end it is opposed to, and contrasted with, the foregoing process; yet as realization it combines the contrasted moments and reconciles their opposition. And this is equally true at every stage of the process. Each phase is related to the foregoing in the same way; so each phase can be represented as opposed to its neighbour (or, for that matter, to any other phase), and each later phase as the reconciliation of such opposition. The process is therefore dialectical in the Hegelian manner.

It thus becomes apparent that every process is a development generating a totality that is immanent in every phase, and throughout the whole course of the process, and which finally embraces the entire process. Thus all relativity implies an absolute and all progression a whole or polyphasic unity which it constitutes and within which it is generated. Pluralism and relativism are only the opposite aspect of monism and absolutism. No satisfactory metaphysic may be either without *ipso facto* implying the other. The real is most truly represented as the unity and reconciliation of these opposites.

8

The difficult question, how system or organization is to be defined, now begins to show promise of an answer. Organization and serial order have proved to be identical, for every serial order is the unfolding of the structure of a system and every system is a scale of serially developing forms, each a more adequate exposition of the principle of organization of the whole. Prior to Collingwood, the attempts of philosophers to characterize system tended towards this position but none, with the exception of Hegel, actually expounded it. Philosophers in all ages (as Collingwood shows) have, as it were inadvertently, provided examples of systems in scalar form, but none except Hegel has actually identified system with scale. The 'Idea' or 'Absolute', in Hegel's philosophy is the system of all systems, and the science of the Idea (i.e. philosophy) must, he says, form a system; 'that is, whilst it gives a bond and principle of unity, it also possesses an internal source of development'.[1] The system for Hegel is essentially dialectical; each phase or category of the dialectic is a provisional definition of the Absolute, and each is a unity of opposites, so that it constitutes a progressive scale of graduated forms, each a specific example of the universal principle of the dialectic. Hegel's late nineteenth-century followers, however, for the most part, fall short of this conception, concentrating, as do Bradley and Bosanquet, on the universal as the type of system, which in virtue of its systematic character, they call 'concrete'. But their best efforts to describe this do not get beyond such analogies as spatial patterns, or worlds, or universes of discourse, each of which is a good example, but none of which adequately reveals the principle of internal development on which Hegel insisted. These writers did, of course, assert that the most adequate example of the con-

[1] *Encyclopädie*, § 14 (Wallace's translation of '*nur als sich in sich entfaltend und in Einheit zusammennemend und haltend*'.)

crete universal was a dynamic system and was best represented by a mind of a personality, but they failed to show satisfactorily why this kind of system or dynamic structure should be identified with the universal of logic. Not until Collingwood expounded his theory of the scale of forms was the relation of genus and species seen to be embodied in the serial unfolding of the scale. This throws new light on both conceptions, rehabilitates the doctrine of the concrete universal in a more intelligible form, and points the way to new developments in dialectical logic.

For Whitehead nature (at least) was a system,[1] and he understood the word in terms of the 'ingression of objects into events', or the mutual prehension of actual entities and the ingredience of each into the real internal constitution of every other. This is the notion of system (as Whitehead repeatedly says) with which physics makes us familiar, and which is logically prior to the particulars that in their mutual interrelation constitute it. He insists also upon process and concrescence, but concrescence, as described, is internal to 'actual occasions' (or entities) and process is largely transition from one such occasion to the next ('time as perpetually perishing, endurance as re-creation' . . .[2]). The scale of forms is never emphasized by Whitehead and the relation of successive concrescent occasions to the ultimate realization of potentialities in the 'Consequent Nature of God' is never made clear. Moreover, universals in the form of 'eternal objects' remain abstract potentialities of definiteness. As prehended in actual entities they seem (according to his account) to be undifferentiated qualities. Their relation to process and to concrescence is obscure, and Whitehead seemed never to recognize and need for its clarification. He does, however, relate eternal objects, through the mental pole of entities which their prehension constitutes, to appetition; and he does insist that they are the source of novelty in the course of the process. Novelty is not asserted to be necessarily progress, though this sometimes seems to be the implication; and whether it is or not, it also depends in some obscure way upon the order of eternal objects in God's Primordial Nature. Here there is faint adumbration of a scale of forms, but in Whitehead's own writing we do not get beyond obscure suggestions and undeveloped implications of the sort of theory of polyphasic unity that I am attempting to develop.

[1] *Vide The Concept of Nature* (Cambridge, 1930), p. 146.
[2] *Process and Reality* (Cambridge, 1929), p. 180.

CHAPTER XXIII

SPACE, TIME AND CAUSALITY

I

Space-time as conceived in the theory of relativity is a plenum in the sense that it is the ubiquitous metrical field and as such it is obviously a continuum. At the same time it is a system of relations between contiguous events and is nothing at all apart from them. The amorphous, featureless, eventless space-time of pure mathematics is a pure abstraction and does not exist in nature, but even here relations are between terms embedded inextricably in the continuum. In physics, spatio-temporal relations unquestionably answer to the account given above. Their terms are parts of a continuum and the relations between them are the form of the intervening matrix. The events, which are the terms, are not separable from the metrical field, whose structure is simply the web of their mutual relations. Moreover the structure of the field, in varying degrees of complication is what constitutes energy and matter, their interaction being the flow of changes in this structure, which are the events interrelated. The overlap of terms is, therefore, obvious; but what is not so obvious is how, if at all, the spatio-temporal continuum is, or becomes, a scale.

So far as they are correlated with the number series they do indeed constitute a scale of sorts, but one which at first sight, does not clearly answer to the description so far given of a scale of forms. Yet it may well be questioned whether space-time, as such, is anything more than a measuring scale—a metric. The field, of course, is a theatre of activity, and in order to describe it determinately, its features must be co-ordinated mathematically. The means of such co-ordination is the application to it of a co-ordinate system in which numerical relations can be assigned to those features. It is primarily the co-ordinate system that we think of (whether vaguely or precisely), when we think of space-time. The particular co-ordinate system used is, within limits arbitrary, but not wholly so, for it may be dictated to some extent by the form of the field. This is what is known as the curvature of space-time and is nothing other than the geometrical properties of the field as physically measured.

As a metric, then, space-time is scalariform in the same way as the number series, but as curved it takes on the character of a scale with progressive change in a certain direction—for that is precisely what curvature is—which can be expressed as a mathematical function. Curved space-time thus has polyphasic unity, and is the primitive type of a scale of forms—a scale (or procession) of changes of direction (or some analogous structure of relationships) governed by a principle of order. Increase in curvature with intensity of field and density of matter gives a new continuum of complexities of the original continuum and develops a scale of forms of a higher order.

This new scale gives rise to no break in continuity. The curvature of space-time is self-closing, giving a universe which is finite but unbounded, so that the Kantian antinomies do not arise. Within this whole every limited local region has curvature of a degree and kind which is a specific manifestation of the comprehensive formula. In restricted regions far from matter the curvature is minimal; as the volume considered increases and the field structure becomes more complex, there is continuous approach to the universal form. So a scale is generated in which each successive limited particular is a specific gradation more adequately expressive of the totality. Increase in curvature, however, is the counterpart (or alternative expression) of increase in complexity of the field, which again is the manifestation of energy, so that each particular region represents an energy system, as does the entire universe taken as a whole. Appropriately selected, each energy system is a specific example, or special case, of a universal equation representing matter-or-energy in general,[1] and a series of energy systems results, from radiant energy through the gamut of elementary particles and their combinations into atoms of increasing complexity, to still more elaborate structures. As each successive system is more inclusive than the last the scale progressively approaches the universe as a whole and so each is in a degree, more or less adequately, expressive of the totality. This is the more apparent when we realize that state, or structure of the physical system, determines the disposition and character of the distinguishable parts within it, so that each relatively partial system within the more comprehensive is determined in its form and condition by its participation in the whole.

The second-order series of material forms is thus, equally

[1] Cf., above, p. 127.

with the first-order series, a scale of specific manifestations of a universal formula to which each, according to its position on the scale, is more or less adequate. The first order series, regarded merely as a scale of space-time curvatures, is thus an abstraction, which while it is itself a complete scale of forms is also the first phase of the higher order scale. This hierarchical relationship of scales is repeated as we go on from the physical to the biotic and from the biotic to the mental, and is the consequence of progressive self-enfoldment to which attention has already been drawn.

2

It is this progressive self-enfoldment that gives its peculiar character to time. As the fourth dimension of the space-time continuum which is finite in extent, time is not infinite regression to the past nor progression into the future. Yet the scale of forms consequent upon self-enfoldment presents itself, at least in some aspects, as a temporal sequence, which *prima facie* is linear and continuous without suggestion of curvature or that intimate relation to space that forbids infinite regression at the physico-mathematical level. This apparent discrepancy in the nature of time calls for elucidation.

For relativity physics space-time is four-dimensional because the diversification of space—the specification of distance—is a temporal process. Measurement of length involves motion and motion is temporal as well as spatial. The diversity of space is thus consequent upon motion, or its infusion with time; and instantaneous co-existence of its parts is an impossibility, for it would eliminate measurement and contradict their diversity, which (for space) is synonymous with distance. In space-time, therefore, time is the diversifying factor and it is apparent that the very existence of diversity involves time.

On the other hand, without diversity, or change of some kind, time is impossible, for lapse without change is an absurdity. What endures unchanged does so only in relation to changes in other things with which its duration is correlated. The truth of the matter seems to be that time and change are identical, and as diversity manifests itself physically only either spatially or temporally, and spatial diversity is the infusion of time into space, time may be seen as essentially the principle of differentiation in the real.

Wherever differentiation manifests itself, therefore, it will do so serially, and the progression of the scale of forms consequent upon self-enfoldment will always have at least a temporal aspect. As space is impregnated with time so are all the elaborations of the space-time continuum, and the diversification of the scale itself is a temporal movement. As differentiation is always differentiation of a totality and diversity is always within a unified continuum, so time is never bare change, but is always ordered change. Thus it is never an infinite progression because diversification takes the form of a scale and each phase is a specific manifestation of a whole which embraces the entire scale and regulates the internal detail. The scale is always a progression towards completion and fulfil- ment—the most adequate expression of the principle of order. To suppose otherwise would be to postulate change without order, which is in principle random change; and that, in the last resort (it has been argued above), is indistinguishable from homogeneity. If we are to avoid the fallacy of spurious homogeneity, therefore, we must realize that all process is self-fulfilling—the generation of a whole—and must equally be self-completing, like the space-time continuum. The scalar and serial presentation of the phases is simply the operation within the system of the principle of differ- entiation, which is time; and differentiation is always, of necessity, correlative to order and coherence. The differentiation of space by time established by Relativity is the same in principle as the differentiation of every whole into a scale of forms serially presented as a temporal process.

3

There is, however, no temporal process unless the distinguished elements are serially identifiable and systematically related. Bare succession, as has been said, is not time. What constitutes temporal succession is a serial order, and while the changes themselves are constituted by the qualitative development of the material in which they occur, their temporal order is determined by the application of a metric to the process so as to relate events to one another as a continuous order. Such correlation of changes with a metrical scale is possible only if there is a rule of succession linking the phases of the process and determining their order. This is just another aspect of the heterogeneity of the continuum and is the source of the cause-effect relationship. The heterogeneity of the continuum issues in a developing process, and the principle of development which dictates how one phase will give rise to the next is the rule of progression. This is the causal principle, which Kant held to be one of necessary connection because if the sequence were contingent the temporal order could not be objectively determined. If this is correct it entails that the sequence could not be objectively other than it is, which seems implausible and is often denied. If the connection is imagined as obtaining between two single, punctiform and otherwise isolated events, taken in abstraction from all other connections, it is difficult to see what necessity can mean—or, for that matter, what sort of connection it could be. Thus Hume failed to find any, and alleged only constant conjunction. But there are no such isolated events, only systems, within which elements, dependent for their character, disposition and mutual relation upon the principle of order, are distinguished. Contemporary physical theory makes this plain.

In relativity theory the temporal element in space-time—the infusion of time which diversifies space—derives from the velocity of light, the motion of which is a causal process. Light signals used to determine distances are propagated through space by the spreading of a wave front. Time and causal progression are thus inseparably linked. A wave is not an event but is a system of events all inseparably and intimately connected with one another according to a principle of organization. More accurately it is a structured process. Every wave propagation is a spatio-temporal process, not simply linear but four dimensional, every detail within which is what it is only because the whole wave system is what it is. Within this system there are no isolable events nor even separable linear trains. Attempts to delineate trajectories (of photons) within it can succeed, if at all, only as derivative from the system. The causal sequence, therefore, is not of atomic or punctiform events (like those contemplated by Hume) but of elements within, or developing states of, a system, the whole of which enters into every state and determines the elements and their mutual relations. The relation between cause and effect is never simple but always multiplex. It is the complex relationship between distinguishable (but indissolubly linked) elements within a system, by the whole of which that relationship is governed.

Causal laws are not discoverable, therefore, by observation simply of atomic events in linear succession, and they cannot be expressed in terms merely of constant conjunctions (E as a general rule following *C*). In contemporary science a causal law is expressed in a mathematical equation as the function of variable quantities. Such a function defines either the organizing principle of a system in a determinate state or the manner in which its state systematically changes in consequence of systematic relations between internal and external parameters.

'It is not in any sameness of causes and effects that the constancy of scientific laws consists, but in sameness of relations. And even "sameness of relations" is too simple a phrase; "sameness of differential equations" is the only correct phrase.'[1]

This was Bertrand Russell's judgment fifty years ago.

When more complicated systems than the spreading light wave are considered; when we come to matter waves, wave-packets and the intricate field system of the atom, attempts to isolate particles and events fail altogether. What Schrödinger called the 'continuous description' demanded by the linear conception of causation cannot be carried out, and to give a coherent account of the facts the scientist must give precedence to the energy system over the distinguishable particles or packets within it. It becomes describable as a standing wave or as a system of such waves. The emission of electrons from a radio-active nucleus or their passage through a screen cannot be predicted in detail if they are regarded as single events or precise trajectories but only in terms of probability estimates calculated on the basis of the structure of the total system and expressed in terms of ψ-functions. So Max Planck denies that merely local relations are sufficient for the formulation of causal laws—no more so, he says, 'than would be the microscopic investigation of the different parts of a picture in order to make clear its meaning'.[2] Only by taking into account the system as a whole can an adequate version of such laws be obtained. No theory of science can therefore be adequate which represents scientific laws as expressing no more than generalizations from the observed constant conjunction of events.[3]

Causation is thus a relation between successive states of a system, or between one feature of the system in one state with

[1] Bertrand Russell, *Mysticism and Logic*, 'On the notion of Cause'.
[2] *Vide The Universe in the Light of Modern Physics*, § III.
[3] Cf. Braithwaite, *Scientific Explanation*, p. 11, to which reference was made in the Introduction (p. 21 above).

a corresponding feature in a subsequent state. In either case the relation is structural having breadth and depth and pattern as well as linear succession. It follows that there are no causal chains but only causal networks and proliferations, and that events are linked not in successive pairs but in interlacing complexes. In every case the determining factor is the structure of the system, and necessity arises from the impossibility of altering a single nexus without subverting the entire system. No two of the distinguishable relata depend upon themselves alone for their relation which is an inextricable participant in a larger containing relational web. Within this web, and given the law of its construction, it is never possible that any nexus could be other than it is and the rest remain the same. It is, therefore, never possible, when the system as a whole is fully known, to conceive that a given causal factor in a nexus could be linked with a different effect, as it cannot be conceived, given the law of gravity and the disposition and motion of the bodies in the solar system to date, that within that system, undisturbed by any intrusion from without, the Earth could suddenly reverse its motion. (The intrusion of some external factor would, of course, have to be explained in terms of some wider system within which the same kind of necessity would hold.)

Question may be raised as to the transition from one state of a system to the next subsequent state. This is where, in quantum physics the 'jump' occurs which seems at first sight to be inexplicable in terms either of causal law or of the system to which the successive states belong. This is the problem of continuous description discussed by Schrödinger and, it will be remembered, resolved by him in terms of resonance waves,[1] which essentially involve the conception of a comprehensive system including the successive states of the two subordinate systems. 'The current view', he says, 'which privileges the "sharp energy states", is self-contradictory, at least in the language it uses. . . . We found it self-contradictory in that it cannot be maintained both for the whole and for the parts; we are left to choose and apply the privilege the way it is most convenient.'[2] The choice of the whole as the privileged entity is further dictated by the Exclusion Principle; and the answer to the question whether, by making this choice, the problem of continuous description can finally be solved is one for the future progress in the science to supply.

[1] 'Are there Quantum Jumps?', *B.S.P.S.* III, 1952.   [2] *Ibid.*, p. 123.

The necessary connection involved in the causal nexus is thus a necessity imposed by the pattern or *gestalt* within which the nexus occurs. In other words, or from a slightly different angle, it is the necessity by which a principle of organization differentiates the totality which it organizes. This diversification of a system according to determinate rules of procedure is precisely what issues as a scale of forms and its efflorescence produces the sequence of changes the succession of which time orders and measures. The rule governs the order and so provides the principle of objective succession upon which Kant insisted. The changes themselves are the process of activity of the real—the temporal aspect of the metrical field—but time proper is the metric itself. The fact that different metrics can be applied in different cases is no more than the fact that local times may differ; but time itself is the system of temporal relations, which, in generalized form, are relations of before and after. In the course of the process of change, these relations do not change and are, in fact, irreversible, not because the temporal reality is static—quite the reverse, because the metric is a fixed scale, within which the divisions and demarcations stand in mutual relations that are of necessity unalterable.

4

Causation and development are not different processes, and the distinction between them is largely epistemological rather than metaphysical. When we regard the system as a whole and the process of its self-differentiation we see it as development. When we focus attention upon a single distinguishable feature, or a narrow group of such features, and attempt to trace the course of change that they undergo in abstraction from their dependence upon other elements in the system, we see the sequence of changes as one of causes and effects. A causal chain is an abstract tracing of a single thread of connection within the woven pattern. But as the course of its windings is dependent upon the pattern as a whole and not simply upon its own prior movement, any such causal analysis is to some extent a distortion of the facts, at least so far as it omits from the account much that is relevant to their determination.

Polyphasic unity, moreover, is characterized by relevant variation and maintains its integrity through plasticity and adaptation. This propensity is the more marked the higher we proceed up the scale of forms. The necessity is therefore never Laplacian rigid necessity excluding possible alternatives. Even at the physical level it expresses itself in probabilities (which are, however, not arbitrary but are quite precisely defined by the character of the system). What actually occurs in fact follows the rule, but as the rule is not one of connection between two terms only, modifications elsewhere would have required a different sequence also in accordance with the rule. It is a necessity therefore which does not settle everything from the beginning, though it does prescribe determinate rules of procedure for the diversification of the system, proceeding from the central principle of organization. Novelty (as demanded by Bergson and Whitehead) is, therefore, not ruled out, but it is never capricious or irrelevant to principle.

It follows that the necessity implicit in causation is not inimical to freedom of action at the level of intelligent mind. Here relevant variation is most labile and most characteristic of activity. Intelligent determination of action is precisely that which gives most scope for the exercise of discretion and untrammelled judgment; and so, by widening the range of applicability of the organizing principle governing the activity, it bestows upon the agent the sort of freedom that issues in responsible choice.

Recent discussions of freedom have altogether missed the possibility of a sort of determinism which is compatible with human moral responsibility. Professor J. J. C. Smart has argued that the doctrine of free will is unmeaning because it advocates a position which is excluded by two opposite alternatives exhausting all possibilities.[1] These he defines as (i) determinism in the Laplacian sense:

'it is in principle possible to make a sufficiently precise determination of the state of a sufficiently wide region of the universe at time t_0, and sufficient laws of nature are in principle ascertainable to enable a super-human calculator to be able to predict any event occurring within that region at an already given time t_1.'

and (ii) 'pure chance', which is the contradiction of (i):

'there are some events that even a superhuman calculator could not predict, however precise his knowledge of however wide a region of the universe at some previous time.'[2]

[1] 'Free-will, Praise and Blame', *Mind*, LXX, No. 279, July, 1961.
[2] *Ibid.*, pp. 293-4.

He then contends that if any event is determined in sense (i) it cannot logically be pure chance in sense (ii), and *vice versa*. Indeterminists rightly consider moral responsibility to be incompatible with both (i) and (ii), and allege some third possibility, which Smart holds to be logically excluded and incapable of any precise meaning.

But this disjunction is not as exhaustive as Smart thinks. If events are not determined as Laplace maintained they were, in the old mechanistic fashion of classical physics, it does not follow that there is no alternative except 'pure chance'. Even logically this is not the case.

Professor Smart symbolizes as follows:

'p: This event happened as a result of unbroken causal continuity.

q: This event happened by pure chance.

That is, q if and only if not-p.

But p or not-p.

So p or q, and not both not-p and not-q.'

Yet, if 'causal continuity' is restricted to the Laplacian sense of determination, the propositions are not necessarily contradictories and the argument is specious. An event cannot happen by pure chance unless it is uncaused, but it could conceivably be caused in some other way than the Laplacian. There may be some form of interdependence between events besides that of mechanical causation, some form that excludes both mechanical causation and pure chance. That this is impossible and inconceivable Smart has done nothing to prove. Consequently, though we might admit 'q if and only if not p', 'only q if not p' is untrue, for not-p, though necessary, is not the sufficient condition of q. 'Both p and q' is certainly false, but 'Neither p nor q' may very well be true.

This false disjunction affects Smart's subsequent discussion of the phrase 'could have done otherwise'. If I drop a valuable china plate and it does not break, I say 'it could have broken', but by this I do not mean that whether it broke or not was undetermined and that whichever happened would have been uncaused; whereas, says Smart, the indeterminist will only admit '*genuinely* could have done otherwise' if causal conditions are excluded and the agent is able to act differently in despite of them. But it does not follow that if we reject the meaning of 'could have done otherwise' which implies 'if causal conditions had been different' we are inevitably committed to 'could have done otherwise though all antecendents remained the same'. The alternative possibility might depend on a possible different organization of the same antecedent causal factors, or a different interpretation of the same perceived or imagined situation. And this would not necessarily be Laplacian determination. The source of the organization of antecedent determinants is certainly not pure chance, nor is it possible to conceive it as Laplacian causation.

Whether a plate breaks or not may always, without undue risk of error, be regarded as a simple mechanical question. The plate never chooses to break or not to break. But drop a cat, and whether or not it lands on its feet may well depend on something more complex than just a train of purely mechanical causes, though nobody would wish to say that it was in no way causally determined. A man falling from a height may try to save himself or he may let himself go, and what happens in either case will be (as with the cat) partly mechanically determined, but it will certainly not be wholly so determined, because the man's awareness of what is happening and his effort (or lack of it) to modify the result are factors in the situation and are almost certainly not the product purely of mechanical determination. Here 'could have done otherwise' depends on the possible alternative organizations of immensely complex structures of determinants beyond anything involved in the case of the china plate, which is far from an adequate analogy. The indeterminist is undoubtedly wrong in trying to exclude every sort of causation, but it does not follow that Laplacian causation is the only admissible kind.

The foregoing discussion of causation requires a very different conclusion. Determination is of the distinguishable but inseparable element within a system by the organization of the whole, and this includes both a temporal as well as a spatial pattern. It is not determination of one separable element simply by another immediately antecedent to it, not even a sum or complication of such single links of determination. Accordingly the same ostensible elements differently organized may display quite different properties. Alternative possibilities may thus be alternative systems of order within the same set of factors antecedent to the event under investigation.

Biological processes are almost without exception examples of determination of particular detail by the totality or structural form of the whole organism. Phenomena of regeneration, healing, ontogenesis, metabolism, homeostasis, and virtually every aspect of living process, are patently cases of the determination of the behaviour of cells, organs and tissues, or the regulation of physico-chemical processes (both as to their kind and rate of procedure) by the organization of the complete living entity. This sort of structural or organismic determination is quite different from Laplacian causation, not because it is unpredictable in principle, but because knowledge of the disposition and movement of individual parts at t_0 is not enough for inference to their disposition and movement at t_1. The principle of organization, both temporal and spatial, must also be known, and this involves insight into the structural interrelation of all the relevant events and the manner in which those at t_1 fit into the total spatio-temporal pattern.

Now, moral judgment applies only to voluntary action, of which the distinguishing character is deliberate intention. We are responsible only for what we do deliberately and what results from our deliberate action or omission. Deliberate action requires full consciousness, and this involves the operation of the whole personality of the agent, with a high degree of integration of its emotional, habitual and intellectual propensities. This is a stupendously complex organized system built upon and continuous with the physiological system of the human organism, which is itself complex beyond description. Consciousness issues from the activity of the whole of this immensely complicated organization, and without it action cannot rightly qualify as voluntary. Consciousness, moreover, whatever else it may be, is essentially the capacity to grasp data as organized totalities—as *Gestalten*, as objects, as situations, facts and states of affairs—and to react to them as such in organized ways. Our actions are our responses to situations apprehended as such in our awareness; that is, as interpreted by our minds acting as wholes, both intelligently and emotionally. Any presented situation may be variously interpreted and every interpretation is an act of mind, which, though it may be fully determined by physiological, psychological and intellectual factors, is not to be dissected and reduced to these determinants, for they constitute and produce their effects only as a single integrated totality, within and subject to which they are mutually determining. Prediction is possible only so far as we have some insight into the general nature of this organic totality and its propensities, and such prediction is not incompatible with moral responsibility. To foretell a man's actions in the light of one's knowledge of his character casts no aspersions upon his freedom.

If this is the truth of the matter, genuinely open possibilities may exist in various ways. First, the personality can act at different levels of organization: at the level of appetite, of desire, or of deliberate choice between objects of conflicting desires. Each level corresponds to a different degree of 'determinism', in proportion to the amount of self-awareness involved. Secondly, at the higher levels, the constant need to make decisions by a person aware of his desires and of their inevitable incompatibilities leads necessarily to a process of conscious ordering, subordinating, preferring and suppressing. In any particular case of choice, the decision is mediated by this process, past (as perpetuated by habit) as well as contemporary (as embodied in the interpretation and comprehension of the presented situation). Here there is ample scope for alternative readings, alternative evaluations and preferences. None of these is 'uncaused'. None is independent of the innumerable influences and pressures exerted upon the mind of the agent by his own habits and innate dispositions, by social suggestions and importunings. But most of these operate at the level of consciousness and many at a very high level of reflection, and this means that they are themselves the fruit of an organizing activity, the source of which at every level is obscure and everywhere gives the impression of spontaneity and self-activation. All of these influences are mediated through that activity supervenient upon conscious organization of data which is judgment. This spontaneous, self-determining act is the essence of responsible behaviour. In the last resort we are responsible for nothing else but our judgment of right and wrong and our consequent action, and there are always genuinely open possibilities of different judgments corresponding to possible different interpretations of fact and different evaluations of the same objects. But judgment is no more nor less than the final outcome of the spontaneous activity of integration and organization traceable in differing forms at lower levels. Nothing else is compatible with moral responsibility.

If this be so, there is a kind of determination which is not mechanical in the Laplacian sense and which is not destructive of moral freedom. The indeterminist's demand for genuinely open possibilities is the intimation (often confused and sometimes misguided) of this sort of determination manifesting itself in

Q

human action, and of its difference from mechanical causation. But to that there is an alternative other than 'pure chance'. There is organismic determination the determination by the total organized system of a living, knowing being, issuing in conscious judgment and deliberate choice.

CHAPTER XXIV

MIND AND KNOWLEDGE

I

The notion of polyphasic unity, described in Chapter IV as a many-faceted unity, a system in which distinguishable elements are differentiated and interrelated on a definite principle of order, but which are not separable without violation of that principle, consequent destruction of the system and obliteration of the distincta within it—this conception has universal application both to the whole and to the parts of the universe as discovered by the sciences. It now transpires that a polyphasic unity is in essence a scale of forms progressively realizing, with continuous increase of adequacy the principle immanent in whole and part. It is a continuum of activity or process issuing in such a scale, the forms, or phases, of which are mutually related (i) as degrees of realization of the principle, (ii) as distinct specifications of its generic nature, (iii) as mutual opposites and (iv) as the reconciliation of oppositions lower in the scale. Each sublates the lower phases, all of which are carried up into and preserved in mutual interdependence in the higher phase that supersedes them.

These features of polyphasic unity were discovered at every level. The physical universe proves to be a spatio-temporal continuum pervaded by a continuously changing 'curvature', which is manifested as energy and matter. This, again, appears as continuous flux, a complex of sub-microscopic waves, superposition of which produces elementary particles. These are interrelated in energy systems constituting atoms, which combine into molecules. Each phase realizes in some degree the laws or principles of order governing the whole;[1] each is a specific manifestation of physical reality;[2] yet they are in definite ways mutually opposed[3] positive charge to negative, matter to anti-matter, nucleus to satellite electrons. Each successive more complex stage, includes and sustains the more elementary, from radiant energy to the most complex atom, in unbroken hierarchical series.

The biotic sphere reveals the same general character but

---

[1] *Vide* pp. 97, 127, 144 above. [2] *Vide* p. 158 above.
[3] *Vide ibid.*

does so more fully and adequately.[1] Its constituent systems are more coherent and organically whole. They are more obviously species of generic forms and lend themselves more easily to a system of classification based on this relationship. The species constitute an evolutionary continuum of increasing complexity and integration, and the tree of life as a whole is a series of overlapping and ramifying deployments each preserving and incorporating earlier forms in hierarchical series. Again there is opposition.[2] and all the features of polyphasic unity that have been listed and demonstrated are once more in evidence.

The biotic sphere, moreover, displays more adequately the other features of polyphasic unity. The organism is more coherent than any physical whole. Its organs are more interdependent and even less separable than physical parts. It is self-maintaining and its stability is achieved by relevant variation of what would otherwise be a highly unstable dynamic equilibrium. Evolution of life is more recognizably continuous and progressive than anything in the purely physical sphere. The genera are more obviously self-specifying. Its oppositions are more subtle and acute—plant to animal, invertebrate to vertebrate, cold-blooded to warm, and so on. Nevertheless, there are still anomalies and inadequacies. Evolution is not direct or linear, much in its course is haphazard and abortive. Specializations adaptive in character prove self-defeating and dysteleological. Reversals of progress and degeneration—albeit always subordinate to the general auturgic nisus—mar and frustrate the assured march of its progress.

Mind is a still more definite and continuous scale. There is direct continuity between physiological activity and behaviour, between instinct and intelligence. Sentience develops directly into perception and perception, along with memory and imagination, into intellect. Moreover the continuity is horizontal as well as vertical, for each form of mind is involved in all. The relations between these forms of specific distinctness, degress of realization, and opposition have been noted above, and their coherence, each in itself and among one another, is so intimate that to speak of separation is nonsensical, and even distinction is made at the price of explicit abstraction. Finally, in the conscious intelligent personality of man at his best and the correlative social order polyphasic unity is exemplified in the highest degree known to science.

The entire gamut of natural forms, from electron to man forms

[1] Cf. Ch. XIV above. [2] *Vide*, p. 281 above.

a similar scale. Each main type of order, physical, chemical, biotic, mental, social, is a species of polyphasic unity and this is what is progressively more fully and typically exemplified. The (provisionally) final form in mind is the most adequate and, therefore, can be regarded as immanent in the more elementary. What is realized in and as mind is potentially and implicitly present in all that precedes it, and that is what is meant by saying that mind develops out of material forms. If this is what Alexander divined when he spoke of time as the mind of space and declared that mind was a developed form of time, he had some inkling of the truth. If this is what Tielhard is trying to convey when he insists on an inward aspect of all things that, as it were, becomes turned outward in the course of development to the conscious mind, he is perhaps, picturesquely and indirectly expressing the same truth. If, moreover, we may identify his 'radial' energy with the immanence throughout the natural orders of that polyphasic unity which is best exemplified in the activity of a mind, we have a scientifically justifiable doctrine without any appeal to mysterious spiritual influences.

2

A position of this sort is not Idealism, if by that is meant a subjectivism which reduces all things to 'ideas', whether of man or of God. Some thinkers have called themselves Idealists, following Hegel for the most part, who have not been subjectivists (as Hegel certainly was not), who have been essentially realistic in their outlook, and who have approached a view such as the one here developed. The name has not stood them in good stead, has misled opponents and has brought their philosophy into disrepute which was largely unmerited. One of the objects of this book has been to re-establish its claim to a scientific and empirical foundation— not sufficiently demonstrated by themselves—if possible, without repeating their errors.

There is no attempt or intention here to reduce (or, if it be preferred, elevate) matter and life to thought. They are what science shows them to be; and what they have in common with mind is what mind realizes by developing out of them. They are all quite distinct species and are even in mutual opposition, although—or because—they are also degrees of realization, of what finally emerges. Still less is it suggested that consciousness is present, in however primitive a form, in the physical world or even in all forms of life. Admittedly it is not possible to pin-point the appearance of sentience in the scale, nor yet of percipience, though the continuity can hardly be gainsaid. But to postulate consciousness and mind *ab initio* except as purely potential, and as immanent, would be to deny development and to go counter to the description of polyphasic unity on which we are insisting.

If the theory is not Idealism still less is it Panpsychism. Consciousness is dependent on the prior development of sentience and sentience on a very high grade of integration of organic process. To postulate either at lower levels would be simply to fly in the face of the available evidence without explaining anything or rendering the mutual relation of developmental phases more intelligible—rather the contrary. It is only by recognizing and insisting upon the differences that the unity and continuity of the whole can be maintained. Reductionism is certainly to be shunned.

On the other hand, the position here advocated is just as little a form of materialism. Dialectical materialists might claim it as their own. If it is, so much the better for their theory, but not for the name they give it. For dialectic is essentially proleptic and teleological. It is the whole that explains the part and the outcome of the dialectical development that determines the process. Unless this were so there would be no dialectic at all, and no process. It has been argued above that the nisus of development is the nisus to the whole, and that progress is effected through the inadequacy of the partial and elementary phases which carries with it a sort of disequilibrium—a strain in the direction of closure and completion. Such a condition is detectable at all levels: in the correction of physico-chemical disequilibria, in the auturgy of living systems —their homeostasis and their exogenous adaptability—in the organization of the sensory field (as demonstrated by Gestalt psychology), and in the equilibrial 'groupings' of intelligent operations. It is always the immanence of the developing whole that provides the drive of the process—*conatus in suo esse perseverare*. Dialectic, therefore, can never be 'materialistic', if that means a reduction of mental activity to physico-chemical process. This is obviously as ruinous a reductionism as any.

If, on the other hand, by dialectical materialism, all that is meant is that the dialectic begins from and proceeds out of material forms, that in its course these forms, by complexification, self-enfoldment and integration into more cohesive and unified systems, become transformed and acquire new properties and capacities impossible at the merely physico-chemical level; if all that is intended is that the material elements are sustained and sublated in the higher complexes and persist as inseparable moments within them, then to speak of materialism is to empty that word of its proper significance, which is essentially the *denial* of any such transformation and dialectical progress. Dialectical materialism is thus a *contradictio terminorum*, and those who profess to believe in it must, to be consistent, adhere either to materialism or to dialectic, but cannot retain them both.

Finally, the position we are expounding is not a form of emergent evolutionism and rejects Bergsonian vitalism. No mysterious new qualities are postulated as emerging inexplicably with each new concrescence. New qualities and powers do indeed arise with new complexities and levels of integration, but their 'emergence' is not ineluctable. It is not, of course, always explicable as soon as it is detected, but the novelty is attributable to the new form of organization and once that is fully understood it should be scientifically comprehensible. Moreover, the novelty is a continuous outgrowth from the foregoing phase. It is not a discrete supervenient addition in principle unaccountable in terms of its contributory factors. Certainly, it is not rendered intelligible by analysis alone. It is a product of synthesis and can be explained only by principles of synthesis. Potentiality in the earlier and more primitive of the later and more elaborate must, however, be presumed and the aim of science is always to trace the continuity between them in as great detail as possible. Emergent Evolutionists may not wish to assert otherwise, but their best exponents never succeed in making 'emergence' rationally intelligible and so fail to maintain the continuity of their postulated scale of forms.

Bergson's theory succumbs to a kindred defect. *L'élan vital*, to the end, remains a mystery. It urges the evolutionary process on in no intelligible or assignable direction, and while continuously producing novelty, it does so apparently by magic, for the theory offers no explanatory principle for the production of new forms. Bergson bitterly opposed holism and the idea that at any stage *tout est donné*. The notions that the ultimate totality could be implicit in the elementary forms, or that it could be the source of the forward drive of evolution, were abhorrent to him. His aversion was the fruit of an insight penetrating but one-sided, for it is very true that the world is no 'block universe' and is not all given immediately as one enormous datum. It is a progressive scale evolving through a continuous process of activity. Its detail, which is inexhaustibly various, generates itself seriatim. Nevertheless, its trend is persistently upstream in the direction of order and concrescence, the development (as the word implies) is towards more adequately self-maintaining complex organisms, complete and more self-sufficient totalities. Consequently the scale itself and as a whole can consistently be comprehended only as self-complete and ultimately one. Because he missed this necessary implication of finality and all-inclusive wholeness, Bergson's teleology was endless and so self-contradictory. He failed to recognize the inevitable correlation of development and totality, of process and concrescence.

3

Despite superficial likenesses, the theory here advocated must not be mistaken for any one-sided idealism or materialism, vitalism or mechanism, though it may perhaps claim with some justification to reconcile their differences. It does maintain that the universe is a single and complete system, immeasurably and bewilderingly diversified—a unity in and through prodigious multiplicity—that it is *in toto* a polyphasic unity, and so a scale of forms. The 'stuff' of which it is made manifests itself as a perpetually active process generating the scale. The tendency of the process and the ascent of the scale is in the direction of intelligent mind, which is a late phase. Thus, as always in a scale of this description, the general principle governing and immanent in its whole course is more fully realized in its later gradations. If so, this principle must be that of rational coherence, as (for our knowledge) best displayed in the work of the intellect. Its immanence throughout the scale gives point and propriety to Hegel's dictum: 'The real is the rational and the rational is the real', which is very far from meaning that everything in the world is just as it should be. On the contrary the real can be rational and the rational can be realized only through a constant striving towards better and more rational forms. Every partial manifestation is subject to improvement and presents a perpetual challenge and stimulation to further effort.

Such a metaphysic finds its foundations in modern science. Systems like those of Lloyd Morgan, Alexander, Bergson and Whitehead were directly inspired by scientific findings, though some of them over-stressed certain aspects of the truth at the expense of others; and even more literary philosophers, like F. H. Bradley, Bernard Bosanquet and R. G. Collingwood were strongly influenced by science and were able to divine its implications. In this study the attempt has been made to examine the scientific foundations in some detail and to make the connection between the scientific theories and the philosophical consequences more apparent. The resulting philosophical system ought now to be worked out in detail. The outline given here suggests lines of advance affording a theory of logic, of knowledge and science, of value and of religion, the full exposition of which would require many volumes. If sufficient has now been done to provide a foundation on which to build a theory of scientific knowledge I shall be content for the present, and shall devote another volume to that purpose in the hope of finding more complete answers to some of the questions with which this book began. We may conclude with a brief consideration of the position of science in the scheme of things so far discovered and reserve the more detailed study of its procedures and criteria for later development.

4

The results of researches in the various sciences have given rise to a conception of the universe as a whole, in which man's mind with its knowledge has a place. Properly to understand the character of science and the validity of its theories it should be seen in the light of this world-concept. In this final section we shall consider the bearing of the scientific world-picture on the status of science itself. It must however immediately occur to the reader that there is danger here of circular argument. Can we establish the validity of science by an appeal to science itself. If the sciences are in any way faulty or deficient in their professed disclosure of the truth, any world-picture that results from their findings will be to that extent misleading, and any theory of science based upon it untrustworthy. No escape from this predicament is to be found, however, by attempting to lay down a theory of knowledge in advance of scientific investigation, for to rely on some presumed inherent propensity of the mind to formulate its own rules and criteria would be equally circular. We cannot step out of the charmed circle of our knowledge in order to find criteria for its validation elsewhere and any theory of knowledge must be self-reflective and somehow self-validating. Our

Q*

only expedient can be to turn the circle of the argument to good effect, to examine the consequences for human knowledge which flow from the world-picture evolved by science and to see whether the latter provides the conditions for its own discovery. There have been epistemologies in plenty that have proved self-contradictory by committing the epistemologist's fallacy—that is, by laying down conditions and criteria for knowledge on which the theory itself would be impossible. We made acquaintance with some of these in Chapter XIX. To arrive at a theory which is not self-refuting would be no small accomplishment. In fact it is difficult to see how a theory of knowledge could be more firmly established.

To gain some idea of the position of science in the scheme of things revealed by science itself, we must briefly retrace our steps, and note once more the main direction of evolutionary progression.

The second law of thermodynamics asserts that the entropy of a physical system can only increase. On the other hand, the special character of life is its ability to maintain the level of entropy in open systems, or even decrease it. Its typical products are always improbable; often so improbable as to beggar the imagination and defy explanation. Whereas the probable course of physical process is towards disorder, life creates and maintains order at the expense of its physico-chemical environment. It appears to extract message from noise. This is perhaps the latest discovery of biology. As Medawar (op. cit.) declares 'What we want, and are very slowly beginning to get, is a comprehensive theory of the forms in which new genetical information comes into being'. The progressive generation of 'information', the distinguishing character of living process, is also an apt description of the entire scale of forms continuous from physical change to mental activity. Thus its final product is information, in the full sense of the word: Knowledge—the work of the human intellect.

Knowledge, we have seen, is the organization in consciousness of the contents of the psychical field, issuing in the appearance of objects to perception. The psychical field is the concentration and sublimation in feeling of the physiological activities of the organism in response to the influences affecting it from an environment extending from it as centre without limit. So the organism constitutes a focus of the universe from a particular point-of-view. The feeling phase of its integrative activity thus contains a universe in suspension—implicit—a confused unarticulated manifold, which becomes progressively disentangled and ordered by the activity of attention in perception, and by the work of the intellect in knowledge.

Throughout the developmental process in the sphere of mind, the object of awareness is the immediately prior phase or form in the scale, with all its sublated implications of the foregoing lower phases. The object of perception is constructed from the contents of feeling; the objects of imagination and memory are past perceptual experiences (never merely repeated but always reconstructed and sometimes, in fantasy, into new patterns); the objects of thinking are the products of perception, imagination and memory, which it transforms by analysis, abstraction, generalization and resynthesis into coherent systems of knowledge—the sciences.

The object of the sciences, therefore, is the world as perceived; and, as the intellect is a late form in the total scale, it comprehends those that precede it and develops explicitly the structure of their organization. As we saw in Chapter XXI the effect of intelligence is objectification, in contrast to the subjectivity of feeling and perception, and the achievement of the sciences is consequently the discovery of reality. Its method and procedure have next to be investigated, in order to determine how this discovery is made. The central question is how errors are detected and corrected. By what criterion is success recognizable and measurable? These matters will be the subject of the succeeding volume.

In the course of our present investigation, as far as we have come, clues and indications have emerged that point the direction next to be taken. As the work of intelligence, scientific thinking will be systematic in a high degree. That in itself is no very startling discovery; but what may be more important is the new view of the nature of system that has come to light. It has long been recognized that systematic thinking is the mark of science, but what should qualify as a system has never been unambiguously decided. We now discover that a system is a developing scale of forms increasing in polyphasic coherence, and we should look for the exemplification of this type of structure, with a high degree of explicit elaboration, in the methods and advancement of scientific thinking.

As the forms become more complex and more fully integrated in their sequence along the scale, so should these properties be

evident in the product of scientific thinking. Its object will, therefore, have to be diversified in great detail, and its method must be
penetratingly analytic. At the same time it must interrelate the
elaborated details in a single and unified system, of which coherence
and consistency will be especially characteristic. Its method will
thus also be comprehensively synthetic. So it should be productive
of wholes, which grow and develop by mutual incorporation and
constructive synthesis. The progressive elaboration of these wholes
will constitute a scale of forms, and the same structure should
reveal itself internally to each phase.

The truth of a theory is the degree to which it presents the
actual nature of the world, and if we may rely upon the account
of the development of experience given in the last section, this
cannot be discovered by simple reference to the more primitive
and confused forms of sentient experience, but only through
further systematization. If the objectivity and 'reality' of a concept
is its rational character then truth should consist in the success
with which theory can account within its system for every aspect
and detail of what appears in perceptual experience.

Consequently, it will follow that science depends on and
develops the products of observation and to be successful, or
true, must account for all the facts. A place must be found in
its system for every appearance, and the system must be fully integrated and consistent with itself. It is, in short, in the coherence
and comprehensiveness of the system that we should seek the
criterion of truth. The relevance of observation will be, first, in
that it is the starting-point of theory, and, secondly, in that no
observation may be exempt from explanation within the system
and all must fit in without mutual collision. We shall not, however,
expect to find a clean break between observation and theory
(perception and thought), for they will be forms in a continuous
scale. They are species of knowledge, indeed, and therefore
distinct, in mutual contrast and, so far opposed, yet overlapping,
gradations of theoretical adequacy. Observation is never wholly
devoid of interpretation (or theory), as has already been found,[1]
and no theory of any merit ever floats completely loose from
observed phenomena.

The truth, the disclosure of the actual nature of the real, is the
ultimate goal of science, for the achievement of which perceptual
experience is examined, analysed, ordered and systematized. We

[1] *Vide* pp. 407 ff. above.

do not stumble upon reality in sensuous perception and then somehow use it as the touchstone of theories independently invented. The truth is the consummation and completion of the scale and, as such, transcends while it includes the lower forms, in which it is also immanent. Empirical science is not itself this consummation, but is relatively to it a lower form. Its truth is the immanence in it of the universal principle that science strives to exemplify as adequately as it can; but what science seeks may well lie beyond its limits, and the search may well lead the mind to further phases in the scale, such as religion and philosophy, which adumbrate a fulfilment in a yet more distant and more profound beyond.

Such, in general outline, are the features we may expect a theory of science to display which is based upon the world-view developed in these pages. But to avoid, as far as possible, the accusation of circularity even though circularity of some kind is in the end unavoidable, we shall in the sequel try to develop a theory based upon the study of actual cases of scientific discovery and not directly by developing the consequences of what has been set out above. If the result corroborates what is written here, both will be more credible. Moreover, the method adopted may properly claim to be empirical. It will arrive at results by examining the relevant facts—the actual procedures of practising scientists—and will make no attempt to lay down fundamental principles *a priori*. So it may hope to escape the error of some so-called Empiricisms which prescribe *ab initio* the principles on which they allege knowledge to be gained and then attempt to fit the procedures of the sciences into their home-made Procrustean bed.

INDEX OF NAMES

INDEX OF SUBJECTS

Digestion 274, 291
Dimension, fifth, 89; fourth, 89
Diploid 172
Directive-state 510–15
Discontinuity 124 f.
Disintegration 231
Disorder 150, 174, 197, 206, 210, 231
Disposition 238, 441. See also Cognitive
Distance 77, 102; correlative to temporal lapse 72 f., 76 f., 466
Distinction 284, 483
Diuresis 219
DNA 170, 244
Dominance 244
Doppler Effect 46, 94
Drosophila 243 n. 4, 282
Dualism, psycho-physical 289
Duration 51, 56, 59, 471
Dynamics 141

E

Ecologist. See Ecology
Ecology 252
Egg (ovum) 206, 211 f., 249, 259, 269, 281; mosaic, 209, 210
Ego. See Self.
Eigenfunction. See Function
Eigenvalue 113
Élan vital (life-force) 228, 260, 264, 452, 487
Eleaticism 63
Electrodynamics 61, 107, 143
Electromagnetics 111
Electron 100, 109, 111, 140, 145, 149, 152, 155, 157; dimensions of, 107; radius of, 105; satellite, 128, 146
  beam, 384
  microscope 111
Element, chemical 111
Embryo 211, 269
Embryogenesis. See Embryology
Embryology 208 f., 273
Emergence 69, 452; theory of, 451, 487 f., not advocated, 309
Emotion 310, 324 f.; relation to bodily change, 309; tension in, 324 f.
Empathy 403
Empiricism 21, 22, *23–8*, 39, 45, 69, 120, 379, 391, 432, 451, 493
Empiricists. See Empiricism
End 181, 262, 267

Endoskeleton 281
Energy 38 f., 50, 58, 67, 98, 100, 105, *109–41*, 147, 149, 151, 153 f., 156, 158, 173, 182, 188, 199, 206, 210, 250; free, 174, 178; 'radial', 150, 152, 175, 225, 248, 328, 485; radiant, 146, 150, 198; 'tangential', 150
Engram 235
Enroulement sur soi-même. See Self-enfoldment
Entropy 149, 173 f., 183, 207, 210, 216, 242, 386, 417, 490; negative, 151, 386, 445
Environment 180, 183, 229, 232, 242 f., 249 ff., 253, 264, 275, 277, 282; behavioural, 347, 349, 388 f., 419, 461; external, 213, 217, 243, 252, 266; 'geographical', see physical; internal, 183, 213, 217 ff., 252, 281; physical, 346, 388 f., 419
Enzyme 170 f., 188 ff., 191 ff., 197; adaptive, 246
Epidermis 212
Epigenesis 245 f.
Epiphenomenalism 289, 302
Epistemology 31, 41, 80, 96, 101, 108, 110, 114, 117, 120, 123 f., 282, 284, 317, 341, 414; appearance fundamental to, 349, 370; physiological, 379
Epistemological fallacy 378, 388, 490
Equilibrial axis 401, 403
Equilibrium 218, 222 f., 324 f.; between organism and environment, 437; of mind, 436 f.
Equipotentiality 213, 215, 321
Equivalence, Principle of, 53 f.
Erythrocytes (Erythron) 177, 201, 212, 221
Ether. See Aether
Ethology 342, 351–66
Events 71; atomic, 473; past, identification of, 421 f., dating of, 421
Evidence 412 f.
Evolution 92 ff., 153, 174, 183, 185 f., 190, 192, 194, 197, 199, 207 f., 225, *226–58*, 259 f., 266, 387, 484, 487; scale of, 296; of life, 296; of mind, 296, 425
Exclusion Principle 39, 98, *131 et seq.*, 150, 153, 157
Existentialism 445
Exoskeleton 281